Authors Herman Kahn and Anthony J. Wiener

HERMAN KAHN is director of the Hudson Institute and one of the founders of the "new science" of strategy games and predicting for policy for decision-makers. His previous books, *On Thermonuclear War, Thinking About the Unthinkable,* and *On Escalation: Metaphors and Scenarios,* are definitive contributions and have shaped our national defense planning and public policy-making for over ten years not only through their specific recommendations but also through the general methodology that Mr. Kahn, and others in centers like the RAND Corporation, created after World War II.

ANTHONY J. WIENER is chairman of the Research Management Council at the Hudson Institute and was one of the Institute's founding members. He has been a research associate of the U.S. Joint Commission on Mental Illness and Health and has directed research projects and written reports to the government and to foundations on issues such as international crises, NATO problems, arms control, poverty, economic development, organization for research and development, and social psychiatry.

DANIEL BELL, who contributes an introduction to *The Year 2000,* is professor of sociology at Columbia University and chairman of the Commission on the Year 2000. He has been one of the most influential intellectuals engaged in the formation of public policy and the new science of decision-making. His seminal study *The End of Ideology* ranks as a modern sociological classic.

THE YEAR 2000

A FRAMEWORK FOR SPECULATION
ON THE NEXT THIRTY-THREE YEARS

THE YEAR 2000

A Framework for Speculation
on the Next Thirty-Three Years

By Herman Kahn and Anthony J. Wiener

with contributions from other staff members of the Hudson Institute

INTRODUCTION BY DANIEL BELL

———————————✳———————————

THE MACMILLAN COMPANY, NEW YORK

COLLIER-MACMILLAN LIMITED, LONDON

We are glad to acknowledge the following authors and publishers for permission to
quote from their copyrighted works:

David Allison, "The Civilian Technology Lag," in *International Science and Technology, December* 1963; James C. G. Coniff, "The World of the Unborn," *New York Times Magazine,* January 8, 1967; Richard A. Easterlin, "Effects of Population Growth on the Economic Development of Developing Countries," in the *Annals* of the American Academy of Political and Social Science, *World Population,* January 1967; Sigmund Freud, from *Civilization and Its Discontents,* Volume 21 of the Standard Edition of *The Complete Psychological Works of Sigmund Freud* (London: Hogarth Press, 1930). Copyright Sigmund Freud Copyrights Ltd., the Estate of Mr. James Strachey and W. W. Norton and Company, Inc. All rights reserved; Col. J. F. C. Fuller, *Atlantis: America and the Future* (New York: E. P. Dutton and Co., 1925); Pierre Gallois, *The Balance of Terror: Strategy for the Nuclear Age* (Boston: Houghton Mifflin and Co., 1961); Herman Kahn, "Central European Outbreak Scenario," from *On Escalation* (New York: Frederick A. Praeger; London: Pall Mall Press, 1965); Walter Kaufmann, trans., *Goethe's Faust* (Garden City, N.Y.: Doubleday and Co., 1961); David Krech, "Controlling the Mind Controllers," in *Think,* July-August 1966. Reprinted by permission from *Think Magazine,* published by IBM. Copyright 1966 by International Business Machines Corporation; Colin Legum, *Pan-Africanism,* rev. ed. (London: Pall Mall Press; New York: Frederick A. Praeger, 1965); Ben-Ami Lipetz, "Information Storage and Retrieval," in *Scientific American.* Copyright © 1966 by Scientific American, Inc. All rights reserved; M. Stanley Livingston, *The Development of Particle Accelerators* (New York: Dover Books, 1966); Robert K. Merton, *Social Theory and Social Structure,* 1956 rev. ed. (Glencoe, Ill.: Free Press, 1949); Marvin Minsky, "Artificial Intelligence," in *Scientific American.* Copyright © 1966 by Scientific American, Inc. All rights reserved; Edmund Stillman and William Pfaff, *The Politics of Hysteria* (New York: Harper and Row, 1964); M. W. Thring, "A Robot Around the House," in Nigel Calder, ed., *The World in 1984* (Baltimore: Penguin Books, 1965), Vol. 2, and *The New Scientist;* Unsigned articles from: *The New Scientist,* February 9, 1967; *The New York Times,* © 1961, 1965, 1966, 1967, The New York Times Company. Reprinted by permission; *The Washington Post,* October 31, 1966; *U.S. News & World Report,* © Copyright 1966, U.S. News and World Report, Inc., from issue of February 21, 1966.

Contents

Detailed Table of Contents

List of Tables

List of Figures

List of Figures

CHAPTER IV. POSTINDUSTRIAL SOCIETY IN THE STANDARD WORLD   185

List of Tables

CHAPTER V. INTERNATIONAL POLITICS IN THE STANDARD WORLD

List of Tables

List of Figures

List of Tables

CHAPTER VII. SOME POSSIBILITIES FOR NUCLEAR WARS

CHAPTER VIII. OTHER TWENTY-FIRST CENTURY NIGHTMARES

Preface and Acknowledgments

This book is simply what the subtitle says—"a framework for speculation." It is far from an exhaustive set of conjectures about every important element of the future; still less is it an attempt to "predict" any partciular aspect of the future. In subsequent work we intend to build upon this study by filling in the framework, here and there, and by enlarging upon, qualifying, discarding, or making a better case for various speculations that are merely sketched here. In this initial report, however, our emphasis is necessarily methodological, synoptic, and contextual—as we explain below, our attempt is to be "heuristic," "propaedeutic," and "paradigmatic." We have emphasized problems, not solutions. Thus our conclusions contain, among other things, a program for further study. In this respect, and in others, this book may not seem "balanced" or "finished." Nevertheless we think it is worth publishing because it contains enough of interest to be worth reading; because it may stimulate others to further work on the subject; because it is the first report in a continuing program of work, and subsequent reports in the Hudson Institute series on Alternative World Futures will need to refer to this framework and to revise and build upon it; and because the task we set ourselves, if taken too seriously, could never be finished.

While we alone are responsible for the defects of this report, we were fortunate in receiving constructive criticism and contributions from many of our colleagues. William Pfaff was our co-author at an early stage of the project; signs of his work remain apparent at many points in the manuscript. The "Rationale for Disarray Worlds" of Chapter VI remains almost entirely his. Morton A. Kaplan was an especially constructive and diligent critic. He was the original dreamer of the section on "Social Controls" of our "Twenty-First Century Nightmares," and his suggestions are embodied at many other points in the book, especially in the chapter on the future of the international system. In our discussion of future technology we made use of welcome suggestions from John Menke and knowledgeable friends outside Hudson Institute, Robert W. Prehoda and G. Harry Stine. David A. Robison also collaborated with us in portions of Chapter II, contributing ideas such as his diagrams of synergisms, and selecting noteworthy items from comprehensive files collected by Jane Kahn. Chapter III was written in collaboration with Institute economists Mark Wehle and Gus Weiss, who contributed many ideas and made meticulous and labor-intensive contributions to our quantitative projections, despite occasional uneasiness about what they were asked to assume.

We must also admit that Edmund Stillman, an indomitable and persuasive collaborator in many previous projects, has influenced our views on international prospects; evidence of his impact is clearly discernible in Chapter V. Max Singer, equally tenacious, and keeper of the conscience of conceptual clarity, tried several times to get us to do better than we could, especially in our comments on nuclear proliferation.

We are also grateful to Frank Armbruster and Raymond D. Gastil for contributing the scenarios appended to Chapter VI; to our former colleague Felix Kaufmann, who called our attention to additional aspects of the comparisons with the classical period; and to Ronald Ridker for some earlier work done at Hudson Institute on economic projections. Nancy Engel de Janosi prepared the index and made many substantive contributions. Mary Mitchell is to be warmly thanked for successfully supervising the typing of the manuscript, under crisis conditions, while several other documents also had to be produced. We owe much to many colleagues and friends who reacted helpfully to this material when it was in early draft or lecture form.

Finally, we are indebted to the American Academy of Arts and Sciences, the Carnegie Corporation, and the Corning Glass Works Foundation for grants in support of this project. We also wish to express our appreciation to Daniel Bell, Chairman of the Commission on the Year 2000; and John Voss, Executive Officer of the American Academy of Arts and Sciences, for their helpfulness and patience as we revised our revised revisions.

H.K.
A.J.W.

Croton-on-Hudson
New York
July 1967

Introduction

DANIEL BELL

Chairman of the Commission on the Year 2000
American Academy of Arts and Sciences

More than forty years ago, Kegan Paul in England and E. P. Dutton in New York published a series of small books, about eighty in number, entitled *Today and Tomorrow,* in which some outstanding minds of the time made predictions about the future. The titles were romantic and metaphorical, and this provided a clue to the style and contents of the series. Almost all the volumes used something Greek—a figure of myth or speech—to personify or typify his subject. J. B. S. Haldane wrote *Daedalus, or Science and the Future;* Bertrand Russell *Icarus, or the Future of Science.* The series ranged widely: Bonamy Dobrée on *Timotheus, or the Future of the Theatre;* Vernon Lee on *Proteus or the Future of Intelligence;* R. McNair Wilson on *Pygmalion or the Doctor of the Future.* Name the subject, and it was covered: food, clothes, architecture, war, peace, Jews, India, labor, machines, and even crime (entitled biblically, in this case, as *Cain*). Some of the books, obviously written for other occasions, were dragged in by the heels, such as Robert Graves' *Lars Porsena, or the Future of Swearing and Improper Language;* some were squeezed into the procrustean bed, such as *Nuntius, or Advertising and Its Future,* by Gilbert Russell; whereas others were squarely at the heart of the enterprise, such as *Sibylla, or the Revival of Prophecy* by C. A. Mace and *The Future of Futurism* by John Rodker [1] ("he has accomplished a considerable feat in writing on such a vague subject," wrote T. S. Eliot in the old London *Nation*).

What is striking about these volumes is their fanciful character, the personal and even prejudiced judgments, the airy and even comical tone, as if the idea of speculating about the future had a somewhat absurd but pleasant quality—in effect, a lack of seriousness. This is not to say that all the books

---

[1] Futurism, it should be pointed out, did not have the contemporary meaning (*circa* 1967) of organized studies of the future, but derived from the movement initiated by Marinetti in 1913, which sought to destroy the entire past in art (and even in society) and which glorified motion, action, violence, and the future. The idea has recurred in the "new" sensibility, which decries enduring art, glorifies "negation," and jumbles all genres.

were simply playful or positive. Russell's volume on the future of science, for example, was deeply pessimistic, for he refused to believe that the progress of science must be a boon to mankind. But in no sense were these books meant to be anything more than "opinion." There was no notion of how one could go, in Plato's sense of the divided line, from "becoming" to "being."

The essays on science and technology had a greater purchase on reality than the others. J. B. S. Haldane, for example, writing in 1923, made the stunning prediction that the center of science would pass from mathematical physics to biology. And in his projections of the future Haldane specified that progress in medicine would practically abolish infectious diseases ("though owing to Hindu opposition, parts of India were still quite unhealthy up to 1980 or so"), that new discoveries in nitrogen fixation would multiply crop yields, and that "by 1951" biologists would be able to produce "ectogenic" children through artificial insemination and the maintenance of female ovaries in the laboratory. (It is clear that Haldane's persuasive "scenarios" were the source of Aldous Huxley's frightening vision in *Brave New World*.) H. Stafford Hatfield, in his *Automaton, or the Future of Mechanical Man* (published in 1928), brilliantly anticipated cybernetic mechanisms that "perceive a change in conditions, such as size or composition of material, and immediately adjust the tool so as to meet correctly the changed conditions," and sketched an automaton that reads manuscripts of different sizes and type faces, automatically regulates traffic, and the like.

The essays on society were feeble. Arthur Shadwell, in his *Typhoeus, or the Future of Socialism* (1929), wrote an intelligent but conventional polemic on the difficulties of planning, but he believed, being a rational man, that this would mean a halt in the activities of the state, for example, in the Soviet Union. He assumed that Russia's failure to deal with the *kulaks* (i.e., the "rich" peasants) would stop the nascent development of collective farms, and there is not a hint of the forced industrialization in the Soviet Union that would begin the very year his small volume was published. *Atlantis, America and the Future*, by Colonel J. F. C. Fuller (1925), is full of portentous historical metaphors about the rise of a new Rome out of the materialism of America. ("Today Japan may be Carthage, but I cannot imagine Japan begetting a Hannibal. If she only could, then this New Rome might save Europe, before the orgy of the Red Cult slimes over her.") He is fond of inept biological metaphors about nations; like human beings, they go through childhood and adolescence, and since every nation as it grows up has to "step over the threshold of religion," soon, it would appear, though it may be a long time yet, the United States will be plunged into a religious war. Protestant will attack Catholic, and out of this hideous conflict will arise the form of religion best suited to the spiritual needs of the nation. Some think it will be the Methodist Episcopal Church, 'because this is unique already and is only to be found in the United States,' " [2]

This uneven competence in the series is apparent as well in the writings of H. G. Wells, the man who inspired all these efforts. In his earlier book *Anticipations,* written exactly at the turn of the century, Wells predicted some social changes with startling accuracy, and fell flat on his face with others. The reason is that Wells was one of the first writers to see the importance of technology and to derive social consequences from specific innovations. (In contemporary jargon, he relied on this as his independent variable.) The nature of technology is that it is cumulative and it becomes diffused. It is cumulative because there is a simple test of functional efficiency (greater utilization of energy, least cost, and the like), which dictates the replacement of one product by another, and it diffuses (these rates can be charted) because the savings in time, money, and effort are quickly apparent to all. (The Connecticut Yankee at King Arthur's Court was able to introduce quickly all kinds of wonderful inventions from the nineteenth century, but he foundered when he sought to change the religion and the monarchy—a lesson in the comparative recalcitrance of technology and belief systems in social change.)

Wells based most of his predictions on the revolutionary consequences of the changes in transportation both in "eclipsing" distance and spreading the span of organization. "No one who has studied the civil history of the nineteenth century," he wrote, "will deny how far-reaching the consequences of change in transit may be, and no one who has studied the military performances of General Buller and General De Wet but will see that upon transport, upon locomotion, may also hang the most momentous issues of politics and war. The growth of our great cities, the rapid popu-

---

[2] Colonel (later General) Fuller reflected a prejudice about America that was quite widespread in upper-class English circles in the 1920's, but he was more outspoken about it than most. Its theme, which he used as a basis for prediction, was America's loss of "character" because of the "mongrelization" of the country. Colonel Fuller writes, for example:

"The American gentleman, and by gentleman I mean a man of breeding and culture, is a most attractive character, perhaps partly due to his rarity. Generally he comes of old British stock and is proud of his ancestry. He is courtly and generous, hospitable, and well-mannered. Unfortunately this class is dwindling, as is generally the Anglo-Saxon stock. The exorbitant price of houses and the dearth of servants, has much to do with this, for no man, who respects his wife or values comfort, can indulge in the luxury of a family in an apartment flat of two rooms or in a hotel.

"If the Anglo-Saxon stock is dwindling, the Latin stock is increasing, and the Hebrew stock is rivalling the sand on the sea shore. New York, sometimes called Jew York, is crawling with Israelites. At Coney Island I literally saw square miles of naked Jews, all stumpy, all of a type, all quite impossible. The Negro problem may be a serious one, but surely the Jewish problem is far more so? In less than a generation New York will be a New Jerusalem, of this there can be no doubt."

lating of America, the entry of China into the field of European politics, are, for example, quite obviously and directly consequences of new methods of locomotion."

But this reliance on technology gave a mechanistic cast to Wells's thinking, and led him to make some horrendous errors as well. Correctly regarding war as the great centralizing feature of a society, Wells remarked: "War in the past was a thing of days and heroisms; battles and campaigns rested in the hand of the great commander. . . . War in the future will be a question of preparation, of long years of foresight and disciplined imagination . . . it will depend less and less on controlling personalities and driving emotions, and more and more upon the intelligence and personal quality of a great number of skilled men."

But this insight into the rationalization of the art of war led him to confuse all politics with technology. In picturing the Napoleonic figure of the past ("He will sweep aside parliaments and demogogues, carry the nation to glory, reconstruct it as an empire, and hold it together by circulating his profile and organizing further successes"), Wells says confidently: "Nothing of this sort is going to happen. . . . The world is no more to be recast by chance individuals than a city is to be lit by sky-rockets. The purpose of things emerges upon spacious issues, and the day of individual leaders is past." In this respect, Aristotle and Max Weber are still better guides to politics than Wells.

Reviewing the prophets of the past, one finds lacking in almost all of them—at least in their sociological predictions—any notion of how a society hangs together, how its parts are related to one another, which elements are more susceptible to change than others, and, equally important, any sense of method. They are not systematic, and they have no awareness of the nature of social systems: their boundaries, the interplay of values, motivation, and resources, the levels of social organization, and the constraints of custom and privilege on change. If there is a decisive difference between the future studies that are now under way and those of the past, it consists in a growing sophistication about methodology and an effort to define the boundaries—intersections and interactions—of social systems that come into contact with each other.

The recent interest in the future is quite novel. Men have always tried to chart the stars or read the entrails of animals in order to know their fate. And in the 1920's, as I have indicated, the idea of prophesying the future had a puckish air. But for about a quarter of a century there was little interest in the future. Men were preoccupied with a worldwide depression, were caught up in the horrors of death camps and fascism, and battered by the storms of war. It was enough, as the Abbé Sieyès remarked of an earlier tumult, simply to survive. In his August Comte lecture seven years ago, on

War and Industrial Society, Raymond Aron remarked: "We are too much obsessed by the 20th century to spend time speculating about the twenty-first. Long-range historical predictions have gone out of fashion."

It is true that the apocalyptic modes of thought that Aron had in mind—the fancies of Spengler, Toynbee, and Sorokin—are no longer pursued so avidly—though the recent popularity of Teilhard de Chardin, with his vision of mental evolution replacing physical evolution (and its science-fiction counterpart in the writings of Arthur C. Clarke, particularly *The City and the Stars*), might give us some pause on that account. But in the past five years there has been an enormous spate of writing on the future, and, more important, half a dozen or so institutions have been created to deal seriously and consistently with problems of the future. In France there is the *Prospectives* group founded by Gaston Berger and the *Futuribles* project directed by Bertrand de Jouvenel. In England the Social Science Research Council has set up the Committee on the Next Thirty Years. In the United States the organization called Resources for the Future, set up with the aid of the Ford Foundation, has done a notable series of studies (principally *Resources in America's Future* by Hans H. Landsberg, Leonard L. Fischman, and Joseph L. Fisher); the RAND Corporation has sponsored the Delphi prediction studies of Olaf Helmer and T. J. Gordon (available most readily in the volume *Social Technology* by Olaf Helmer); the American Academy of Arts and Science has created the Commission on the Year 2000, and the Hudson Institute, directed by Herman Kahn, has plunged full scale into studies of the future.

How does one explain this resurgence of interest in "the future"? Some of this is due, undoubtedly, to the lure of the millennial number of the year 2000, which is but thirty-three years away; two-thirds of all Americans now alive will probably witness the turn of that chiliastic year. Some is due to the romance of space—the awareness that within this generation men will stand upon the moon, and before the end of the century they may even reach out for Venus and Mars. Important as these factors are to the imaginative context of men's efforts—the recurrence of an impulse toward omnipotence—there are more prosaic, yet, paradoxically, more important reasons for this new upsurge. It arises from the simple fact that every society today is consciously committed to economic growth, to raising the standard of living of its people, and therefore to the planning, direction, and control of social change. What makes the present studies, therefore, so completely different from those of the past is that they are oriented to specific social-policy purposes; and along with this new dimension, they are fashioned, self-consciously, by a new methodology that gives the promise of providing a more reliable foundation for realistic alternatives and choices, if not for exact prediction.

Most theories of social change—and these were derived principally from the nineteenth century—have dealt with impersonal processes—theories of evolution, immanence, cycles, and the like. What is distinctive about the middle of the twentieth century is the deliberate intervention of human instruments, principally government, to control change for specified ends. With the growth of modern communication and transportation, we are more quickly aware of the linked consequences of change, and the need to anticipate these and to plan for them from the community to the national level. But the recognition of the need for planning involves an added dimension as well—the nature of time. The rebuilding of American cities, for example, involves a thirty-five-year cycle. The expansion of medical services, as another example, involves fifteen-year planning—the time it takes for a young man to enter college and complete his medical board exams. In fact, especially in a post-industrial society, where human capital is the scarcest resource, planning necessarily involves long-run commitments and, with equal necessity, it requires long-run forecasting.

But planning, by its very nature, is not a mechanical process. Central to it is the problem of choice—both for the ends desired and for the allocation of resources. Thus planning and rationality are one. All this puts us on the threshold of an ancient and persistent human quest: to choose our futures. And what is central, therefore, to the present future studies is not an effort to "predict" the future, as if this were some far-flung rug of time unrolled to some distant point, but the effort to sketch "alternative futures"—in other words, the likely results of different choices, so that the polity can understand the costs and consequences of different desires. A large part of America, since the end of World War II, has been reshaped by the desire of millions of Americans to own their own homes, on separate plots of ground—a consequence, in part, of the pastoral myths in America's past and the moralistic Protestant fear of the "big city." But few persons were aware of the large costs of such a change: the problem of travel time and of roadways; of vast new service needs, such as schools, water, police; of the sprawling and chaotic growth of townships and the like. Nor was there an effort to sketch the total costs of alternative plans: cluster-type suburban developments, or concentrated high-rise densities with large open spaces. It may well be that even if such alternatives were presented, most Americans would still have chosen the present dispersal of suburbia, but the polity would have gained a clearer idea of the range of problems involved. Hence the heart of the present future studies, whether of domestic or of international affairs, is the effort to chart "alternative futures" as the condition for policy choices.

Along with this has come a new sophistication in methodology. We have begun to assemble statistical time-series both to plot trend lines and to extrapolate likely developments. The existence of a trend is no necessary guarantee that it will continue; but knowledge of trends and curves gives us more knowledge of likely developments. Along with time-series, we have begun to construct "models" or likely combinations of trends and developments in order to uncover the connections and causal relations between variables. And finally, with such simple techniques as the Delphi method, we seek to impose some "controls" by checking the informed guesses of one set of observers with those of others.

This volume, by Herman Kahn and Anthony Wiener and their associates, arises out of the joint interest of the American Academy of Arts and Sciences and the Hudson Institute in sketching "alternative futures." In October 1965, the Academy created the Commission on the Year 2000, composed of thirty individuals, to stimulate such research. Discussions at the first plenary session of the Commission established the need for statistical and other "baselines for the future"; that is, a compilation of likely and possible future developments that the Commission could take as a starting point for more detailed consideration of policy consequences and alternatives. Mr. Kahn, a member of the Commission, was asked to undertake this task; and this research is the result.

This volume serves a double task. It fits into the ongoing work of the Commission on the Year 2000, and it is the foundation for continuing studies by the Hudson Institute in its own program. The Commission on the Year 2000 has produced five volumes of working papers. These include preliminary memoranda by this writer, transcripts of the plenary discussions, and about sixty papers by members of the Commission and invited participants on various aspects of the future. A selection of these materials has been published as the Summer 1967 issue of *Daedalus,* the magazine of the Academy, under the title of *Towards the Year 2000: Work in Progress,* and it will be issued as one of the *Daedalus* series of books published by Houghton Mifflin. The Commission on the Year 2000 has now entered the second phase of its project with the creation of eight working groups to undertake detailed consideration of problems under the following rubrics: the adequacy of governmental structure, the changing nature of values and rights, the intellectual institutions of a post-industrial society; the life-cycle of the individual; the international system; the social consequences of the computer; the problems of biomedical engineering, and the future organization of science and technology. These working groups take as predicate the assumption that the United States is becoming a post-industrial society, which I have defined as one in which the organization of theoretical knowledge becomes paramount for innovation in the society, and in which intellectual institutions become central in the social structure.[3] The statistical baselines and alternative futures are sketched in this volume. Messrs.

---

[3] For an elaboration of the theme, see my essays, "Notes on the Post-Industrial Society" in *The Public Interest,* Numbers 6 and 7, Winter and Spring 1967.

Kahn and Wiener, in the accompanying preface, indicate the role of this volume in the further plans of the Hudson Institute.

Apart from the substantive material which the Hudson Institute researchers have assembled—and their data on population trends, gross national product, literacy, military power, technological extrapolations, and so on are a unique service for students of social trends—what is especially noteworthy about this volume is the variety of methodological innovations that they have introduced. For the authors have skillfully employed a novel combination of history with statistical techniques to create some extraordinary sketches about the future.

Their efforts and conclusions underscore a crucial point about future studies. No one pretends that single "events" can be predicted. These are often contingent and even irrational. Nor can one predict what historians call "turning points" in the lives of men or nations—those events (e.g., the success or failure of a revolution) that can move nations in new directions. But all such events are constrained by various contexts: of resources, of customs, of will. And they are shaped, as well, by basic trends in human society: the growth of science, literacy, economic interdependence, and the like. This volume, therefore, is not an exercise in prophecy; it is an effort to sketch the constraints of social choice.

In his famous distinction between *fortuna* and *virtù* (in Chapter 25 of *The Prince*), Machiavelli argued that half of men's actions are ruled by chance, and the other half are governed by men themselves. This volume, and the work of the Commission on the Year 2000, is an effort to change that balance.

Columbia University
July 1967

THE YEAR 2000

A FRAMEWORK FOR SPECULATION
ON THE NEXT THIRTY-THREE YEARS

CHAPTER I

Change and Continuity

A. WHY SPECULATE FAR AHEAD?

There are many good reasons for trying to imagine what the world may be like over the next thirty-three years. The most important, of course, is to try to predict conditions in reasonable detail and to evaluate how outcomes depend on current policy choices. If only this were feasible, we could expect with reasonable reliability to change the future through appropriate policy changes today.[1] Unfortunately, the uncertainties in any study looking more than five or ten years ahead are usually so great that the simple chain of prediction, policy change, and new prediction is very tenuous indeed.

It is not that the period beyond the next decade (the approximate limit of usefulness of most policy research studies) is too far away to be of interest. It is short in terms of many human concerns: a child born this year will be only thirty-two years old on January 1, 2000, and many of today's adults will probably still be taking active roles in the first third of the twenty-first century. Useful or interesting as such long-range predictions would be, it is simply too difficult to make them well, and even more difficult to estimate how this relatively distant future depends on current policies.

Nevertheless, at the minimum, such studies, even if only partially successful, contribute to interesting lectures, provocative teaching, and stimulating conversation, all of which can broaden horizons and increase creativity —by no means negligible benefits. More important, these studies can affect basic beliefs, assumptions, and emphases. Probably most important, at least for us at Hudson Institute, is that long-range studies provide a context in which to do five- to ten-year studies that can and do influence policy choices. Thus a long-range perspective is useful to policy-planners and policy re-

[1] Of course, there is no doubt that actions taken today can change the future. The problem, to which we return in our concluding chapter, is that the changes may be unintended, undesirable, and unpredictable.

I

search analysts generally. Line decision-makers, in government and industry, in contrast to staff analysts, will ordinarily find extremely long-range studies less useful; they may be still less useful, in a narrow professional sense, for various specialists, though even here they can still be of some heuristic value.

Another important, but unfortunately often unattainable, objective for a long-range study is to anticipate some problem early enough for effective planning. Whether this can be accomplished more or less directly (as opposed to stimulating or providing a perspective for a later study or plan) depends, of course, on the issue and the question: some variables change much more slowly and reliably than others, and some questions need much better answers than others. Trends or events that depend on large, aggregative phenomena are often more amenable to long-range planning than those that depend on unique circumstances or special sequences of events. Projects, such as educating an individual, carrying out city planning, projecting recreational demands, formulating antipollution, or perhaps population control policies, can normally be usefully considered much further in advance than problems of international relations or subtle and complex national security issues. This is true because gross, long-term trends are far more recognizable and projectable than complex sequences of unique events, such as those that will determine tomorrow morning's headlines.

There are also problems of timing. Programs, policies, and doctrines, as well as governmental and military systems, usually change relatively slowly in response to current decisions, yet at the same time are changing rapidly as a result of decisions made in the past. In the late 1950's and early 1960's decisions were made on political and strategic programs (and military procurement) that will play a large part in determining the foreign alliances, political commitments, and military capabilities of the United States in the late 1960's and early 1970's. Today decisions are being made that will heavily influence our situation and commitments in the early and mid 1970's. Thus between now and about 1970 we are working in a changing context, and with changing instrumentalities, which were largely decided upon in the quite different conditions of at least five years ago. At the same time, our current needs and decisions find relatively little immediate response. In short, we can often do least to change sociopolitical situations that are closest to us and about which we know the most, while we may have the greatest influence over those future situations of which we know relatively little, even about our preferences. Thus to paraphrase the old French adage *"si la vieillesse pouvait; si la jeunesse savait"*—if the past only could; if the present only knew.

One answer, a partial one, to these problems at the national policy level is deliberately to build greater flexibility into both systems and programs. To the extent that we succeed in this, policy-makers and decision-makers of the future will be freed from some of the material, technological, and political constraints which otherwise could prevent them from responding appropriately to the circumstances in which they find themselves. Although this kind of flexibility is extremely valuable, it is difficult to achieve and may be expensive in both resources and, in some cases, the sacrifice of advantages associated with commitment strategies or the need for continuity. It is certainly expensive in thought. If it is desirable for a decision-maker to be able to "muddle through," how—in this world of accelerating changes and global political involvements—does he acquire the capability for muddling through? What are the parameters of that flexibility which all concede the policy-maker of the future is likely to need? One answer, as suggested in Chapter X, is to plan in a way that accommodates a large range of events. Options should be provided not only for the important long-run choices which are most likely to occur, but also for less likely choices insofar as they would present significant dangers or opportunities, and if preserving the options would not require giving up too much in current terms.

Thus in policy research we are not only concerned with anticipating future events and attempting to make the desirable more likely and the undesirable less likely. We are also trying to put policy-makers in a position to deal with whatever future actually arises, to be able to alleviate the bad and exploit the good. In doing this, one clearly cannot be satisfied with linear or simple projections: a range of futures must be considered. One may try to affect the likelihood of various futures by decisions made today, but in addition one attempts to design programs able to cope more or less well with possibilities that are less likely but that would present important problems, dangers, or opportunities if they materialized.

New and rapidly innovating technologies; vast political, social, and economic upheavals accompanying the worldwide mushrooming of population; the continued development of mass communication; and the less spectacular but equally consequential processes of urbanization, industrialization, and modernization are obvious facets of the second half of this century. It is a truism that the pace with which such changes are taking place has reduced the reliability of practical experience as a guide to public policy and has diminished the usefulness of conventional judgment in dealing with social problems. On the other hand, traditional or unalterable factors in man, societies, and culture continue to play important, even decisive, roles.

Policy-makers in many fields, given so much new information to assimilate, so many new variables to assess, and so little experience directly relevant to the new problems, can no longer be as confident of the applicability of traditional wisdom and can no longer rely as much on the intuitively derived judgments that once seemed adequate to resolve issues and to achieve fairly well-understood social goals. It is very difficult not to underestimate or overestimate the overall significance of new developments and tendencies: scientists, engineers, and managers who deal directly with modern technology and who are also interested in broad policy issues often seem to overestimate its likely social consequences, and go to extremes of optimism or pessimism, while those more oriented to the cultural heritage— whether they are unschooled conservatives or liberal, literary intellectuals— equally often seem to bank too heavily on historical continuity and social inertia. The problem, of course, is to sort out what changes from what continues, and to discern what is continuous in the changes themselves.

This kind of study of the long-range future has, after some decades of disrepute, become once again a matter of scholarly interest. Indeed it has become fashionable if not faddist. More or less systematic and serious efforts to explore the shape and possibilities of the future are under way in several places in the United States, Europe, and Japan. One thing which distinguishes some of these new efforts from the earlier work, or speculation, of individual writers and thinkers is their emphasis on sustained, cooperative, and relatively systematic effort. Several disciplines are enlisted in a common effort of analysis and interactive speculation. These efforts are hardly likely to replace individual visions of the future of the kind we already know, such as those of H. G. Wells, Aldous Huxley, and George Orwell, to take only the best-known recent examples in English. Such personal works of imagination—nearly all of them in fact passionately aimed at changing the future—are likely to prove more influential than more systematic and "reasonable," but correspondingly more prosaic, efforts. On the other hand, a properly led and integrated interdisciplinary project is more likely to incorporate the relevant insights, if any, from a range of academic and technical disciplines. It is also more likely, if this is an objective of the study, to address realistic policy issues in the form in which they are likely to arise. Sometimes, of course, such projects are trying to study important issues whether or not they have yet been perceived or felt to be important. In this case, while a competent interdisciplinary study is not necessarily more likely than a political fantasy to arouse the interest and concern of decision-makers, the former should, at least, contain recommendations in a form decision-makers can eventually use.

Of course, such interdisciplinary research may fail to achieve its objectives. For example, much interdisciplinary research results in congeries of reports rather than in integrated and unified discussions. Interdisciplinary projects that are organized as committees of equals are most likely to have this difficulty.

There is also a risk of falling between the stools of rigor and relevance: one may relax the requirement of being academically "sound" and "well grounded" so far (perhaps in order to be able to address interesting and important issues) that the work is of low quality; on the other hand, one may try so hard to be explicit and "objective" (perhaps so that there will be tangible empirical and analytical issues about which to argue) that the project is ultimately diverted from the more interesting and important issues—those that are hard to formulate and perhaps even partially "unresearchable." Despite these difficulties, good policy research projects are indeed more likely to produce hard documentation, explicit issues, or relatively objective speculation. The argument will then be carefully formulated and more productive than a discussion concerning intuitive assumptions, tastes, or values. (Such discussions are not necessarily futile, but it is difficult to avoid conducting them so abstractly, irrelevantly, or otherwise out of context that issues are not joined. It is rare for any cumulative growth in understanding to result from a series of such discussions.) And while only the great novelists and prophets can impart an intense sense of drama and excitement, even quite minor poets, seers, and publicists may achieve some of this quality. We hope that in this venture into speculation we have not been so austere as to exclude this flavor entirely, or so interested in the important, or sensational, as to be irresponsible.

B. METHOD: STANDARD PROJECTIONS AND MULTIFOLD TRENDS

In this study we have used several interrelated devices to facilitate making systematic conjectures about the future. The most important, of course, is simply to think about the problem—to seek to identify important long-term trends which seem likely to continue. These trends include the worldwide spread of a more or less secular humanism, the institutionalization of scientific and technological innovation, the expectation of continuous economic growth, and the like. For our purposes we have identified a complex, long-term "multifold trend" consisting of thirteen interrelated elements.

In addition, we have considered how the problem of projecting one-third century ahead might have appeared in 1933, 1900, and so on, in order to get a sense of the current and future pace of change and the likelihood of unexpected developments, and to identify significant clusters of events, qualitative changes in the combination of trends, and emergent properties, such as the increasing self-consciousness of time and history.

Next we have attempted to construct significant baselines, statistical where possible, to project key variables in society. These include population, literacy, gross national product, energy sources, military strength, and the like; these variables and their growth rates tend both to furnish and to constrain the possibilities for any society. By selecting extrapolations of current or emerging tendencies that grow continuously out of today's world and reflect the multifold trend and our current expectations, we create a "surprise-free" projection—one that seems less surprising than any other specific possibility. Consistent with this projection, we describe a "standard world" and several "canonical variations," designed to raise certain issues.

We have used two approaches common in the study of political-military and other kinds of public policy problems—the scenario and the systematic context, or "alternative future." These methodological devices are especially valuable in the study and evaluation of the interaction of complex and/or uncertain factors. Scenarios are hypothetical sequences of events constructed for the purpose of focusing attention on causal processes and decision-points. They answer two kinds of questions: (1) Precisely how might some hypothetical situation come about, step by step? and (2) What alternatives exist, for each actor, at each step, for preventing, diverting, or facilitating the process? "Alternative futures" can be used for generating additional scenarios, for setting forth and discussing criteria, for the systematic comparison of various alternative policies (or alternative combinations of assumptions and objectives), or for the analysis and examination of specific issues. They are also of interest in making assumptions and contexts explicit, as should be done, for example, in any analysis of "directions and destinations." With a set of alternative futures and scenarios that lead to them by alternative routes, one may see better what is to be avoided or facilitated, and one may also gain a useful perspective on the kinds of decisions that may be necessary, and the points in time after which various branching-points will have been passed.

We have found it useful to construct a range of future contexts that include not only some of the main expectations (both hopes and fears) of policy-planners, but also other cases of interest. By constructing a "concrete" series of named futures and treating all the factors involved in an internally consistent fashion, we hope to be better able to understand not only the separate factors and their interactions, but important consequences of these that are often overlooked in general or abstract analyses and discussions. By making potential directions and destinations clearer, the construction of these contexts can also lead to better understanding of the significance of current emphases, of the major alternatives, and of how different these may be.

1. The Basic, Long-Term Multifold Trend

The basic trends of Western society, most of which can be traced back as far as the twelfth or eleventh centuries, can be seen as part of a common, complex trend of interacting elements. For analytic purposes, however, we shall separate them into thirteen rubrics, as shown in Table 1. Obviously one might wish to group these elements into fewer and more abstract categories, or to refine the analysis by identifying or distinguishing many more aspects. From the point of view of looking toward the future, the important consideration is that, as basic trends, these elements seem likely to continue at least for the next thirty-three years, though some may saturate or begin to recede beyond that point.

TABLE I

There Is a Basic, Long-Term Multifold Trend Toward:

1. Increasingly Sensate (empirical, this-worldly, secular, humanistic, pragmatic, utilitarian, contractual, epicurean or hedonistic, and the like) cultures
2. Bourgeois, bureaucratic, "meritocratic," democratic (and nationalistic?) elites
3. Accumulation of scientific and technological knowledge
4. Institutionalization of change, especially research, development, innovation, and diffusion
5. Worldwide industrialization and modernization
6. Increasing affluence and (recently) leisure
7. Population growth
8. Urbanization and (soon) the growth of megalopolises
9. Decreasing importance of primary and (recently) secondary occupations
10. Literacy and education
11. Increasing capability for mass destruction
12. Increasing tempo of change
13. Increasing universality of the multifold trend

The terminology presents problems that we hope to clarify later in this chapter, in which we shall discuss the thirteen elements in some detail. Despite the fact that none of our discussion of the multifold trend depends on the acceptance of any formal theory of history, we will also find it useful to illuminate some of the issues that will arise in the continuation of the trends by reference to various more or less systematic and comprehensive theories of long-term, historical change. Having identified certain rather general trends, however, the question arises: How do we extrapolate from these to a point several decades ahead?

2. Surprise-Free Projections and the Standard World

In projecting beyond the next decade, whether studying general trends and contexts or very specific areas, we must choose—perhaps more or less arbitrarily—among many plausible alternatives those which ought to be studied in greater detail. We have discussed some of the methodology of such choices in *Selected Papers from the Hudson Institute*, Volume II-A of the Working Papers of the Commission on the year 2000 of the American

Academy of Arts and Sciences.[2] While we shall not repeat that discussion here, it is worth stressing that our uses of "future worlds" or "standardized contexts" are, like our references to historical theories, mostly heuristic, and are intended to be used as vehicles for further discussion, explication of underlying assumptions, and systematic consideration of major alternatives.

One problem of long-range speculation is that the subjective curve of probabilities often seems flat. That is, no particular course of events may seem much likely than a large range of others. In order to avoid the dilemma of Buridan's ass, who starved midway between two bales of hay because he could not decide which one he preferred, we must then make arbitrary choices among almost equally interesting, important, or plausible possibilities. That is, if we are to explore any predictions at all, we must to some extent "make them up." Clearly, the most salient of the projections we can make is one that is "surprise-free"; nevertheless it would be very surprising if in any thirty-three-year period the real world did not produce many political and technological surprises.

For the skeptical reader this "surprise-free" projection may be useful chiefly as a norm for comparison and disagreement. While the surprise-free projection is similar in spirit to the "naïve projection" of the economist, which assumes a continuation of current tendencies, it is more complex in that it also includes the implications of whatever empirical and theoretical considerations affect our expectations. (For example, a "naïve" projection of world population to 2000 would be about 7.2 billion, but our "surprise-free" projection would be 6.4 billion, and a persuasive case could be made for a somewhat lower figure.) Then while still staying within this general surprise-free projection one can specify one or more "standard" worlds for even more intensive study.

It is important, or useful, to make up such descriptions and name them, in part because the shared literature of any audience may not contain a sufficiently varied or precise set of referents. We shall present two kinds of contexts here, the "Standard World" and the "Canonical Variations." Our own Standard World, adumbrated throughout the volume, reflects our own expectations, of course, and we have tried to make these explicit as much as possible. Several of our colleagues at Hudson Institute share these expectations, wholly or in part. In a larger and more comprehensive study, any important set of attitudes that is held by any important consensus about the range and possible projections of happenings that would broadly, if roughly, encompass the salient factors of the real world might be considered as defining an alternative "standard" world.

[2] See especially Section C-5 of Herman Kahn, "On Alternative World Futures." This paper will also appear in Morton A. Kaplan, ed., *New Approaches to International Relations*, to be published by St. Martin's Press in 1968.

3. *The Canonical Variations*

Each of the major alternatives to the Standard World that we will consider can be put into one of three categories: (*A*) more "Integrated," (*B*) more "Inward-Looking," and (*C*) in greater "Disarray." The models in these categories envisage, respectively:

(*A*) a relatively peaceful, relatively prosperous, relatively arms-controlled world with a relatively high degree of consultation among nations, and the existence of political coordination or even integration among all, or almost all, the major and/or minor powers;

(*B*) almost as peaceful and prosperous a world, but with little arms control or general coordination; and

(*C*) a relatively troubled and violent world, but one in which no large central wars have occurred.

Table II lists the eight Canonical Variations.

TABLE II
Canonical Variations

A. More Integrated
  1. Stability-oriented
  2. Development-oriented
B. More Inward-Looking
  3. With an eroded Communist movement
  4. With an eroded democratic morale and
       some Communist dynamism
  5. With a dynamic Europe and/or Japan
C. Greater Disarray
  6. With an eroded Communist movement
  7. With a dynamic Communist movement and
       some erosion of democratic morale
  8. With a dynamic Europe and/or Japan

By focusing attention on each of the above possibilities in turn, we get a sense of comparative structures and of a range of possibilities while remaining within or fairly close to the "surprise-free" projections. Yet it should be clear that only a Procrustean theory could attempt to define the next ten to fifteen years (much less the next thirty-three) in terms of such single themes. The reality will undoubtedly be one in which one theme alternates with another, or there is a dialectical contention among political trends, or open conflict. But for our standardized and canonical contexts (and for some but not all of the scenarios that lead to them), we assume that there is little fluctuation from simple secular trends.

In these projections we assume that the ten major powers (which we have divided into the categories super, large, and intermediate) develop more or less according to Figure 1. One might have wanted to assume that the "Integrated World" develops more rapidly and with smaller disparities in income than the "Inward-Looking World," and that this in turn develops more rapidly than the "Disarray World." While this is reasonable, it is not by any means inevitable.

Figure 1 shows how the ten largest nations compared in GNP and population in 1965 (numerals in circles), and the points they seem most likely to reach by the year 2000 (numerals in ellipses). The numbers identifying each country are in the order of our medium or "best estimate" projections for GNP in 2000; except that the differences among Canada, India, and Italy are not significant. The ellipses indicate a range of reasonable uncertainty for each year 2000 projection. In 1965, for example, the United States had a GNP of $692 billion (by United Nations definition), population of about 195 million, and per capita GNP of $3,560. By the year 2000 its GNP could be up to more than $4,500 billion (almost the top of the chart) with more than $12,000 per capita GNP; or assuming the lowest "reasonable" growth rate, GNP could be less than $1,400 billion and GNP per capita under $5,000. The range in population estimates is narrower—291 to 361 million. Our "best estimate" for the United States is for a GNP close to the top of the "reasonable range" and for a relatively moderate population growth—$3,200 billion and 318 million people. (Chapter III contains more detailed figures.) The ellipses for India and China slope backward because they are more likely to achieve relatively high GNP growth if they can limit population. The descriptions for the GNP per capita ranges will be explained on page 58.

Finally we separate the 135 nations of the world into two classes—old (about 55) and new (about 80). Old nations are those that have had a relatively continuous existence at least since World War I; new nations are for the most part post-World War II creations or ancient countries recently emerged from colonial status. We consider West Germany to be an old nation; East Germany, China (newly integrated), Taiwan, India (newly independent), Egypt, and so on to be new. We also assume (again in all worlds, and for the 1967-2000 period as a whole) the fulfillment of certain widespread current expectations: that there will be more or less sustained economic growth, among all the major (and most minor) nations; and more or less sustained (but usually tapering off) population growth; and that except in periods of actual war or great crisis there will be freedom of the seas with foreign commerce moving freely and without explicit reliance on national naval or other military power. We assume that there will be few and minor frontier changes, if any, in the old nations, chiefly because of general conditions of political stability or inertia rather than because of the

FIGURE 1
"SURPRISE-FREE" PROJECTIONS
FOR THE TEN MAJOR COUNTRIES

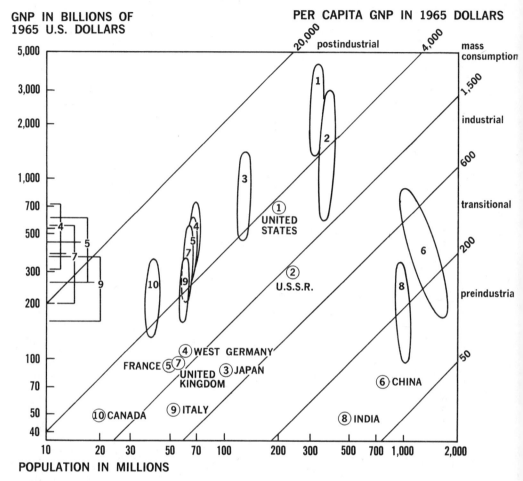

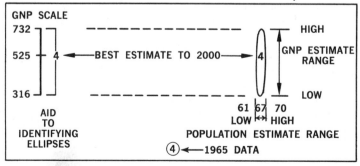

LEGEND (EXAMPLE IS WEST GERMANY)

balance—or lack of balance—of local military situations. We assume that most of the old nations will not be called on to use military power to advance their national interests—at least in any simple or direct way. Obviously nations may nonetheless experience benefits, or disutilities, from military power, for example, from their ability implicitly or explicitly to protect (or threaten) various other nations; and some small nations may obtain security benefits, or disutilities, from having sizable national military forces, for example, from being a more valuable ally or from feeling freer to accept or reject offers of protection by larger nations. But by and large, for *most* of the old nations (and many of the new), national security is assumed to be free—derived from the general condition of stability rather than a nation's own efforts.

Of course, this stability, if it exists or is to continue, will be maintained, in part, by the willingness of various nations (especially the United States or the Soviet Union) to intervene judiciously when situations arise that threaten the general equilibrium. Presumably the balance could be tipped by one of these nations trying either too hard or not hard enough—by failing to check forces tending to instability or by intervening too readily in an attempt to control events.

The Canonical Variations, while also standardized, do not necessarily describe a particular consensus, but only a set or collection of assumptions, trends, or possibilities to which it is useful to give a name. The one Standard and eight Canonical Worlds described in this volume represent in our judgment a sort of minimum range of variation for a reasonably systematic discussion. In fact, we have occasion to go outside this range; but we believe that the range represented does include the most salient possibilities at least in the next decade or so, and that most of these possibilities could be extended for some purposes into the 1980's and even to the year 2000 and perhaps beyond. The reason for the restriction in time is that it is difficult to take any simple collection of constant trends and maintain that these are likely to be continuously dominating themes over the next thirty-three years. While such "straight line" (or often actually exponential) trends are not impossible, modern history in particular does seem to have certain cyclical or ebb-and-flow characteristics in time periods as short as decades. We have not, as yet, formulated any Standard or Canonical Worlds with these latter characteristics, but we have included scenarios of this type in Chapters VI and VII.

This study thus will present some fairly simple "surprise-free" political projections (Standard Worlds) and some nearly surprise-free Canonical Variations; together these represent a range of not implausible developments from existing conditions. Their narrow range of variance is for present purposes their merit as well as their disadvantage. The fact that they are surprise-free, or nearly surprise-free, makes them generally acceptable for use and discussion, but we should be quite clear that as we extrapolate these projections beyond the next decade into the mid-1980's and to the year 2000 (and even in some cases to 2020), the assumption that no grave surprises or great crises will occur becomes increasingly untenable. But this does not make these worlds entirely useless. They provide specific cases, or examples, with which one can disagree as well as agree, vary from as well as use without change, make use of to emphasize specific contradictions as well as to illustrate or elaborate hypotheses.

We have done what we could to construct our Standard World of tendencies that are currently dominant. On the other hand, it is possible that it more or less naïvely canonizes the perceptions and assessments of the moment, and it is likely to be heavily influenced by hopes and fears of the moment—even perhaps emphasizing present trends that are waning or events that have already lost their importance. Our most important caveat, however, is that *almost any day has some chance of bringing up some new crisis or unexpected event that becomes a historical turning-point, diverting current tendencies so that expectations for the distant future must shift.* Over any period of decades at least one such shift, and probably several, are likely—and the turning-point may come at any moment. Thus any study of the distant future may date rapidly.

C. SOME PERSPECTIVES ON HISTORICAL CHANGE

1. *The First Two-Thirds of the Twentieth Century*

We are attempting in this study to speculate about the next third of the twentieth century and, to a very limited degree, about the first third of the century following it. Even more, we are trying to create a framework and context for further speculation by ourselves and by others. Some perspective on the problem may be gained by considering what a "surprise-free" projection might have been like in 1933 or 1900. The following tables list features of those periods that furnish points of comparison.

Many would argue that the world of 1900 was close to being a political, cultural, and economic unit. Almost all parts of it were in intimate contact —at least with the United States, Western Europe, Russia, or Japan. One might think of this as a worldwide "Western" empire; the world being dominated by the major powers of Western and Central Europe, the United States (a direct extension of West European culture), and two Westernized non-Western societies, Japan and Russia. (While the latter was, of course, geographically and in many ways culturally an integral part of Europe, the acculturative impact of the postfeudal West's contact with Russia justifies thinking of it as, in 1900, a partly Westernized Russo-Byzantine culture.)

TABLE III

Year 1900

One world (Western-dominated), though with many unassimilated, traditional cultures

Industrial, colonial, or "protected" societies

Declining United Kingdom and France—rising Germany, United States, Russia, and Japan

Parliamentary government and Christianity

Basic feeling in almost all classes of the white race (and in many non-white) of optimism, security, progress, order, and physical supremacy of Western culture, and a belief in rational and moral domestic and foreign politics, and perhaps most important of all, a relative absence of guilt feelings

Intellectual acceptance of the ideas of Adam Smith, Darwin, and the Enlightenment by the West

It is interesting to note that the only two non-Western countries which had successfully begun to industrialize by 1900—Japan and Russia—did so more to serve the purposes of national security than to increase their standard of living. Except possibly for Turkey, Iran, Thailand, Ethiopia, and some Latin American countries, every nation which by 1900 had failed to industrialize was either in colonial status, a protectorate, or a *de facto* dependency. Successful industrialization was widely perceived as a matter of national independence if not national survival. By contrast, one of the difficulties nations experience in attempting to industrialize in the 1960's is that this pressure for survival has been much reduced, while the pressure of the "revolution of rising expectations" is often relatively weak, if it is the sole motivation for social reform, sustained national effort, and even individual sacrifice. While in 1900 individuals in many societies were powerfully motivated by a combination of ambition and patriotism, in 1967 similarly placed persons more often seem to feel that much less is at stake. As a result, individuals who dedicate themselves to development are often not sufficiently protected either from cynical criticism which, whether relevant or not, may lead to erosion of morale, or from the competitive demands, whether reasonable or not, of various "nonproductive" private or public activities that divert individuals from concentrating their time and energy on making various entrepreneurial activities or social investments successful. Furthermore, successful individuals do not serve as examples for others to the extent that they have not contributed to a felt public need.

It is an open question how effective material ambition will prove to be in causing various societies to change themselves in the last third of the twentieth century, particularly since many of these societies have a great distance to go. Presumably we shall have to wait several more decades for a verdict on how powerful the "revolution of rising expectations" is as a force for modernization. To date this verdict is an open one for most, but not all, of the non-Western nations. (We shall discuss this further below.)

In the year 1900 it was clear to many, and had been for some time, that the two established great powers of Western Europe, Great Britain and France, were losing power compared to Germany, the United States, Japan, and Russia. Using some terms to be discussed later, one can think of Britain and France as "core" powers of the West, Germany (or at least Prussianized Germany) as "semiperipheral," the United States as "fully peripheral," and Russia and Japan as either fully peripheral or new "mixtures."

So far as systems of government and religion were concerned, the parliamentary ideal was widely accepted. Christianity was almost everywhere triumphant or on the rise in 1900—except in the modernized nations that had been traditionally Christian, where secularization had made important inroads. This attraction toward parliamentarianism and Christianity may have been less a result of the intrinsic appeal of these systems than of the association of these systems with the power and charisma of the unprecedently successful West.

The national self-satisfaction, optimism, and faith in the future of most Western or Westernized people was, to modern eyes, perhaps the most striking characteristic of the year 1900—and one that was soon to disappear in the tragic futilities of World War I and its aftermath. Most likely the loss of optimism stemmed as much from the systematic postwar disillusionment, which reinforced the experience of the war and made psychological recovery almost impossible, as from the immediate or direct effects of the war itself.[3] In any case it seems doubtful that our century, or possibly even the early twenty-first century, will see the revival—at least in the West—of the almost total faith in the existing economic and social system and its leaders. When such revivals of faith and optimism occur, they tend to be restricted to elite groups and to be relatively shallow and transitory in the rest of the society—and/or often associated with aberrant ideologies (e.g., Communism and Fascism).

One reason, of course, for the serene confidence of 1900 was that the widespread acceptance of the theories of Adam Smith and Darwin and of the political values and philosophical assumptions of the Enlightenment provided a convincing rationale for the organization, values, and operations

[3] Contrast, for example, the attitudes of the residents of Hiroshima and Nagasaki today: the former are preoccupied with their historic experience with nuclear weapons, while the latter almost ignore it; yet both cities went through almost the same physical experience. The even more destructive attacks on Dresden and Tokyo, for example, were "conventional," and therefore seem to have left much less psychological residue.

of the bourgeois and imperialist systems. An even more important cause for this faith was the actual success of the system and its seemingly improving prospects—particularly during "la belle epoque," the period from 1901 to 1913 when there took place an extraordinary, almost worldwide, economic growth and prosperity, coupled with impressive scientific and technological advances. Despite the many countertendencies that might be cited, la belle epoque was widely perceived, especially in retrospect, as the culmination point of a century of material, technological, scientific, and, seemingly, ethical progress.

Table IV notes that in contrast to the expectations listed in Table III, the first third of the twentieth century brought some startling and almost totally unexpected events.

TABLE IV

First Third of the Twentieth Century

Russo-Japanese War
"La Belle Epoque" (1901-1913)
Mexican (1910) and Chinese (1911) social (and racial) revolutions
World War I—Europe partly devastated
Five major dynasties (Hohenzollern, Hapsburg, Romanov, Manchu, and Ottoman) dethroned
Emergence of United States as leading world power
Loss of European (and democratic) morale and prestige
Rise of Communism and Soviet Union
Great Depression
Rise of Fascist ideologies and diverse dictatorships
Upsetting impact of new intellectual concepts, such as those of Bohr, de Broglie, Einstein, Freud, and Schroedinger

---

The next third of a century experienced still more unexpected changes and disturbing events, as shown in Table V. An Indian national is quoted as saying of these first two-thirds of the century:

> For us in Asia there have been two epochal events in this century. The first was Japan's defeat of Russia in 1905. The second was China's atom bomb. . . . Asia and India are learning the uses of power in the modern world. The first lesson was taught by Japan in 1905. It demonstrated that an Asian country could master the West's weapons and use them to defeat the West. The second lesson was taught by China. It demonstrated that Asia could equal the West even in advanced military technology . . .[4]

[4] As quoted by Harrison E. Salisbury in the *New York Times,* August 18, 1966.

TABLE V

Second Third of the Twentieth Century

Continued growth of Communism and Fascism
World War II—Europe again devastated
Mass murder and forced population movements
on extraordinary scale before, during, and after
World War II
Intense, nationalistic competition in the develop-
ment and application of radically new technol-
ogies for both peace and war
Decolonization
The Cold War and Neutralism
Shifts in power position
    Rise and decline of Italy, Canada, and India
    Decline and reemergence of Europe
    Decline and reemergence of Japan
    Reunification and centralization of China
    Emergence of
        Two super powers (U.S. and S.U.)
        Five large powers (Japan, W. Germany,
        France, China, U.K.)
        Three intermediate powers (India,
        Italy, Canada)
Post-Keynesian, post-Marxian, and perhaps post-
communal and sophisticated "development" eco-
nomics
Emergence of mass-consumption societies
"Second" wave of industrial revolutions
Chinese achieve nuclear status

The first item on Table IV and the last on Table V emphasize this perspective. To Asia—or at least some Asians—the century began with a nonwhite nation's successfully beating a white nation on its own ground, thus
proving that Europe's four-hundred-year-old military supremacy was not
necessarily permanent; and the second third of the century ended with the
acquisition of nuclear weapons by another nonwhite nation. Both of these
events were seen at the time as of crucial and worldwide significance and,
at least in the first instance, came as a great and unexpected shock. It is
said that in the first decade of the century there were Africans who did not
know what Russia and Japan were, and yet knew that a nonwhite people
had defeated a white nation. A leaflet circulated among the Annamite
population of Indochina during this same period said:

I, your humble servant, an obscure student, having had occasion to study new books and new doctrines, have discovered in a recent history of Japan how they have been able to conquer the impotent Europeans. This is the reason we have formed an organization. . . . We have selected from young Annamites the most energetic, with great capacities for courage, and are sending them to Japan for study. . . . Our only aim is to prepare the population for the future.[5]

It may be noted that many of the items on Tables IV and V would probably not have been predicted by any individual or policy research group "speculating about the next thirty-three years," in either 1900 or 1933.

Most of the items on the two preceding tables require no further comment, but let us note a few points that are suggested.

Probably the great divide was World War I, preceded as it was by the thirteen years that are still known as "la belle epoque," years which were, for almost all the civilized world, an unprecedented era of sustained growth. While some of the period's glory has been dimmed by comparison with the post-World War II era of growth, the years are still remembered nostalgically by many. One of the issues that we shall find worth speculating about is whether or not the period since 1952, which is also an era of unprecedentedly sustained worldwide growth, is the start of a "new" age (as projected in Chapter III) or a temporary high plateau in the ups and downs of the economic cycle.

World War I not only terminated la belle epoque, it shattered the moral and political structure of Europe. One might have thought that the effective triumph of democracy over despotism (or at least unenlightened monarchy) would have created a situation of high morale, but the cost of the war had been too high, particularly the seeming senselessness of many of the tactics, the moral effect of various revisionist and antiwar writers, and the disillusionment with the postwar settlement. The loss of European morale and prestige following 1918 was both grave and worldwide. Many former admirers of European culture, such as the Chinese scholar Yen Fu (who had spent his lifetime translating such authors as J. S. Mill and Adam Smith, and attempting to get his own country to adopt many aspects of Western culture), turned on the West. Yen Fu wrote: "Western culture, after this European war, has been corrupted utterly. It seems to me that in three centuries of progress the peoples of the West have achieved four principles: to be selfish, to kill others, to have little integrity, and to feel little shame." [6]

The pessimism that seized the West was reflected in the popularity of such authors as Spengler. While most Europeans presumably expected that

[5] As quoted in Edmund Stillman and William Pfaff, *The Politics of Hysteria,* (New York: Harper and Row, 1964), p. 103.

[6] As quoted in *ibid.* The genuine (and significant) disillusionment of an admirer of the West should be distinguished from anti-Western cant that stems from other motives.

the Russians or Asians would be the ones to succeed to the West's power, actually an aberrant of Western culture, Naziism, came perilously close to conquering all of Europe, and, in alliance with Japan, becoming predominant in the world. While Fascism, and still more, Nazism are no doubt heretical to the Western tradition, they are as much products of Western culture as, say, pollution is of industry. That is, they are not inevitable, can sometimes be prevented, but result from identifiable and historically continuous religious, ideological, cultural, and structural forces in Western societies—trends that were emphasized by the pessimism and sense of frustration that resulted from World War I.

Despite the widespread belief that it is poverty that creates instability and messianic totalitarian movements, such as Communism and Fascism, historically it was the four nations closest to catching up with or passing the advanced industrial powers, but which also encountered frustrations—Japan, Russia,[7] Germany and Italy—that provided the serious instability of the first half of this century. This may turn out to be the prototype of some possibilities in the next sixty-six years as well. Certainly a better understanding of the dynamics of the situation is provided by avoiding the clichés that the major source of international unrest is poverty and that the process of industrialization cures unrest. Unfortunately there are many cases to the contrary.

The excesses and political pathologies of ideological mass movements such as Communism and Fascism may be as much due to the character of their adherents as to their totalitarian-utopian dogmas and irrationalities. Mass movements often find converts among those who are alienated from society, leading meaningless and purposeless lives, or anxious to "escape" from themselves, perhaps by surrendering themselves to an all-embracing ideal—a movement that requires the submerging of personality to its unity of purpose and action. Specific examples include rootless or restless adolescents; the newly poor; frustrated but ambitious and/or confident classes or minorities; various kinds of misfits and outcasts; nihilists and egoists; and paranoids and opportunists. Such people are created in abundance by the rapid industrialization of almost any traditional culture (e.g., Japan), or even by the forced catching-up of "backward" and still relatively traditional portions of the West (e.g., Prussia and Italy). They are particularly likely to exist in large numbers when the industrialization process is interrupted by a depression or when the more progressive and/or stable elements and values of the society have lost strength, or "charisma," perhaps as a result of war and defeat. (In Chapter IV we conjecture that the problems associated with too rapid acculturation and/or of leading "meaningless and

---

[7] From 1890 to 1914 (except for the years of the Russo-Japanese War, 1904 to 1905) Russia grew in GNP at an average rate of 8 per cent and was thus, in some ways, undergoing a very successful industrialization.

purposeless" lives are likely to rise again, but this time in new forms caused as much by the "success" of industrial society as by defeat and depression.)

Finally, we noted in Table IV that there were many new theories put forth during the first third of the century that were, at least for intellectuals, profoundly upsetting. The self-assured, rationalistic, moralistic, and mechanically minded Victorians were told, in effect, that solid matter is mostly empty; that time is relative and that perfectly accurate clocks run at different speeds; that the world is governed by the probabilistic laws of wave mechanics, rather than by simple deterministic "cause and effect" as suggested by Newtonian mechanics; [8] and finally that a good deal of what passes as rational behavior is actually motivated by unconscious impulses and feelings of a socially unacceptable or reprehensible character. Yet all of these ideas were accepted with astonishingly little disturbance. This may or may not augur well for the capacity to accept still newer concepts and technical developments likely in the near future, a subject discussed in Chapters II and VII. It is interesting to note also that while the new ideas did not seem to unhinge anyone (though of course some psychotics no doubt wove them into their delusions), people were very interested. In the half-century before 1940 hundreds of popular books were published explaining the new ideas. For various reasons this interest, along with the "conflict between religion and science," has almost disappeared since World War II.

The second third of the twentieth century (Table V) ended with two super powers, five large powers, three intermediate powers, and about one hundred twenty small powers. This structure and hierarchy seem likely to characterize the next decade or two as well. In fact, listing Japan and West Germany as the two largest of the five "large" powers is even more appropriate for the mid-1970's than for today.

Let us comment briefly on the strange careers—a sharp rise and a sharp fall—of Italy, Canada, and India, in the middle third of the twentieth century. Italy achieved important international status under Mussolini in the 1930's and lost it in the early 1940's as a result of defeat. Canada achieved great—if implicit and largely unrecognized—influence in the decade after World War II. Canada was then perhaps the third or fourth most influential power in the world, having emerged from World War II as a major industrial and agricultural power with large surplus resources of material, men, and energy, which it contributed to reconstruction, rehabilitation, and peacekeeping. It controlled territory essential to the air defense of the United States. It was, effectively, leader of the small powers of NATO, in part be-

[8] Of course, many physicists now believe that the world is deterministic, but that there are unknowable "hidden variables." However, in the early days of quantum mechanics and the uncertainty principle, many philosophers seized upon the latter as allowing for, or being identical with, free will and thus providing a belated and unexpected answer to the mechanists and determinists of the eighteenth and nineteenth centuries.

cause of its intimacy and influence with the United States, but also because it shared the small powers' perspectives and interests—or at least the small powers thought so and thus were almost always greatly influenced by Canadian example. Finally, Canada played an active and central role in United Nations activities generally, and peacekeeping in particular. Today, however, the economic and political recovery of the rest of the world, the development of ballistic missiles, the erosion of NATO, and the rise of the Afro-Asian bloc in the United Nations have reduced Canada to the least important of the intermediate powers.

India achieved its remarkable status under Prime Minister Nehru who, whether wisely or not, acted in a self-appointed, but widely acknowledged, moral role and was the effective political leader of the Third World. Serious and chronic internal difficulties and failures, morally ambiguous acts by the Indian government, China's attacks, and Nehru's death all combined to reduce India to a status that we would judge to be that of the most important of the intermediate powers.

Perhaps the most significant aspect of the middle third of the twentieth century has been the sustained economic growth achieved in the post-World War II era. This has raised as a real possibility worldwide industrialization and the emergence in more advanced industrial nations of what has been called a postindustrial culture. Some of this economic growth clearly derives from a growing sophistication in governmental economic policies. As even the classical economist Milton Friedman recently said, "We are all Keynesians today, and we are all post-Keynesians as well." If this were not true, and the postwar world had been marked by the same violent swings between prosperity and depression as in the interwar world, we would not now take such a sanguine view of future economic prospects. But now it seems—or at least is widely believed—that, except possibly for China, almost all the Communist and capitalist governments are coming to understand how to keep their economies reasonably stable and growing (i.e., both the capitalists and the Marxists are "revisionist"). While we reject the so-called convergence theory, in which it is argued that Communism and capitalism will come to resemble each other so closely that they will be practically indistinguishable, it is clear that they are borrowing from each other—with the Marxists, however, doing more of the explicit borrowing. (However, the idea of five-year plans seems to have been borrowed from the Marxists.) We believe that current governmental success in economics and planning is a major cause of the emergence of mass-consumption societies in Western Europe, the United States, Japan, and Australia, and is one reason why such societies can be expected to emerge rapidly in the Soviet Union and Eastern Europe.

It is still an open question, however, whether the same thing can be achieved in communal societies, such as China is striving to be, and in the less-developed nations generally. But at least two groups of less-developed nations are now doing so well economically that it is reasonable to think of them as undergoing a kind of second industrial revolution. Thus, as indicated on Table VI, those parts of Europe that were left behind by the Industrial Revolution, or which were "transplanted," are now beginning to catch up.

TABLE VI

Second Wave of Industrial Revolutions

1. Eastern Europe
2. Southern Europe
3. "European Latin America"
   (e.g., mostly the cities)
4. Israel
5. South Korea, Taiwan, Thailand,
   Malaysia, Singapore, Hong Kong,
   and perhaps the Philippines
6. And, to some degree, the rest of the
   Third World (e.g., currently Iran
   and Pakistan)

Even more impressive are the growth rates in the Sinic cultures of the world outside China. (Because of the large Chinese element, these include Malaysia and perhaps the Philippines and Thailand. All the countries listed under item five currently seem able to sustain a growth rate of about 8 per cent, except for the Philippines, which has about 5 per cent.) One can remark—half seriously—that wherever the Chinese (or their culture) have gone in the world they have done well, except in China: there the system was designed by Chinese and even the Chinese cannot beat it. More accurately, as we shall discuss later, for about 2000 years (until around 1800) China was, except for periodic interregna, the preeminent culture in the world by almost any criterion. It may now once more be coming out of an interregnum, but whether it will again achieve its "normal" status must now be judged unlikely or at best an open question.

As Table VI indicates, the rest of the Third World is also growing, but less strongly and consistently.

2. The Last Third of the Twentieth Century and the Beginning of the Next

Let us turn now to the last third of our century. In this chapter we shall consider only a relatively apolitical and "surprise-free" projection. The reader will see what we mean by "relatively apolitical" and "surprise-free" by comparing Table VII with Tables IV and V. Taking the contrasts between Table VII and Tables IV and V seriously suggests that Table VII may be weak as an indicator of what actually will happen, yet it is the freedom from specifically unpredictable surprises that makes the projections useful as a takeoff point for discussion and elaboration.

TABLE VII

Final Third of the Twentieth Century
(Relatively Apolitical and Surprise-Free Projection)

1. Continuation of basic, long-term "multifold trend"
2. Emergence of "postindustrial" culture
3. Worldwide capability for modern technology
4. Very small world: increasing need for regional or worldwide "zoning ordinances" for control of arms, technology, pollution, trade, transportation, population, resource utilization, and the like
5. High (1 to 10 per cent) growth rates in GNP per capita
6. Increasing emphasis on "meaning and purpose"
7. Much turmoil in the "new" and possibly in the industrializing nations
8. Some possibility for sustained "nativist," messianic, or other mass movements
9. Second rise of Japan (to being potentially, nominally, or perhaps actually, the third largest power)
10. Some further rise of Europe and China
11. Emergence of new intermediate powers, such as Brazil, Mexico, Pakistan, Indonesia, East Germany, and Egypt
12. Some decline (relative) of the U.S. and the U.S.S.R.
13. A possible absence of stark "life and death" political and economic issues in the old nations

---

Except for the possibility of the emergence of a postindustrial culture, the listing is "surprise-free"—it assumes the continuation of the multifold trend, but excludes precisely the kinds of dramatic and/or surprising events that dominated the first two-thirds of the century. More specifically, the "surprise-free" projection rules out *major changes in the old nations* that might be caused by possibilities such as those listed in Table VIII.

The first four of these have to do with the "four horsemen of the apocalypse" (conquest, war, famine, and death) of the sixth chapter of the Book of Revelation; the first six are associated with six seals of the book that is the subject of the Revelation. The remaining possibilities are notably modern possibilities. Many of the seventeen are discussed below (particularly in Chapters VII, VIII, and IX), but this volume concentrates for the

---

TABLE VIII

Some Possible Causes of "Surprising" Changes
in the Old Nations

1. Invasion and war
2. Civil strife and revolution
3. Famine
4. Pestilence
5. Despotism (persecution)
6. Natural disaster
7. Depression or economic stagnation
8. Development of "inexpensive" doomsday or near-doomsday machines
9. Development of nuclear "six-gun" weapons technology
10. Resurgence of Communism, or revival of Fascism
11. A racial, North-South, rich-poor, East-West, or other disruptive polarization
12. Economically dynamic China ($\sim$ 10 per cent per year growth)
13. Politically dynamic U.S., U.S.S.R., Japan, West Germany, Brazil, and other powers
14. New religious philosophies and/or other mass movements
15. Development of U.N. or other worldwide organizations
16. Possible regional or other multinational organizations
17. Psychologically upsetting impact of new techniques, ideas, philosophies, and the like

---

most part on the "relatively apolitical" and "surprise-free" projection of Table VII.

If the basic, long-term multifold trend continues or is accelerated during the next thirty-three years, and there are no surprising but not-impossible disruptions of the sort listed above, then a "postindustrial" society seems likely to develop in affluent parts of the world.

Table IX lists some possibilities often associated with the concept of a "postindustrial" society. This term, introduced by Daniel Bell,[9] refers to what may be as important a future change as that caused by industrialization in the eighteenth and early nineteenth centuries.

Aspects of the postindustrial society are discussed further in Chapters IV and V.

To go beyond the next thirty-three years, we can speculate briefly on world society in the first third of the next century.

All the points thus far introduced, including Table X, will be discussed

[9] See *The Reforming of General Education,* (New York: Columbia University Press, 1966), pp. 301 ff.; and his most recent articles on the subject, in *The Public Interest,* Nos. 6 and 7 (1967), and his Introduction to this volume.

TABLE IX
The Postindustrial (or Post-Mass Consumption) Society

1. Per capita income about fifty times the preindustrial
2. Most "economic" activities are tertiary and quaternary (service-oriented), rather than primary or secondary (production-oriented)
3. Business firms no longer the major source of innovation
4. There may be more "consentives" (vs. "marketives")
5. Effective floor on income and welfare
6. Efficiency no longer primary
7. Market plays diminished role compared to public sector and "social accounts"
8. Widespread "cybernation"
9. "Small world"
10. Typical "doubling time" between three and thirty years
11. Learning society
12. Rapid improvement in educational institutions and techniques
13. Erosion (in middle class) of work-oriented, achievement-oriented, advancement-oriented values
14. Erosion of "national interest" values
15. Sensate, secular, humanist, perhaps self-indulgent criteria become central

TABLE X
A Relatively "Surprise-Free" Early Twenty-First Century

1. We expect the rise of new great powers—perhaps Japan, China, a European complex, Brazil, Mexico, or India.
2. There will be new political, perhaps even "philosophical," issues.
3. There will be a leveling off or diminishing of some aspects of the basic, long-term multifold trend, such as urbanization.
4. The postindustrial and industrial worlds will have been largely realized.
5. Some success seems likely with population control, arms control, and some kind of moderately stable international security arrangements, though probably not a "world government."
6. In the industrializing world, disorder, ideology, and irrational movements will probably continue to play disruptive though geographically confined roles.
7. In the U.S. and Western Europe, there will presumably be either a return to certain Hellenic or older European concepts of the good life, or an intensified alienation and search for identity, values, meaning, and purpose, a search made necessary and facilitated by the unprecedented affluence and permissiveness of the postindustrial economy.

in later chapters. The remainder of this chapter will consider some concepts, both substantive and methodological, that are useful in supplying stimulating (sometimes provocative) language and hypotheses, and in setting a context, and then will discuss the items of the multifold trend.

3. *The Heuristic Use of Macrohistory*.

Many readers may be irritated by our form of presentation. Displaying a series of lists, often including items that are not parallel, commenting on many of the topics lightly or not at all and passing on to additional sweeping considerations mentioned in a sentence or two, may try the patience of any reader who wishes to stop and argue seriously about each point. Our comments may seem hopelessly abbreviated; but to deal with any of these issues at greater length, at least in the introductory chapter, would be tedious and would delay us on our route to the distant future. We invite the reader to provide if possible the qualifications and elaborations that are needed and to note our belief that although our arguments could surely be made more accurately, with more complex qualifications and explanations, to do so would not change significantly the points we make and use. Furthermore, we ask to be excused on the ground that what is worth doing at all may be worth doing just well enough to be of some use: that is, the value of a discussion of these matters as a "framework for speculation" may be sufficient even if gained from a "pilot study" that is more broad than deep and occasionally even superficial or oversimplified.

The reader will probably not be surprised that we have our reasons for risking his impatience with our staccato and synoptic style of presentation. We are trying to sketch a broad framework, to outline a context, and therefore we find ourselves continually presenting, in effect, tables of contents for chapters (or libraries) we have not written. Sometimes rather obvious items must be mentioned for the sake of completeness and balance of orientation; sometimes we list unexplored items in order to remind the reader of some of the many things that seem worth mentioning but not worth elaborating in an already long discussion. To strive too much for orderliness and a less eclectic, more deductive line of argument would lend only a surface of clarity and would obscure complexities that should be underlined; moreover, while to be more systematic and more selective might mean to be less disjointed, the gains in smoothness of exposition might be made at the expense of different, and worse forms of oversimplification, abstractness, and aridity. A framework for speculation is no more than that; it ought to raise questions and to present difficulties frankly, and not pretend to completeness or finality that would be impossible to achieve without many more years and volumes of work, if ever.

In speculating on such long-term, large-scale changes as those implicit in our subject, we are involved, whether we like it or not, in matters that have previously been given attention by a long series of macrohistorians or philosophers of history. Despite the fact that none of our discussion of the multifold trend depends strictly on any formal theory of history, we will find it useful to illuminate some of the issues that arise by reference to several more or less systematic and comprehensive theories. Speculations about the future have had a long and varied history, ranging from the literary speculations of Jules Verne and Edward Bellamy to the humanistic and philosophical writings of Arnold Toynbee, Oswald Spengler, Pitirim Sorokin, and Jacob Burckhardt. Many writers have claimed to observe in history some developmental or cyclic patterns [10] of events. Some of these observations have been based on historical study, as in the case of Edward Gibbon, on a philosophy of history as in the case of Toynbee, or on a kind of historical-sociological theory as in the case of Sorokin. Although the observations and philosophical assumptions of the various writers have differed greatly, some of their empirical observations or contentions have had much in common. (For example, when Sorokin finds societies fluctuating among Ideational, Integrated, and Sensate patterns, his categories bear comparison to what Gibbon noted of Rome on a more descriptive level.) If one treats—as we do in this study—the more theoretical and even some of the empirical observations merely as *heuristic metaphors,* regardless of their authors' diverse and more ambitious intentions, they may suggest possible patterns for the future that it would be foolish for us to discount entirely. At the same time, we must reject, as will most of our readers, the claims of our macrohistorians to provide valid comprehensive theories and "explanations" of long-term changes.

Since this volume is intended as a context for speculations about large-scale, long-term changes, we would be wrong either to ignore such insights as may be gleaned from these sources or to treat them too seriously, that is, as rigorous theories the precise details of which are important for us. Treating the theories in this cavalier manner runs the risk of being unfair to our historians without eliminating the risk of being misled by them. Yet we believe such metaphoric and heuristic use better suits the speculative tasks we have set ourselves than would either more rigorous and scrupulous use of such theories or rejecting the partial insights they may afford.

The impact of the continuation of the basic, long-term multifold trend outlined in Table I can be illuminated by reference to these macrohistorical theories. The comparison is intended to help us speculate, explore, and raise questions, without committing us to any particular theory or even perspective. Table XI attempts to provide a reasonably complete categorization of

[10] The cycle in this case usually has a basic time period of one or two thousand years.

perspectives that have been associated with various philosophers of history. We will use them in discussing specific institutions and individual nations as well as in considering civilizations.

We should note that our discussion will be relatively matter of fact, thus leaving out a good deal of the aura of metaphysical or cosmological portentousness that is generally associated with such discussions by advocates of various points of view. For many of those passionately attached to a particular perspective, the charismatic and mystic aspect of *Weltanschauung* that is omitted here is precisely what gives the grand theory its emotional meaning and attractiveness. But since this quality is in part irrelevant to our purposes, in part an obstacle to them, and in any case most difficult to reproduce, we will not attempt to do so.

TABLE XI
Macrohistorical Perspectives on Change

1. Static, traditional, and/or repetitive
2. Progressive: the multifold trend, revolution of rising expectations, utopian, chiliastic, culminating point
3. Decay: not competitive, "hubris," lost golden age, nostalgia, conservatism
4. Rise and fall: cyclic, growth and decay (Quigley Scenario), fluctuation (Sorokin Scenario), "regular" ebb and flow
5. Patternless and unpredictable
6. Typical (empirical) patterns: the multifold trend, irregular ebb and flow, empirical and analytic trend analysis, typical or phenomenological scenarios
7. Eclectic and syncretic: the multifold trend, other trend analyses, other typical patterns (particularly metaphoric use of Quigley and Sorokin Scenarios and of classical history), some current speculations on decline and/or rebirth, and even crypto-historicism

---

We have already indicated that our own viewpoint fits best under categories 6 and 7, though we believe aspect 5 always plays a part. There is, of course, no total rejection of elements 1, 2, 3, and 4, but only a skeptical and limited borrowing from those who emphasize these positions. In other words, while we are interested in the issues raised by those who argue that things are much the same, or who are extremely optimistic, pessimistic, or deterministic, we are as yet unpersuaded by the theoretical and empirical arguments presented for any particular perspective, and presumably will remain unpersuaded.

It is sometimes noted, but only rarely today, that things do not really change; the past continues endlessly into the future. This is certainly true for many issues: people are still born with about the same genetic endowment, must grow up, for the most part in families, usually learn to deal with their impulses in some prescribed way and live in some sort of community, usually form new family relationships and have children, and then in a few decades face death. Yet even such constants as these may be altered by technological and social changes in the next thirty-three or sixty-six years. In any case many other significant aspects of life are either changing or being affected by changes which, as we have noted in the multifold trend, are taking place at an ever increasing rate, while at the same time many things remain basically unchanged.

The most obvious changes today are those which could be labeled progressive. Many people would assume that the multifold trend is an example of progress. This is, of course, a question of values as well as substantive or empirical judgment. But it is becoming more clear that these changes, although they are produced to a great extent by purposive efforts, often lead to undesirable, mixed, or ambiguous as well as desirable results. Other cultures have typically conceived of history as static, cyclic, or as a decline from a golden age. The dominant Western belief is in a future that is better than the past, or even, in a long series of Utopian heresies, in a heaven on earth, and the idea of progress has, of course, spread over the entire world today. This is one of the really important changes that have occurred as a result of the worldwide impact of Western culture.

Many progressives (or "provisional catastrophists")[11] do have a Utopian view of the future—in either terms of current trends or as achievable by design (or social engineering). The endpoint is defined in terms of an earthly paradise, or more transcendentally and chiliastically, as the endpoint of a teleological process. In the latter case, history is implicitly assumed to have a point of culmination. Typically philosophers of history think of their own particular culture or subculture as this culminating point of man's million-year evolution. Thus the Prussian aristocrat, the English Christian, or the American liberal is implicitly (or explicitly) described as history's culminating accomplishment. One can, almost without consideration, reject such notions, though they may be associated with powerful political, philosophical, or religious concepts and movements and have persuaded many intelligent people.

Increasingly common today is the opposite of the idea of progress—the idea of decay. Often decay is only relative to competition. Any individual, institution, nation, or culture which is not competitive with its challengers is likely not only to sense decay but to assume that the decay is widespread, even worldwide. Figure 2 indicates a particular kind of decay, in which England is decaying economically as compared to the other four contemporary large powers. Yet this is a decay during which most Englishmen have

---

[11] People who believe that catastrophe will occur unless something is done, but who also believe that something can be done to prevent this catastrophe.

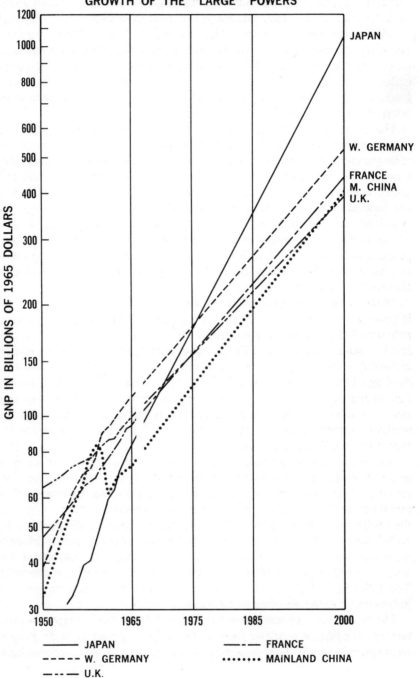

FIGURE 2
POSTWAR ECONOMIC GROWTH AND
ONE PROJECTION OF ECONOMIC
GROWTH OF THE "LARGE" POWERS

JAPAN

W. GERMANY

FRANCE
M. CHINA
U.K.

GNP IN BILLIONS OF 1965 DOLLARS

——— JAPAN   —·— FRANCE
------ W. GERMANY   •••••••• MAINLAND CHINA
—··— U.K.

SOURCE:

For 1950 to 1966, data for China from U.S. government, data for other countries from
United Nations. Projections to 2000 from Table XIII, Chapter 3.

"never had it so good" and their economic condition continues to improve. England is growing economically at about 2 per cent a year—about as fast or faster than in any sustained period of growth in its history. Why then should Englishmen be unhappy? The answer is that in 1945 they were economically the largest of the five nations on the chart. They have now been passed by West Germany, will soon be passed by France and Japan, and perhaps even by China. If current trends continue, before the year 2000 England will have fallen from the richest of the five large powers to the poorest, even while its GNP has quintupled.

This projection of England's relative status is quite plausible. The other four countries seem likely to continue to grow faster than Britain. But if their growth rates were to drop to that of Britain, Britain's growth would be more heartening and very likely much of the contemporary British self-hatred would disappear. England's "decline" would be "cured." If this does not happen, then while many in Britain will criticize the government and bewail the current situation, it would seem that a "cure"—through English efforts to double the growth rate—is unlikely, since no single class or large group is suffering so much or is so unhappy and/or frustrated by conditions in what actually is a prosperous and growing nation to force the necessary changes for faster growth.

Others believe the world is headed for disaster because of the accumulating power over nature (including man) created by the acceleration of technological and economic development. It may be that modern civilization has in effect made the bargain of Faust. An important question may be whether industrial society resembles the medieval Faust—who sold his soul to the devil and was damned—or Goethe's romantic Faust, influenced by the Enlightenment. This embodiment of the modern spirit was saved from damnation by angels, who approved of his restless striving for knowledge and worldly mastery. We shall return to the question of the potential costs of modern man's Faustian powers.

Another intimation of decay derives from the idea common in antiquity of a lost, golden age. Theories of decay may come from nostalgia, or "conservatives" may sense decay because certain values or institutions (such as moral standards, class divisions, and behavioral standards of the young) that they prize, possibly quite properly, have eroded or have disappeared. Finally, a certain bias often affects studies of history or of the future, reflecting preoccupations of the historian or futurist, and causing the analysis to lean toward utopian optimism or to find innumerable evidences of ruin and decay. The belief in the rise or fall of any culture can, of course, be based on judgments of either absolute or competitive trends.

The next figures illustrate two fairly plausible cyclical interpretations of history. The first, *in modified form,* is Aristotle's—gained from his study of one hundred and fifty-eight constitutions of Greek cities. Aristotle concluded that there was no best form of government and that one form of government tended to decay, or to change into another form, more or less plausibly, as indicated by Figure 3. Presumably at almost each point in such a cycle, assuming such cycles really occur, most people—or at least the elites—would have felt so satisfied with the system that they would have regarded it as a culminating point, perhaps self-evidently so.

Figure 4 illustrates very much the same process but focuses on the corresponding belief system of the society. (It may be worth emphasizing again that we use the concepts and sequence shown as a source of conjectures, hypotheses, and analogues without accepting any notion of sequential determination or inevitability.)

We will defer to a later section the discussion of the next item on Table XI, various theories of rise and fall. These theories run counter to the belief held by many people, including the authors, that crucial historical events are often patternless and accidental, but this does not prevent many events, or aspects of events, from falling into typical empirical or theoretical patterns. Whatever the actual underlying mechanisms behind these patterns or associations, one may be able to use them, in effect to reason by analogy—or at least by metaphor—for raising issues, questions, conjectures, and hypotheses, or just to make the discussion richer and more clear. Obviously conditions do not reproduce exactly, but this is true even of the weather. Nonetheless, a simple and fairly reliable way to predict weather is to look at past weather patterns resembling today's, and count the percentage of times that they produced rain and the percentage of times they did not. The result is a "probability" prediction of future weather. No doubt weather is determined by material factors and even here we do not know the "hidden variables" that would resolve the perceived indeterminancy. The indeterminancy in man's affairs is more basic and more complex; we do not have so large an array of analogous prototypes to select from; and, there are important basic secular changes in the general framework in which the events occur (in fact, this is the major point of our multifold trend). Nevertheless in some cases, partially similar or analogous situations may, at least in part, produce partially similar or analogous results—history may not repeat itself, but it may paraphrase.

When Aristotle developed his theory of cycles, he had one hundred and fifty-eight constitutions to study, and a relatively stable basic situation. But our analogies must be based on very limited experience in a rapidly changing situation. The use of such analogies is now more than ever an inherently uncertain and unreliable process and, as applied to the future, might even be systematically deceptive.

We ended Table XI with the term "crypto-historicism" to describe one possible element of the syncretic and eclectic approach we favor. One who is a "crypto"-anything tends to hold some ideology but is unwilling to admit

FIGURE 3
A MODIFIED GREEK THEORY OF POLITICAL CYCLES

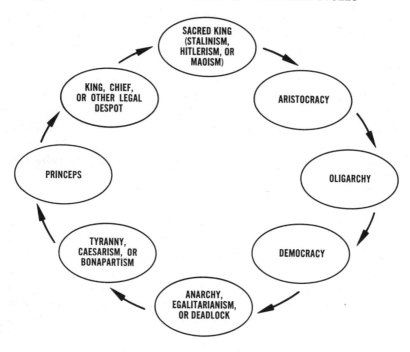

FIGURE 4
A POSSIBLE CYCLE OF BASIC INTELLECTUAL ATTITUDES

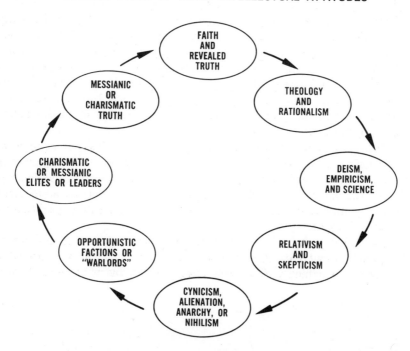

it, because he is uncertain, ashamed, or unaware of his implicit commitment. Whenever any of the above applies, we shall try to drop the "crypto" position and be explicit. In particular we shall try not to use historical analogies or theories for evidence or documentation, or as models. If we slip from this standard, it is unintentionally, but one cannot make use of striking historical analogies without running the risk that they will carry greater psychological force than was explicitly intended. This is, of course, a warning to the readers as well as to ourselves.

D. SOME METHODOLOGICAL COMMENTS ON THE ANALYSIS OF LONG-TERM TRENDS

In the next section, as in much of our study, we depend very heavily on straightforward extrapolations into the future of existing and past trends, often including in this projection an extrapolation of the rate of innovation. The expert is often hostile to this last because extrapolations that depend upon the successful introduction and acceptance of as yet uninvented, undiscovered, or at least unproved innovations, other creative acts, or chancy programs, usually seem irresponsible to him. The expert is usually an expert on the present and sees no compelling reasons for believing that innovations he cannot evaluate or even recognize will necessarily occur. Insofar as he emphasizes the word necessarily, he is, of course, right.

On the other hand, unless specific account is taken of the fact that there will be innovation, creativity, and successful programs of various kinds in the future, we will sharply misunderstand or misestimate the future. Consider, for example, the graph in Figure 5, describing the rate of increase of operating energy in particle accelerators. The curve that is tangent to the curves for the separate technologies is called an "envelope curve" and, of course, represents the actual curve of the overall technological progress.[12] When we predict the future of particle accelerators it is this curve we are trying to predict and not the curve associated with any particular technology. It is, of course, quite clear that at any point in the last *thirty* years an attempt to look five or ten years ahead that ignored the possibility of new techniques would have sharply underestimated the actual progress that was made.

In the recent past—at least in the area of weapon systems and advanced technology—such mistakes of "responsible pessimism" have been more common than overly optimistic extrapolations of the rate of technological development, or of other innovation and creativity. (For another interesting and important example of this kind of systematic underestimation by "re-

[12] Trend analysis through envelope curves is discussed by Robert U. Ayres, "On Technological Forecasting," in *Selected Papers from the Hudson Institute*. This figure is derived from M. Stanley Livingston's Introduction to *The Development of High-Energy Accelerators,* edited by him (New York: Dover Publications, Inc., 1966), p. 3.

FIGURE 5

THE RATE OF INCREASE OF OPERATING ENERGY
IN PARTICLE ACCELERATORS

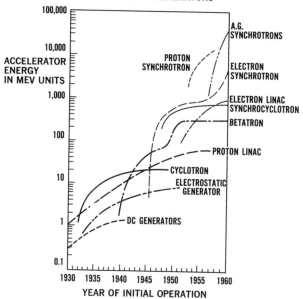

SOURCE:
From M. S. Livingston, as quoted by Gerald Holton in "Scientific
Research and Scholarship: Notes Toward the Design of Proper
Scales," **Daedalus,** Vol. 91, No. 62 (Spring 1962).

sponsible" experts, see almost any non-Japanese discussion of Japanese
growth rates in the decade of the 1950's.) Yet the expert, with detailed
knowledge, often still feels virtually compelled to make predictions that fit
responsibly into known technology and known but unsolved problems. Thus
he is also virtually compelled to ignore the crucial fact that in this kind of
rapidly changing situation it is new technology or other innovation that determines the trend, since it is almost impossible for him to say much about
the nature of new technology or about other untested, or even undiscovered,
innovations. If he understood their nature he would already be using or
investigating them.

Thus there are many areas in which the expert who has specific knowledge very much in mind may actually do less well at forecasting than the
"naïve" journalist, or the "naïve but sophisticated" systems analyst, who
assumes, perhaps implicitly or unconsciously, that innovation and creativity
will occur at a certain rate, even though (or *because*) he does not know
precisely how.

This is not an uncommon situation. For example, at the RAND Corporation in the 1950's many relatively nonexpert individuals made envelop extrapolations of technological progress in various weapon systems, of nuclear
devices, computers, radar, propulsion, aerodynamics efficiency, and the like.
These often aroused great annoyance among many experts who refused to
accept the "simplistic" assumption that such predicted rates of undefined

innovations would be maintained. After all, they knew the technology and did not know persuasive reasons to expect particular specific innovations. Yet it is in fact quite often reasonable, in the light of experience, to have faith that the rate of innovation will not change very much in the area being considered, even though one clearly must worry about saturating (or accelerating) phenomena, and other factors changing the rate of innovation.

There now exist a number of design groups in industrial corporations that look at such envelope curves and ask how their own predictions fit them. But so far as we know, the first systematic use of envelope curves in this way was at the RAND Corporation in the late 1940's. They had, at that time, an almost unique sense of what was going on, of what the "theory" was about.

On the other hand, in extrapolating population trends, most experts—and the systems analysts—now seem to believe that the current rates of growth are probably misleading. Simple projections, for example, yield a world population of more than seven billion by the end of the century. Most experts argue that the figure will actually be between five and a half and six and a half billions, and will most likely be closer to the lower figure. Whether or not they are right, they are persuasive. An even more persuasive example of how foolish naïve, straightforward "envelope" extrapolation can be is given in Figure 6, extrapolating R & D expenditures and GNP. R & D ob-

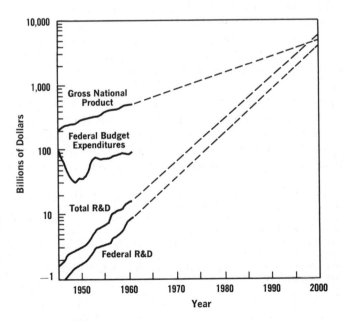

FIGURE 6
GNP AND R&D: FAILURE OF NAIVE EXTRAPOLATION

SOURCE:
BOB, NSF, DOD, Business Statistics, Statistical Abstracts; from David Allison, "The Civilian Technology Lag," *International Science and Technology,* December 1963, p. 24.

viously will not eventually surpass GNP, nor is it likely to be more than 10 per cent of it by the year 2000.[13]

One cannot simply argue that the less sophisticated projection is better than the more expert one, but one can argue that both the sophistication and the expertise must be *about the right things*. Projections must at least consider long- and short-term trends and how they are likely to be modified. One should not ignore these gross trends in favor of explicated and detailed calculations of the future done on a priori and analytic bases, at least not until the calculating machinery for such analytic projections is very sophisticated and long tested.[14]

While real-world trends tend to be partly qualitative, frequently fluctuating, and in any case uncertain, it may still be useful to set forth precise and/or quantitative extrapolations or estimates. These are not ordinarily given because it is believed they represent an exact estimate of appropriate variables and factors, but only to communicate with some precision what we have in mind. If we say that something should range between five and ten, we do not mean that it cannot be less than five or greater than ten. We simply mean that we would be willing to make a bet at say two to one, or five to one, or even twenty-to-one odds, as the case may be, that the variable under discussion will, in fact, range between five and ten. Sometimes it is useful to make even the subjective probability (i.e., the bet) precise and explicit as well. But again we would normally do so because there is widespread understanding and agreement (except perhaps among a few of the experts) about the meaning of the term subjective probability, and not because we have independently calculated or studied carefully and precisely the numerical probability put forth. Putting the assertion in terms of willingness to make a bet with a small sum of money is intended to make clear our degree of certainty; it does not usually suggest just how educated our educated guess is. It tries to communicate how much confidence we feel in the prediction but often not the confidence we feel in our confidence. (The amount we might be willing to risk often indicates the latter confidence.)

Furthermore, quantitative statements necessarily refer to variables that are quantifiable—or to quantifiable aspects or models of a variable. The frequent use of such quantifications does not imply that less quantifiable variables and issues may not be important or even dominant—or that there may not be difficulties of principle in defining the variable to be quantified. It

---

[13] For a systematic discussion of envelope and other methods of predictions, see Daniel Bell, "Twelve Modes of Prediction," in *Daedalus,* 1966; R. U. Ayres, "On Technological Forecasting," and Herman Kahn, "On Alternative World Futures," in *Selected Papers from the Hudson Institute.*

[14] The prediction of future GNP is a good example. Until quite recently gross phenomenological models that used very aggregated data did much better than very detailed input-output models using much more information. Even today the two methods seem competitive.

implies only that we believe that it is still of interest to ask, "what if . . . ,"
or to communicate, quantitatively, some aspect or approximation of an issue,
even if not the whole of it. This kind of communication creates difficulties
and errors—particularly of emphasis—but may still be more useful than
saying that something will be "small" or "unlikely." Thus we use precise
and quantitative statements usually to improve precision in communication,
not because the variable can be precisely measured or estimated, or even
precisely defined.

Finally, there is the matter, which we have already mentioned, of "surprise-free" vs. "most probable" vs. "absolutely probable" trends or estimates. One can think of a surprise-free projection as being as sophisticated
a projection as it seems reasonable to make given the available understanding of current trends. It thus differs, but not in spirit, from the "naïve"
projection of the economists which take current tendencies as certain. For
most of the projections that we are discussing, in which we are looking
twenty to thirty or more years ahead, perhaps the most surprising thing that
could actually happen would be an absence of surprises. Therefore, there is
no implication that a *surprise-free* projection is *likely*. It may, in fact, be the
most likely of the various possible projections; that is to say that when con-
templating a thousand things which could happen, the surprise-free projection may have a probability of much less than one in a hundred, yet be more
probable than any of the other 999 possible occurrences. It could be "most
probable" and still be quite improbable.

It is interesting to note that the authors have found that their own attitudes, and those of some of their colleagues, have changed during the course
of this study toward Table VII, the relatively apolitical and surprise-free
projection for the last third of the century. Our attitude is now much like
that of a weather forecaster who has very inadequate theory and information, but can look out the window and see what the day is like. Weather
forecasters know that the best single prediction in the absence of strong
contrary indications is that current conditions will continue tomorrow. While
this prediction would obviously be very often wrong, it would be better than
any other simple doctrine for predictions. Similarly we would be willing to
wager small sums, at even odds, that the next third of a century will contain
fewer big surprises than either of the previous thirds (i.e., that in this respect
the world is more like 1815 than 1914). Whether this increased optimism is
due to having learned something from doing this study or merely to having
become too used to its assumptions is a matter that the reader must judge
for himself.

Our surprise-free extrapolations are based on the assumptions that the
basic, long-term, multifold trend, listed in Table I, will continue. The elements of this trend should not be thought of as separate phenomena even

though for immediate conceptual, expository, analytic, or other abstract purposes we may consider them separately. For our purposes the trends should be seen as made up of thirteen or more intimately interacting phenomena, or as thirteen explicated aspects of a single complex trend. These aspects are no more than empirical and semianalytical extensions of trends now two or three to seven, eight or even more centuries old in the Western world and that seem likely to hold true for the next thirty-three years, though some of the trends may be beginning to level off or recede—at least in the Western world.

Next, we discuss in more detail the elements of the multifold trend.

E. THE BASIC, LONG-TERM MULTIFOLD TREND

1. *Increasingly Sensate (Empirical, This-Worldly, Secular, Humanistic, Pragmatic, Utilitarian, Contractual, Epicurean or Hedonistic, and the Like) Cultures*

The first item in Table I indicated that there has been a long-term trend toward an increasingly Sensate culture. This term, derived from Sorokin,[15] is best explained by contrasting it to Sorokin's other concepts: "Integrated" (or Idealistic) and "Ideational." These terms are illustrated for the fine arts by Table XII, which relates to each concept terms likely to be used in describing works of arts representative of each category. Of course, usually only some of the words will apply.

It is clear from the lists why Sorokin originally used the term "Idealistic" for what he had also described as "Integrated." We would judge, for example, that Socialist Realism is a modern instance of Integrated, or Idealistic, art.

Our description of "Late Sensate" art may reflect a bias that some of its proponents would probably term square; on the other hand, they might accept the description and justify such art on the ground that it protests the ugliness, emptiness, and excesses of a declining Sensate culture. They feel its role to be justifiably destructive to traditional values. Others might argue that it is simply avant-garde, and hence misunderstood.[16]

[15] Sorokin, Pitirim A., *Social & Cultural Dynamics* (New York: Bedminster Press, 1962), Vol. I, especially Chaps. 7-10. By "Sensate," Sorokin does not intend a connotation of sensual or sensational; worldly, humanistic, or empirical would have been equally useful for our purposes. Sorokin does not make a separate category for "Late Sensate," though he mentions it, and we have added several adjectives to his brief comments on this phase.

[16] Of course, the identical phenomena might be as accurately described as "Late Sensate," or avant-garde, but with very different connotations. Both terms, of course, share a connotation of being the "wave of the future," but this too is an assumption or a hypothesis and not a necessary and obvious conclusion.

TABLE XII

Ideational Art	Idealistic or Integrated Art
Transcendental	Mixed Style
Supersensory	Heroic
Religious	Noble
Symbolic	Uplifting
Allegoric	Sublime
Static	Patriotic
Worshipful	Moralistic
Anonymous	Beautified
Traditional	Flattering
Immanent	Educational

Sensate Art	Late Sensate Art
Worldly	Underworldly
Naturalistic	Protest
Realistic	Revolt
Visual	Overripe
Illusionistic	Extreme
Everyday	Sensation Seeking
Amusing	Titillating
Interesting	Depraved
Erotic	Faddish
Satirical	Violently Novel
Novel	Exhibitionistic
Eclectic	Debased
Syncretic	Vulgar
Fashionable	Ugly
Superb Technique	Debunking
Impressionistic	Nihilistic
Materialistic	Pornographic
Commercial	Sarcastic
Professional	Sadistic

Sorokin argues elsewhere,[17] as Table XIII summarizes, that philosophers of history, while obviously not in basic agreement,[18] have a remarkable de-

[17] In *Modern Historical and Social Philosophies* (New York: Dover, 1963), esp. Chap. XIV, "Areas of Agreement Among Modern Social Philosophers."

[18] For example, Sorokin specifically rejects the idea that cultures necessarily die, or that they go through any specific sequence of cycles. But he also argues, as do other philosophers of history, that the West is currently in something like a "late sensate" stage, and that something like either an Integrated or Ideational stage should soon follow this Sensate stage—thus big changes are in the offing. We would consider this argument as an unproved but interesting, even central, hypothesis.

gree of agreement in language. Each has coined or selected terms that are almost interchangeable and that may be useful in describing empirical phenomena or in formulating issues and hypotheses.

TABLE XIII
Three Standard Cultural Phases

Sorokin	Spengler, Toynbee, *et al.*	Schubart	Berdyaev
1. Ideational	Growth, Spring, Childhood	Ascetic-Messianic	Barbaric-Religious
2. Integrated	Maturity, Summer	Harmonious	Medieval-Renaissance
3. Sensate	Autumn, Winter, Civilization, Decline	Heroic-Promethean	Humanistic-Secular

There are, of course, always minor themes, reluctant or nominal conformers, undergrounds, holdovers, dropout, dissenters, schismatics, heretics, unbelievers, and other deviants or exceptions. (These may be a majority of the population, but still not very visible.)

We have stressed that our use of Sorokin's terminology and that of other philosophers of history should not be taken as implying a belief in a necessary life-cycle for a civilization or culture, or a commitment to other theories of history put forward by these men. The situation is similar to much use and perhaps misuse of the language of psychoanalysis: it has now become useful, and even commonplace, in describing emotions or psychological "mechanisms" to use the language of Freud. Many who reject Freud's theories or who accept them only in the dilute formulations of his revisionists would nevertheless concede that many of his terms are extremely descriptive and pertinent and perhaps essential to serious discussion.

The taste for Late Sensate art today is restricted to small minorities. Some will argue that if an appreciable proportion of a society becomes Late Sensate in many aspects of life, the society is likely to become almost ungovernable. Others see in the growing taste for Late Sensate art a revolt against materialism and conformity and a possible emergence of a new humanism and creativity—of honesty and individuality. We shall have more to say about all of these possibilities later. Discussing the issue now, however, raises the question of the significance—if any—of this growing popularity of Late Sensate art. Is it a harbinger, a symptom, a cause of other changes, or perhaps all three? This in turn raises the more general, and perhaps more basic, question of the uniformity of cultures. To what degree are the various activities of a culture, as listed, for example, on Table XIV, accurately described by the same terms?

TABLE XIV

One Could Also Contrast the Ideational, Integrated
(Idealistic), and Sensate Systems of:

Fine Arts	Family Relationships
Performing Arts	Civic Relationships
Architecture	Literature
Truth	Ethics
Music	Education
Law	Government
Economics	Etc.

One must, of course, also worry about the theory of consistency and leading and lagging sectors, as well as the exceptions previously mentioned.

The notes on Tables XIII and XIV suggest that a culture is usually most deeply held, even, or especially, at its zenith, by an elite—an educated or dominant middle- and upper-class group. Our references to culture thus are usually to "high culture," the music, art, and literature of the educated or dominant classes—or of some other relevant elite—rather than to the more general societal culture spoken of by sociologists and anthropologists. To some degree, in all societies, the public tends to Sensate culture, or, at least in the Ideational or Integrated cultures, to be more inclined to the Sensate than are the middle and, often, the upper classes.

In American society today, high culture clearly tends to be Sensate, though many subgroups have large Integrated and Ideational elements. In general, while a high culture may seem vividly defined to an outside observer, and appear pervasive in a society, the situation may be much more complicated than the outside observer—or the student of history—may be likely to realize. For example, it would appear that in Cromwellian England the majority of the people actually rejected Puritan values, though this rejection would have been almost invisible to the official visitor. Values are often enforced by an elite as well as exhibited by them. The degree of homogeneity and pervasiveness of any particular culture is, in fact, a crucial issue. So is the question of how important the visible elites may be as opposed to the less visible but perhaps more influential. For example, in the United States today there is clearly a strong split between a large group of intellectuals and the government on many issues, but we believe (and have evidence from public opinion polls) that while many intellectuals may hold a "progressive" consensus and dominate discussion in serious journals, they, in fact, are not representative of the country as a whole. This group is certainly not as representative even of intellectuals as the journals of opinion might suggest. This is virtually a universal situation; but at the same time one should not underestimate the importance of the opinions of the alienated portions of the intellectual elite and of the eventual, if not immediate, influence they exert.

While we concede that there are important issues and uncertainties about leading and lagging sectors and the degrees of pervasiveness and homogeneity, we tend to accept, with reservations, the assumption of most philosophers of history that there is, by and large, a considerable congruence or convergence among the various sectors of at least a high culture, or perhaps of any widely held culture. If, for example, a culture is Sensate in art or in systems of truth, it has tended, historically, to be Sensate in systems of government and family as well. Of course, in any particular situation, the exception may be much more important than the general rule, and we will argue later that there are a number of reasons for arguing that modern United States culture may provide such exceptions.

Because of its importance we have set forth in Table XV the major characteristics of Ideational, Sensate, and Late Sensate systems of truth. The Integrated system, which is omitted from the table, would as its name indicates, involve elements of both the Ideational and Sensate systems, and also rely heavily on reasoning, rationality, and deductive logic, as well as inte-

TABLE XV
Three Systems of Truth *

IDEATIONAL	SENSATE	LATE SENSATE
Revealed	Empirical	Cynical
Charismatic	Pragmatic	Disillusioned
Certain	Operational	Nihilistic
Dogmatic	Practical	Chaotic
Mystic	Worldly	Blase
Intuitive	Scientific	Transient
Infallible	Skeptical	Superficial
Religious	Tentative	Weary
Supersensory	Fallible	Sophistic
Unworldly	Sensory	Formalistic
Salvational	Materialistic	Atheistic
Spiritual	Mechanistic	Trivial
Absolute	Relativistic	Changeable
Supernatural	Agnostic	Meaningless
Moral	Instrumental	Alienated
Emotional	Empirically, or	Expedient
Mythic	Logically Verifiable	Absolutely Relativistic

* See, e.g., Sorokin, *Social & Cultural Dynamics,* Vol. I, especially pp. 84-91.

grating the Ideational and Sensate systems of truth. It should be clear by now that the authors are for the most part committed to the dominant Sensate (or better, Early Sensate) assumptions of our society, but are concerned about some already visible social changes that may lead in the direction of an excessively Late Sensate society—though we do not believe "increasingly Sensate" leads necessarily toward Late Sensate.

While the Sensate trend that has come to dominate Western culture does go back seven or eight centuries, its progress has not been uninterrupted. The Reformation, the Counter-Reformation, the Puritan era in England, some aspects of the later Victorian era, and la belle epoque, and to some degree such phenomena as Stalinism, Hitlerism, and Fascism, represented—at least at the time—contradictions to the basic trend of an increasingly Sensate culture. Nevertheless, the long-term, all-embracing Sensate trend would seem to have expanded from the West and to cover now virtually the entire world. Whether this will continue for the next thirty-three or sixty-six years, or whether it will become Late Sensate, are open questions. But when we examine the description of Late Sensate art and Late Sensate truth, it seems plausible that if the implications of this description are valid, any long-term tendencies toward Late Sensate must stabilize, top-out, or even reverse. Otherwise the system must change in other important respects.

We have been using, as many writers do, the terms culture and civilization almost interchangeably. Spengler thinks of culture as more or less identical with the Ideational and Integrated phases of Sorokin, and civilization as corresponding to the Sensate and Late Sensate phases. According to Toynbee, civilization should be defined as the smallest, more or less historically, independent unit of study. By this definition, there is today only one civilization, since as a result of the geographical expansion of the area of modernization mentioned in the multifold trend, the history of every country of the world is inextricably mixed with that of Western civilization. However, in 1500 there were presumably seven major civilizations in existence (Western, Moslem, Indian, Sinic, Inca, Aztec, and Russo-Byzantine). Other civilizations are assumed to have disappeared; that is, their existence as an independent unit was terminated (Sumerian, Egyptian, Classical, Mycenaean, and some of the earlier Indian and Chinese civilizations); yet their culture lives on in their successors. We will not enter into the controversies over definitions, but will take all of our examples from Classical and Western civilization since these are the ones most important to us and with which we are most familiar. However, it should be remembered that the same points are often made by philosophers of history who draw their examples from other cultures.

Many of the philosophers of history believe that new civilizations are created in areas where two cultures "mix," or where a "barbarian" group invades and conquers an established culture. It is argued that in such circumstances (1) a freedom of choice and a flexibility of outlook may prevail that is conducive to new designs for living, working, or fighting; (2) in particular, the new group can adopt institutions and/or techniques without also accepting a lot of unnecessary traditions and vested interests; (3) the new people may have some sort of "barbaric vigor"; and (4) conditions of flux may be especially conducive to the rise of efficient and charismatic leaders.

Classical civilization grew out of the mixture of an earlier Mycenaean form with that of later conquerors, while modern Western civilization had its roots in the impact of Roman civilization on Germanic and other Northern invaders. When a new culture starts, one can often distinguish a relatively clear-cut "core" area, which in the case of Classical civilization can be taken as Ionia (basically Athens), or even the entire Greek area, including—if one wishes—Greek colonies in southern Italy, the Black Sea, and the eastern Mediterranean. The core area for Western civilization is presumably Northern Italy, France, Western Germany, the Netherlands, and England. It has been noted by many historical philosophers that a peripheral area sometimes becomes more dynamic and aggressive than any of the nations of the core area and succeeds in conquering most or all of the core area. Later a still more peripheral area invades and conquers, and finally a completely peripheral area does the same. In the case of Classical civilization, this sequence is presumably illustrated by Athens, Macedonia, and Rome. In the case of Western civilization the sequence was never carried through, although "semiperipheral" England made a good attempt to dominate the Continent, as did semiperipheral Germany, and then in quite a different way, the wholly peripheral United States.

One such author, Carroll Quigley,[19] whose terminology (but not necessarily theories) we use, lays great emphasis on the notion of an "instrument of expansion." In the case of Classical civilization he thinks of this instrument as slavery. He argues that there are, in the case of Western civilization, three phases of instrumental expansion; and that each phase can be thought of as a "rebirth" of the civilization. These are: feudal system (970 to 1270), commercial capitalism and mercantilism (1440 to 1700), and industrialism (1730 to 1929). We would suggest that historians of the future may add a fourth and contemporary phase, starting after World War I or World War II, in the United States. Here the instrument of expansion might be labeled "modern management and production techniques." (One is tempted to use the more romantic terms "cybernation and technology," but while these ideas are included they are much too narrow to cover the relevant factors, especially since by "management" we intend to include the management of economy by governmental and other authorities.)

Quigley's concept of "institutionalization" holds that after a time the "instrument of expansion" as defined above is subverted or corrupted by

[19] *The Evolution of Civilizations* (New York: Macmillan Company, 1961).

those who operate it and it becomes an institution of which the major purpose is to serve the interests of the operators. One could argue that this happens to almost all instruments of expansion. It is Quigley's thesis that unless this institution is then superceded by a new instrument of expansion, the civilization enters a declining phase.

Let us ask what this hypothesis might suggest about the current situation. On the one hand, there are the symptoms of Late Sensate culture, communicating to some a feeling of likely decline; on the other, there is also clear evidence of enormous economic expansion using modern management and production techniques; finally there are new pressures conducive both to dehumanization and anonymity and the reinforcement of the right of the individual to fulfill his own values and purposes, if necessary even against the will of the community.

Table XVI summarizes what we will call "Quigley's scenario."

TABLE XVI

Quigley's "Scenario"

1. Mixture
2. Gestation
3. Expansion
4. Age of Conflict
5. Universal Empire
6. Decay
7. Invasion

Quigley argues that civilizations are almost immune to invasion and conquest in Stages Three, Four, and Five, but are vulnerable in Stages One, Two, and Six. That is, it is easy to "arrest" an incipient civilization or to conquer one that is decaying. These terms may be quite useful descriptively and as hypotheses, whatever the merits of Quigley's arguments for the mechanisms of change.

We would suggest that it is interesting to consider Quigley's "scenario" for present purposes as merely a classification system, ignoring the substantive content intended by Quigley. For example, let us consider any historical situation in which a universal empire has been conquered. It is clear that it must have been invaded, and it is clear that in examining the society at the time of the successful invasion one will find evidences that could be interpreted as decay, particularly if the empire has lasted over a long period of time and there have been changes from the original culture. Therefore one might argue that the invasion succeeded because the empire decayed. Of course, it might have also been true that the invaders succeeded because they had a competent leader, a dynamic ideology, or some other advantage. Even if the invaders had not been competent enough to destroy the empire at its heyday, it might still be true that if they had not had their particular leaders or ideology the empire would have had some breathing space in which it might have recovered from its so-called decay. In this sense the conquest might have been fortuitous or accidental.

It also seems quite clear that this universal empire, or the state that put it together, must have arisen from some place; and it seems unlikely, unless the empire is very limited geographically (as in Egypt), that the original culture will always remain dominant. There will also be reasons for conjecturing that much of the time the conquering power will arise from what we have called the "mixture" area.

One of the most frequent reasons for the success of such a power in its mission of conquest is that the core area is preoccupied with internal conflicts, and fails to unite to face the potential conqueror. An invasion in another period, meeting a united opposition, would have failed. Thus Quigley's scenario is a priori reasonable; we should not be surprised that many situations can be fitted into these categories, especially if we take a broad and shallow view and do not inspect details so closely as to miss the forest for the trees, or conclude that unique aggregations of trees can never be forests.

Scenarios such as this are, of course, especially prone to the fallacy of *post hoc ergo propter hoc*. This issue of causation and inevitability will presumably not arise in most of our discussions except possibly by connotation since we are interested in categorization, not in prediction, when we use these terms.

Sorokin's "scenario," which we summarize here in outline form, also furnishes an interesting hypothesis.

TABLE XVII

Sorokin's "Scenario" *

1. Late Sensate Chaos
2. Increasing Polarization
3. Crisis
4. Ordeal
5. Catharsis
6. Charisma
7. A New Religiosity

* Sorokin, *Social & Cultural Dynamics*, I, 775-779.

Sorokin and almost all of the nineteenth- and twentieth-century philosophers of history seem to believe it likely that some new kind of "religious" stage will follow a termination of Sensate culture. This stage could be spiritual and intellectual, rather than arising out of technology, as Julian Huxley; or it could be a properly religious, simple development of Christianity, (as early Arnold Toynbee); or it could be a new synthesis of East and West, as later Toynbee, or something completely different. In any case, it is usually argued that there will be some unpleasant events between the Late Sensate chaos and the new religiosity. That is, most macrohistorians seem to hold, with Sorokin, that our civilization will not continue along the multifold or any other trend, but will either be "terminated" or have a more or less painful rebirth following a time of chaos, anarchy, nihilism, and irrationality. During this period there will be a tendency for some individuals to polarize around ethical and altruistic values and for others to focus on materialism, sensualism, selfishness, and egotism. Sorokin uses the terms ordeal and catharsis in describing the process. Eventually a new and charismatic idea will arise and be used to create either an Ideational or Integrated (Idealistic) society—a new culture or a resurrection of the old.

It would be possible to put together a picture of the future, using plausible, contemporary evidence, which fits expectations of either a new "instrument of expansion" or of "Late Sensate" chaos. In later chapters we will cite indications of a revival of respect for the individual as well as signs of the increasing blurring of the distinction between persons and things. As one would expect, it is not going to be possible to make any very persuasive or rigorous predictions on this most basic of issues, though we hope through discussion to shed some light on some aspects of this issue and at least stimulate thinking on others.

2. Bourgeois, Bureaucratic, "Meritocratic," Democratic (and Nationalistic?) Elites

By bourgeois we mean holding economic values and ideologies of the kind that characterized the new middle classes which emerged from the breakup of feudal society—values of personal and family achievement, financial prudence, economic calculation, commercial foresight, and "business" and professional success as a moral imperative. (The emergence of bourgeois elites in this sense is vividly described in works such as R. H. Tawney's *Religion and the Rise of Capitalism*, Max Weber's *The Protestant Ethic*, and Karl Marx and Friedrich Engels' *Communist Manifesto*.) Although Marx and Engels might have been surprised, it is now clear that these values can (and perhaps must) also be present in socialist or communist economies, especially if they are industrialized and "revisionist." By democratic we mean having a popular political base, which can also be totalitarian, or tyrannical (in the classical sense), provided it is not merely imposed from above, and providing some economic mobility and relative equality in access to opportunity. Bureaucratic and meritocratic administrations also characterize modern industrial societies, whether capitalist or communist.

Bourgeois democracy tends to rest on some form of "social contract" concept of the relationship between the people and their government. The people hire and fire their governments, and no group has theocratic (Ideational) or aristocratic (Integrated) claims on the government. Democratic government clearly is also an expression of democratic "ideology"— it is sustained by the idea of the "consent" of the governed. The idea is contractual; the factors of sacredness, occultness, or charisma, are restricted. Sorokin argues that the emphasis on contractual relationships of the people to their government can be found in all aspects of a Sensate society, including the intrafamilial relationship. For example, the influential view that any two "consenting adults" can have any sexual relationship they wish so long as they do not harm third parties or each other in a serious way is a typically Sensate concept. So too is the notion that marriage is a secular contract which may be dissolved at any time the individuals see fit. If the marriage has resulted in children, dominant ("elite") American and European opinion today seems to be that so long as the children are reasonably looked after, the individuals should have the right to dissolve the marriage without excessive interference from the state or church. (Polls indicate that many Catholics accept a slightly modified version of this view.) The issue is regarded as completely personal and purely bilateral. If both sides have good personal reasons to terminate their contract, it is both unjust and unwise for government or church to treat their personal relationship as a social fact for which the community requires continued recognition.

Nationalistic values are also associated with the rise of the middle class. Kings used nationalism to gain allies among the middle class against the nobles, the church, the emperor, or enemy states. The nationalist idea later involved a recognition that the people (the nation) have the contractual right to government of (and by) their own kind and eventually to self-government—or that the right to govern has to be justified as representing the will of the people and serving the general welfare. Even the totalitarian nationalism of Mussolini, Hitler, Stalin, and the Japanese officer corps usually made its basic appeal to, and in any case found its greatest response from the middle class, or, in the case of the Japanese, the agrarian middle class.

One can argue that the long-term nationalist trend today is on the decline, at least in what might be thought of as the NATO area, though this remains in many ways an open issue. (The West European nations could conceivably become more nationalist in the future, and a European political community might emerge that would be nationalist in the sense that "Europe" becomes the "nation.") In any case, Late Sensate culture carries implications of cosmopolitanism and pacifism and lack of particularist ethics or loyalties, except on a shifting, contractual basis. Nevertheless it is probably safe to argue that over the next thirty-three years nationalism will increase in most of the underdeveloped and developing worlds, at least in the minimal sense that modern systems of public education and mass communication will tend to integrate even the most peripheral groups into national languages and cultures.

3. Accumulation of Scientific and Technical Knowledge

4. Institutionalization of Change, Especially Research, Development, Innovation, and Diffusion

In order to provide a quick impression of science and technology (with an emphasis on technology) in the last third of the twentieth century, we list in Table XVIII one hundred areas in which it is probable that technological innovation will occur in the next thirty-three years. In Chapter II we shall return to these topics for fuller discussion.

Each item in the list has the following characteristics:

(1) It is important enough to make, by itself, a significant change in the next thirty-three years. The difference might lie mainly in being spectacular (e.g., transoceanic rocket transportation in twenty or thirty minutes rather than supersonic in two or three hours); in being ubiquitous (e.g., widespread use of paper clothes); in enabling a large number of different things to be done (e.g., super materials); in a general and significant increase in productivity (e.g., cybernation); or simply in being important to specific individuals (e.g., convenient artificial kidneys).

(2) A responsible opinion can be found to argue a great likelihood that the innovation will be achieved before the year 2000—usually long before. (We would probably agree with about 90-95 per cent of these estimates.)

(3) Each warrants the description technological innovation, revolution, or breakthrough. None is simply an obvious minor improvement on what currently exists.

The list is deliberately eclectic and disordered because this communicates a more accurate description of what we know about these future possibilities than the superficial appearance of order and understanding that would be given by a somewhat differently ordered list. Indeed since, as detailed in Chapter II, serendipities and unexpected synergisms play an important role, reading this eclectic and disordered list is almost a simulation of the process of innovation and diffusion.

We should also note that the one hundred areas are not entirely randomly ordered. Most people would consider the first twenty-five as (largely) unambiguous examples of progress or human benefit. A few would question even these. The first item, for example, lasers and masers, might make possible a particularly effective kind of ballistic missile defense, and thus, some believe, could accelerate the Soviet-American arms race. Or the expansion of tropical agriculture and forestry, as suggested in the eighth item, could mean a geographical shift in economic and military power as well as a dislocation of competitive industries. Indeed nearly all the areas of innovation could involve adjustment difficulties of this kind. Nevertheless there probably would be a consensus among readers that the first twenty-five areas do represent progress—at least for those who are in favor of "progress."

The next twenty-five innovations would clearly have controversial consequences; many would argue that government policy might better restrain or discourage innovation or diffusion here. As discussed in Chapters II, IV, and VIII, these twenty-five "controversial areas" raise issues of accelerated nuclear proliferation; of loss of privacy; of excessive governmental and/or private power over individuals; of dangerously vulnerable, deceptive, and degradable overcentralization; of decisions becoming necessary that are too large, complex, important, uncertain, or comprehensive to be left to mere mortals (whether acting privately or publicly, individually or in organizations); of new capabilities that are so inherently dangerous that they are likely to be disastrously abused; of too rapid or cataclysmic change for smooth adjustment, and so on.

The last fifty items are included in part because they are intrinsically interesting and in part to demonstrate that it is fairly easy to produce a long list of items of innovation that entail nontrivial consequences.

TABLE XVIII

*One Hundred Technical Innovations Very Likely
in the Last Third of the Twentieth Century*

1. Multiple applications of lasers and masers for sensing, measuring, communication, cutting, heating, welding, power transmission, illumination, destructive (defensive), and other purposes
2. Extreme high-strength and/or high-temperature structural materials
3. New or improved superperformance fabrics (papers, fibers, and plastics)
4. New or improved materials for equipment and appliances (plastics, glasses, alloys, ceramics, intermetallics, and cermets)

TABLE XVIII (*continued*)

5. New airborne vehicles (ground-effect machines, VTOL and STOL, super-helicopters, giant and/or supersonic jets)
6. Extensive commercial application of shaped-charge explosives
7. More reliable and longer-range weather forecasting
8. Intensive and/or extensive expansion of tropical agriculture and forestry
9. New sources of power for fixed installations (e.g., magnetohydrodynamic, thermionic and thermoelectric, and radioactivity)
10. New sources of power for ground transportation (storage battery, fuel cell, propulsion [or support] by electro-magnetic fields, jet engine, turbine, and the like)
11. Extensive and intensive worldwide use of high altitude cameras for mapping, prospecting, census, land use, and geological investigations
12. New methods of water transportation (such as large submarines, flexible and special purpose "container ships," or more extensive use of large automated single-purpose bulk cargo ships)
13. Major reduction in hereditary and congenital defects
14. Extensive use of cyborg techniques (mechanical aids or substitutes for human organs, senses, limbs, or other components)
15. New techniques for preserving or improving the environment
16. Relatively effective appetite and weight control
17. New techniques and institutions for adult education
18. New and useful plant and animal species
19. Human "hibernation" for short periods (hours or days) for medical purposes
20. Inexpensive design and procurement of "one of a kind" items through use of computerized analysis and automated production
21. Controlled and/or supereffective relaxation and sleep
22. More sophisticated architectural engineering (e.g., geodesic domes, "fancy" stressed shells, pressurized skins, and esoteric materials)
23. New or improved uses of the oceans (mining, extraction of minerals, controlled "farming," source of energy, and the like)
24. Three-dimensional photography, illustrations, movies, and television
25. Automated or more mechanized housekeeping and home maintenance
26. Widespread use of nuclear reactors for power
27. Use of nuclear explosives for excavation and mining, generation of power, creation of high temperature–high-pressure environments, and/or as a source of neutrons or other radiation
28. General use of automation and cybernation in management and production
29. Extensive and intensive centralization (or automatic interconnection) of current and past personal and business information in high-speed data processors
30. Other new and possibly pervasive techniques for surveillance, monitoring, and control of individuals and organizations

T A B L E X V I I I (*continued*)

31. Some control of weather and/or climate
32. Other (permanent or temporary) changes—or experiments—with the overall environment (e.g., the "permanent" increase in C-14 and temporary creation of other radioactivity by nuclear explosions, the increasing generation of CO_2 in the atmosphere, projects Starfire, West Ford, and Storm Fury)
33. New and more reliable "educational" and propaganda techniques for affecting human behavior—public and private
34. Practical use of direct electronic communication with and stimulation of the brain
35. Human hibernation for relatively extensive periods (months to years)
36. Cheap and widely available central war weapons and weapon systems
37. New and relatively effective counterinsurgency techniques (and perhaps also insurgency techniques)
38. New techniques for very cheap, convenient, and reliable birth control
39. New, more varied, and more reliable drugs for control of fatigue, relaxation, alertness, mood, personality, perceptions, fantasies, and other psychobiological states
40. Capability to choose the sex of unborn children
41. Improved capability to "change" sex of children and/or adults
42. Other genetic control and/or influence over the "basic constitution" of an individual
43. New techniques and institutions for the education of children
44. General and substantial increase in life expectancy, postponement of aging, and limited rejuvenation
45. Generally acceptable and competitive synthetic foods and beverages (e.g., carbohydrates, fats, proteins, enzymes, vitamins, coffee, tea, cocoa, and alcoholic liquor)
46. "High quality" medical care for undeveloped areas (e.g., use of medical aides and technicians, referral hospitals, broad spectrum antibiotics, and artificial blood plasma)
47. Design and extensive use of responsive and supercontrolled environments for private and public use (for pleasurable, educational, and vocational purposes)
48. Physically nonharmful methods of overindulging
49. Simple techniques for extensive and "permanent" cosmetological changes (features, "figures," perhaps complexion and even skin color, and even physique)
50. More extensive use of transplantation of human organs
51. Permanent manned satellite and lunar installations—interplanetary travel
52. Application of space life systems or similar techniques to terrestrial installations
53. Permanent inhabited undersea installations and perhaps even colonies
54. Automated grocery and department stores

TABLE XVIII (*continued*)

55. Extensive use of robots and machines "slaved" to humans
56. New uses of underground "tunnels" for private and public transportation and other purposes
57. Automated universal (real time) credit, audit and banking systems
58. Chemical methods for improving memory and learning
59. Greater use of underground buildings
60. New and improved materials and equipment for buildings and interiors (e.g., variable transmission glass, heating and cooling by thermoelectric effect, and electroluminescent and phosphorescent lighting)
61. Widespread use of cryogenics
62. Improved chemical control of some mental illnesses and some aspects of senility
63. Mechanical and chemical methods for improving human analytical ability more or less directly
64. Inexpensive and rapid techniques for making tunnels and underground cavities in earth and/or rock
65. Major improvements in earth moving and construction equipment generally
66. New techniques for keeping physically fit and/or acquiring physical skills
67. Commercial extraction of oil from shale
68. Recoverable boosters for economic space launching
69. Individual flying platforms
70. Simple inexpensive home video recording and playing
71. Inexpensive high-capacity, worldwide, regional, and local (home and business) communication (perhaps using satellites, lasers, and light pipes)
72. Practical home and business use of "wired" video communication for both telephone and TV (possibly including retrieval of taped material from libraries or other sources) and rapid transmission and reception of facsimiles (possibly including news, library material, commercial announcements, instantaneous mail delivery, other printouts, and so on)
73. Practical large-scale desalinization
74. Pervasive business use of computers for the storage, processing, and retrieval of information
75. Shared time (public and interconnected?) computers generally available to home and business on a metered basis
76. Other widespread use of computers for intellectual and professional assistance (translation, teaching, literature search, medical diagnosis, traffic control, crime detection, computation, design, analysis and to some degree as intellectual collaborator generally)
77. General availability of inexpensive transuranic and other esoteric elements
78. Space defense systems
79. Inexpensive and reasonably effective ground-based BMD
80. Very low-cost buildings for home and business use
81. Personal "pagers" (perhaps even two-way pocket phones) and other per-

TABLE XVIII (*continued*)

sonal electronic equipment for communication, computing, and data processing program

82. Direct broadcasts from satellites to home receivers
83. Inexpensive (less than $20), long lasting, very small battery operated TV receivers
84. Home computers to "run" household and communicate with outside world
85. Maintenance-free, longlife electronic and other equipment
86. Home education via video and computerized and programmed learning
87. Stimulated and planned and perhaps programmed dreams
88. Inexpensive (less than one cent a page), rapid high-quality black and white reproduction; followed by color and high-detailed photography reproduction—perhaps for home as well as office use
89. Widespread use of improved fluid amplifiers
90. Conference TV (both closed circuit and public communication system)
91. Flexible penology without necessarily using prisons (by use of modern methods of surveillance, monitoring, and control)
92. Common use of (longlived?) individual power source for lights, appliances, and machines
93. Inexpensive worldwide transportation of humans and cargo
94. Inexpensive road-free (and facility-free) transportation
95. New methods for rapid language teaching
96. Extensive genetic control for plants and animals
97. New biological and chemical methods to identify, trace, incapacitate, or annoy people for police and military uses
98. New and possibly very simple methods for lethal biological and chemical warfare
99. Artificial moons and other methods for lighting large areas at night
100. Extensive use of "biological processes" in the extraction and processing of minerals

The following are areas in which technological success by the year 2000 seems substantially less likely (even money bets, give or take a factor of five), but where, if it occurred, it would be quite important, are these:

TABLE XIX

Some Less Likely but Important Possibilities

1. "True" artificial intelligence
2. Practical use of sustained fusion to produce neutrons and/or energy
3. Artificial growth of new limbs and organs (either in situ or for later transplantation)
4. Room temperature superconductors

TABLE XIX (*continued*)

5. Major use of rockets for commercial or private transportation (either terrestrial or extraterrestrial)
6. Effective chemical or biological treatment for most mental illnesses
7. Almost complete control of marginal changes in heredity
8. Suspended animation (for years or centuries)
9. Practical materials with nearly "theoretical limit" strength
10. Conversion of mammals (humans?) to fluid breathers
11. Direct input into human memory banks
12. Direct augmentation of human mental capacity by the mechanical or electrical interconnection of the brain with a computer
13. Major rejuvenation and/or significant extension of vigor and life span—say 100 to 150 years
14. Chemical or biological control of character or intelligence
15. Automated highways
16. Extensive use of moving sidewalks for local transportation
17. Substantial manned lunar or planetary installations
18. Electric power available for less than .3 mill per kilowatt hour
19. Verification of some extrasensory phenomena
20. Planetary engineering
21. Modification of the solar system
22. Practical laboratory conception and nurturing of animal (human?) foetuses
23. Production of a drug equivalent to Huxley's soma
24. A technological equivalent of telepathy
25. Some direct control of individual thought processes

We list below ten radical possibilities, some of which hardly make sense. We do not believe that any of them will occur by the year 2000, or perhaps ever. But some of them are discussed today; and such a list does emphasize the fact that some dramatic and radical innovation must be expected. The list may suggest how surprising and exciting (or outrageous) such an event might prove.

TABLE XX

Ten Far-Out Possibilities

1. Life expectancy extended to substantially more than 150 years (immortality?)
2. Almost complete genetic control (but still homo sapiens)
3. Major modification of human species (no longer homo sapiens)
4. Antigravity (or practical use of gravity waves) *
5. Interstellar travel

TABLE XX (*continued*)

6. Electric power available for less than .03 mill per kw hour
7. Practical and routine use of extrasensory phenomena
8. Laboratory creation of artificial live plants and animals
9. Lifetime immunization against practically all diseases
10. Substantial lunar or planetary bases or colonies

* As usually envisaged this would make possible a perpetual motion machine and therefore the creation of energy out of nothing. We do not envisage this as even a far-out possibility, but include antigravity, even though it annoys some physicist friends, as an example of some totally new use of a basic phenomena or the seeming violation of a basic law.

And finally there is the possibility—more far-fetched than popular science fiction would have it, but impossible to exclude—of a discovery of extra-terrestrial life; or, much more extreme, of communication with extraterrestrial intelligence.

These lists make only the obvious point that as a result of the long-term trends toward accumulation of scientific and technological knowledge and the institutionalization of change through research, development, innovation, and diffusion, many important new things are likely to happen in the next few decades. It is worth while asking specifically what the consequences of each item—and their synergistic interactions—might be. We shall return to these topics in Chapter II.

5. *Worldwide Industrialization and Modernization*

6. *Increasing Affluence and (Recently) Leisure*

We might conceive of nations at the end of this century as divided into the five classes indicated by Table XXI. The preindustrial countries are in the condition one might think of as historically "normal." Many people—Kenneth Boulding, Peter Drucker, J. M. Keynes, for example—have pointed out that for the last ten thousand years or so, excluding the last two or three centuries, no large human society has ever produced more than the equivalent of some $200 per capita per year, nor dropped much below about $50 per capita per year for any appreciable period of time. Kenneth Boulding points out that, from his point of view, Indonesia represents "normal civilization"—or "civilization"—since it has a population of some one hundred million people, roughly that of the Han Empire or the Roman Empire, and an average per capita income of about one hundred dollars per year. Thus most Indonesians live in a manner recognizable to both the Romans and the Han Chinese, and if Indonesians could visit such economies, they would find much that is familiar.

TABLE XXI

Five Levels of Income and Industrial Development in the Year 2000

1. Preindustrial	$50 to $200 per capita
2. Partially industrialized or transitional	$200 to $600 per capita
3. Industrial	$600 to perhaps $1,500 per capita
4. Mass consumption or advanced industrial	Perhaps $1,500 to something more than $4,000 per capita
5. Postindustrial	Something over $4,000 to perhaps $20,000 per capita

---

With industrialization mankind broke out of this pattern. We shall consider partially industrialized societies (which we somewhat arbitrarily, but in accordance with custom, define as those with incomes between $200 and $600 per capita) as probably in a "transition" stage, without assuming that they will necessarily continue to industrialize. Walt W. Rostow described the "take-off" as occurring when the proportion of net investment to national income rises to more than 10 per cent, when there is some development of the manufacturing sector, and when an appropriate institutional structure emerges.[20] Our groupings are in terms of levels of per capita income, a convenient criterion, although clearly not one that identifies any "threshold" for economic take-off. (In fact, per capita income is only loosely correlated with the proportion of national product invested.)[21]

We call (even more arbitrarily, and certainly inaccurately as a generalization) societies with between six hundred and fifteen hundred dollars per capita income, industrialized. Yet they are short of the mass consumption stage. Theirs is roughly the condition of America in the 1920's, or Europe immediately after World War II. Many preindustrial and partially industrialized societies may also, of course, have dual economies.[22] Northern and Southern Italy are examples, and this problem—though here defined in terms of urban-rural differences— is still worse in such areas as Latin America today, and promises to get even worse in the future. It may be worst of all by the year 2000 in the six most populous, less developed countries: China, India, Pakistan, Indonesia, Brazil, and Nigeria. These now contain, and in the future will probably continue to contain, about half the world's

[20] W. W. Rostow, *The Stages of Economic Growth* (Cambridge: The University Press, 1960).

[21] C. P. Kindelberger, *Economic Development,* 2d ed. (New York: McGraw-Hill, Inc., 1965), p. 98.

[22] If a country has large unexploited "frontier" areas as well—as many in Africa and Latin America do—we might call it a triple economy.

population, are now preindustrial, and will presumably be partially industrialized by the year 2000. The problem of relatively great development in major cities and much less in lesser cities and rural areas is already evident in these countries. Thus despite important differences in average development one can argue that most great cities today have achieved startlingly similar conditions of modernization. Cities, such as Rio de Janeiro, Bangkok, and Athens, are clearly twentieth-century phenomena and have many of the virtues and problems of the major cities of the United States: twentieth-century slums, computers, labor displaced by automation, great universities, skilled engineers and scientists, a trend toward tertiary and quaternary occupations, startlingly similar price structures for many commodities and activities, and so on; while the rural areas can be thought of as "modified sixteenth century"—modified by the addition of the bulldozer, the electric lights, the transistor radio, and the crop-dusting plane—but largely unchanged or entering, rapidly or slowly, the eighteenth or nineteenth centuries.

Post-World War II has seen the emergence of the so-called mass-consumption society, first in the United States and then in Western Europe and Japan. Again arbitrarily, but reasonably, we shall define a mass-consumption society, today, as one with between $1,500 and $4,000 per capita. Japan, although it has less than $1,000 per capita, is by every superficial appearance a mass consumption society today; while the Soviet Union, with a per capita income of around $1,500, seems far short of that condition. Similarly $4,000 per capita will probably be sufficient for transition to a postindustrial economy in countries like Great Britain or the Scandinavian group, while those with more ambitious goals, in terms of world power (e.g., the Soviet Union), stronger traditions of economic striving (e.g., West Germany), or higher expectations of productive affluence (e.g., the United States) would not become "postindustrial" until higher levels of affluence had been reached. Obviously these definitions cannot be taken too seriously; not only are there exceptions today, but there may be more in the future.

From our point of view, probably the most interesting classification on Table XXI is that of the postindustrial society. We shall discuss this at some length in chapters to follow. Some other characteristics of the postindustrial society have already been noted on Table IX.

Table XXII indicates a rather impressionistic, but not wholly unreasonable, economic ranking for the nations of the world in the year 2000. The figures express national populations in millions, and the total world population is estimated at 6.4 billion. The descriptions are, on the whole, optimistic, and we would not care to defend in detail the specific rank order we have suggested. The numbers identifying each group correspond roughly to the levels of income of the previous table.

TABLE XXII

Six Economic Groupings in Year 2000 (Millions of People)

(5) Visibly Postindustrial		(3) Mature Industrial	
U.S.	320	Union of South Africa	50
Japan	120	Mexico, Uruguay, Chile,	
Canada	35	Cuba, Colombia, Peru,	
Scandinavia and		Panama, Jamaica, etc.	250
Switzerland	30	N. Vietnam, S. Vietnam,	
France, W. Germany,		Thailand, the Philip-	
Benelux	160	pines, etc.	250
	665	Turkey	75
		Lebanon, Iraq, Iran, etc.	75
(5) Early Postindustrial			700
United Kingdom	55		
Soviet Union	350	(2) Large and Partially	
Italy, Austria	70	Industrialized	
E. Germany,		Brazil	210
Czechoslovakia	35	Pakistan	250
Israel	5	China	1,300
Australia, New Zealand	25	India	950
	540	Indonesia	240
		U.A.R.	70
(4) Mass Consumption		Nigeria	160
Spain, Portugal, Poland,			3,180
Yugoslavia, Cyprus,			
Greece, Bulgaria, Hun-		(1) Preindustrial or Small and	
gary, Ireland	180	Partially Industrialized	
Argentina, Venezuela	60	Rest of Africa	350
Taiwan, N. Korea,		Rest of Arab World	100
S. Korea, Hong Kong,		Rest of Asia	300
Malaysia, Singapore	160	Rest of Latin America	100
	400		850

Some issues that arise from the interactions among nations in different stages of development are discussed in Chapter V. If the above scenario is realized, the year 2000 will find a rather large island of wealth surrounded by "misery," at least relative to the developed world and to "rising expectations." Even these poor countries, however, for the most part will enjoy great improvements over their traditional standards of living. The postindustrial and industrial societies will contain about 40 per cent of the world's population: more than 90 per cent of the world's population will live in nations that have broken out of the historical $50-$200 per capita range. Yet at the same time the absolute gap in living standards, between countries or sectors of countries with developed (industrial, postindustrial, mass consumption) economies and those at preindustrial levels, will have widened abysmally. (See the "dichotomized standard world" in Chapter III.)

7. Population Growth

8. Urbanization and (Soon) the Growth of Megalopolises

One issue with which futurists are much concerned, but which we shall touch on only in passing, is urbanization and related phenomena. The United States in the year 2000 will probably see at least three gargantuan "megalopolises" that we have labeled—only half frivolously—"Boswash," "Chipitts," and "Sansan." Boswash refers to the megalopolis that will extend between Boston and Washington and might contain almost one-quarter of the United States' population (perhaps about eighty million people). (We might even call it "Portport" on the grounds that this megalopolis really stretches from Portland, Maine, to Portsmouth, Virginia.) Chipitts is another developing megalopolis, concentrated around the Great Lakes, which may stretch from Chicago to Pittsburgh, and possibly also north to the Toronto region of Canada, thereby including Detroit, Toledo, Cleveland, Akron, Buffalo, and Rochester. The United States portion of this megalopolis seems likely to contain more than one-eighth of the United States' population (or upward of forty million people). Sansan would be a Pacific megalopolis that would presumably stretch initially from San Diego to Santa Barbara, and ultimately from San Francisco to Santa Barbara, and should contain one-sixteenth or so of the United States' population (perhaps twenty million people).

All three of these megalopolises will show their maritime origins. Boswash (or Portport) is an extremely narrow strip on the North Atlantic coast. Chipitts is primarily on all the shores of Lake Erie and on the southern and western shores of Lake Michigan and Lake Ontario, and may be connected to the Ohio River. It is, of course, separated from Boswash by the Appalachian Mountains and their foothills, including most of Maine, New Hampshire, and Vermont, and much of northern and central New York, central Pennsylvania, western Virginia, West Virginia, and Kentucky. This region will presumably provide playgrounds and second homes for the better off or lucky of both megalopolises, as well as attractive sites for aesthetically or recreationally minded "postindustrial" organizations taking advantage of improved communication and transportation. Sansan is an even narrower strip on the West Coast which might actually join the San Francisco area. Chipitts and Boswash might also join through a Buffalo-Finger Lakes-Hudson Valley corridor through the Appalachian barrier. (There may also be a rather "suburban," low-density megalopolis in Florida).

One would also expect that while all three would be recognizably American in culture, they would be quite distinguishable in subcultures. Sansan will presumably provide an informal "barbecue" culture, which has sometimes been called "wholesome degeneracy," as well as a large and self-conscious Beatnik, new Left, hip, Bohemian group. Chipitts, which recently has been having very successful architectural and urban renewal programs, will probably still have traces of both the "Bible belt" and the "raw and lusty vitality" referred to by Carl Sandburg. Boswash will be "cosmopolitan," of course, the home of New York liberals; Boston bankers; both tired and creative intellectuals in publishing, entertainment, and the arts; liberal Republicans; the industrial, legal, financial, and academic establishment typified by the Committee on Economic Development and the Council on Foreign Relations; political Washington; and relatively subdued "drop-out" and alienated enclaves.

The three megalopolises should contain roughly one-half of the total United States' population, including the overwhelming majority of the most technologically and scientifically advanced, prosperous, intellectual, and creative elements. Even Sansan will have a larger total income than all but five or six nations. Any study of the United States in the year 2000 may largely be a study of Boswash, Chipitts, and Sansan.

Such structures will be typical of other countries as well. Thus most of southeastern England is likely to be one megalopolis, though in this case it may be called a conurbation. Doubtless the Japanese will want to find a word for the Tokyo-Osaka strip. Most people in the world, however, will still live in more traditional urban areas. Yet most of the developed world's population, perhaps 80 or 90 per cent, will be urbanized by the end of the century. This trend clearly must level-off, if for no other reason than that virtually all the people will have been urbanized.[23] Suburbia, then as now, will be a special kind of low-density urban living, easily distinguished from rural patterns.

9. Decreasing Importance of Primary and (Recently) Secondary Occupations

Closely related to current trends toward very large urban agglomerations is the declining importance of primary and secondary occupations, and the growing importance of what are normally called "tertiary" occupations, though we shall distinguish between tertiary and "quaternary" occupations. The primary occupations, of course, are fishing, forestry, hunting, agriculture, and mining. Secondary occupations are concerned with processing the products of a primary occupation. A tertiary occupation, in our terms, is a service rendered to primary and secondary occupations, while "quaternary"

[23] Some demographers expect that the underdeveloped world will also achieve 80 to 90 per cent urbanization by the middle of the twenty-first century.

occupations are those that render services to tertiary occupations or to each other. There will undoubtedly be a large shift to the latter group. Since these occupations are heavily concentrated among various levels and agencies of government, the professions, the nonprofit private groups, and the like, this implies, in conjunction with other things, a shift from the private business enterprise as the major source of innovation, attention, prominence, and reward in society. Lessened emphasis on primary occupations will be accompanied by a lessened dependence on access to expensive or inconvenient raw materials (rather than a situation of desperate shortages of usable or available raw materials). This, in turn, will make many factors of geography and location less crucial for the nation as a whole.

The distinction between tertiary and quaternary occupations may seem to be an artificial one since it is customary simply to lump these together as service industries. We make the distinction in order to emphasize the extraordinary degree to which the service sector of a modern economy operates by "people taking in each other's laundry," rather than by "servicing" primary and secondary activities. At the extreme is the vision held by some enthusiasts for automation in which all material goods are supplied automatically and without charge, and all economic activities are services rendered to others in service industries, rather than to primary and secondary industries. This would be a purely quaternary economy. This is very far from both today's reality and the likely future. But to a much lesser degree even today, and more so in the future, a major portion of the most productive and creative people will be engaged in what can be thought of as quaternary activities. This creates a special difficulty in estimating the GNP (as does the growing service sector in general). For example, one can imagine a young boy raising two "$50,000 cats" that he trades for one "$100,000 dog." If these artificial prices ever happen to be recorded in the country's economic transactions, the GNP would go up somewhat artificially and misleading by $200,000. Some of the activities that are going on in a highly developed quaternary economy are, at least conceptually, not too different from this example—one can examine the inputs but there is no objective measure of the output.

10. *Literacy and Education*

There are, of course, close relationships among all the elements of the multifold trend; they are parts of the same process. Increasing literacy and higher education has an obvious relationship to all the other trends, especially to the institutionalization of innovation and the emphasis on quaternary functions in the postindustrial occupational structure. In the United States we no longer tend to ask if a person is literate; we assume he is. And we tend to assume that younger people have had at least an eighth-grade education. Certainly, if current poverty programs succeed, and perhaps independently of them, we may soon be able to assume that most people have had a twelve-year high school education.[24] In fact, currently something like 40 per cent of American youth supposedly get some college experience.

On the one hand, this emphasis on education opens up the possibilities for increased personal creativity and fulfillment; continued rapid economic growth; and, perhaps even more important, that of most people's vocations being interesting, intellectually demanding, and filled with nonmonetary rewards. On the other hand, there can be serious problems—as well as advantages—in such a trend.

An overemphasis on education can result in shallow intellectualism; Mandarism (the intellectual as "father and mother of his country"); an overemphasis on "book learning" (conceptual world and documented information rather than existential world and perceived orally or transmitted information); an expansion and prolongation of the adolescent subculture; a meritocracy; excessive theorizing, intellectual and/or educated parochialism; alienation from one's own culture or subculture; and other alienation from the practical world.

Not all of these "problems" can occur simultaneously in the same individual or perhaps even in the same culture or subculture, but all of them can occur and many of them seem to be occurring today in various parts of the world.

11. *Increasing Capability for Mass Destruction*

12. *Increasing Tempo of Change*

13. *Increasing Universality of the Multifold Trend*

These aspects of the multifold trend are almost self-explanatory. We shall return to these themes in subsequent chapters.

Up to this point we have treated each of the thirteen aspects of the multifold trend (see Table I) as being on a more or less equivalent footing, though many would argue that some of these are causes or independent variables, and that others are effects, perhaps even trivial effects.

Until about two hundred years ago, it would have been even more difficult to determine which was cause and which was effect; after that, technology and economic development gained a momentum which made them seem most conspicuous to many observers. Yet the accumulation of scientific and technological knowledge; the institutionalization of change through research, development, innovation, and diffusion; and worldwide industrialization, modernization, and increasing affluence could take place

[24] See "Notes on World-Wide School Enrollment and Illiteracy, and U.S. School and College Graduates to Year 2000," by Mark Wehle and Laurie Rockett, in *Selected Papers from the Hudson Institute.*

only within a rather special cultural and structural setting—which was, as we have suggested, a culture that had tended to become Sensate, empirical, this worldly, utilitarian, and manipulative of nature, and a social structure characterized by the increasing dominance of economically minded (bourgeois), bureaucratic, and democratic elites.

Of course, the system in which worldwide social changes take place is far more complicated than can be suggested by any effort to identify a limited number of abstract "trends," let alone to specify which of the abstractions "causes" the others. It is enough to describe processes of change that seem likely to continue, and to give rise to further change.

It may be fair, though crudely sweeping, to say that of these trends it was first the Renaissance ("Sensate") and then the Reformation (bourgeois) that were important, next the Industrial Revolution, economic growth, and technology that became, not "causes" of the other trends, but at least the most prominent of them. To continue in this vein, it may be the last three items of Table I—increasing capability for mass destruction, increasing tempo of change, and increasing universality of the multifold trend—that in the future will have the most spectacular and conceivably destabilizing consequences.

In any case, the long-term, cumulative operation of elements of the multifold trend will ultimately create differences in degree that at some point will amount to qualitative changes in some or all of the elements. If thousand-year patterns described by macrohistorians remain relevant to our own society, these qualitative changes may still be some centuries away. Yet Western industrial society is the first to have routinized extremely rapid and cumulative economic and technological development Perhaps we have thereby acquired an institutionalized capacity to adapt to change indefinitely. On the other hand, we may be undergoing an unusually rapid acceleration to potentially disastrous points of culmination and reversal—or irreversibility—of trends. Avoiding such junctures will depend in part on the capacity of our own and future generations to perceive long-term trends, to anticipate emergent crises, and to respond to them appropriately. It will also depend, of course, on factors beyond the control of any or even all policy-makers; we may be lucky enough to escape disasters temporarily or permanently in spite of shortsighted social policies, or so unfortunate that our best efforts will not be good enough.

In the following chapters we continue our discussion of issues that may be raised by continuation of the multifold trend and other future possibilities, and in our final chapter we make some suggestions for improving policy-makers' capacities for coping with both projected and unexpected difficulties and dangers.

CHAPTER II

Comments on Science and Technology

A. INTRODUCTION

In this chapter we continue the discussion of the third, fourth, and twelfth aspects of our multifold trend: the accumulation of scientific and technological knowledge, the institutionalization of change—especially research, development, innovation, and diffusion—and the increasing tempo of change. There is, of course, no dearth of books on the future of science and technology.[1] We are not going to attempt to summarize this voluminous literature in this chapter. The three lists—Tables XVIII, XIX, and XX—in Chapter I were intended to suggest something of the range of likely and less likely possibilities for technological innovation.

In this chapter we shall restrict ourselves to some limited observations about some general issues and six selected areas of technology: (1) nuclear power; (2) central war; (3) electronics, computers, information processing, and automation; (4) lasers; (5) holography; and (6) the biological manipulation of man, which have been chosen to illustrate the range of issues that arise. But before discussing these areas we should probably make some comments about the general character of the three lists presented in Chapter I.

The impression of disorder and eclecticism that is fostered by our almost unstructured list of one hundred areas may be somewhat exaggerated.

---

[1] Of special interest in this connection is the report of the President's Commission on Technology and Automation. For a good description of the technology itself, see Robert Prehoda's *Designing the Future, the Role of Technological Forecasting,* to be published by Chilton Books in late 1967. A series of articles by John Kettle in the *Monetary Times* of Canada, 1967, also gives a good picture, and see also Nigel Calder, ed., *The World in 1984, The Complete New Scientist Series,* 2 vols. (Harmondsworth, England: Penguin Books, 1965).

Clearly we could have given a more organized and orderly presentation. For example, we could have divided the various items into functional groupings, or we could have emphasized the basic technologies and technological interactions among various areas and thus also indicated, to some extent, how the various areas depend on the body of scientific and technical knowledge as a whole. This might have also suggested how many of the innovations depend on each other or are otherwise closely correlated, and that there is indeed a rather broad and relatively concerted movement taking place in the advancement of science and technology.

Of course, innovation and discovery inevitably entail a certain amount of disorder. But by deliberately not displaying any of the regularities and relations that do exist we may have appeared to understate the order. However, while we have indeed left out aspects of orderliness, we have not really overstated the disorder. The appearance of the lists does reflect something about current understanding of the advance of science and technology and their applications. It is often only in retrospect that the relations seem clear; our expectations and activity are often sporadic, eclectic, unintegrated, and startlingly incomplete. Thus a study in 1937 totally missed not only the computer but atomic energy, antibiotics, radar, and jet propulsion, nearly all of which had been around in principle and waiting for development.

There is another reason why, despite their length, our three lists no doubt understimate the advance of technology and overestimate our understanding of this advance. They give little sense of the importance of interactions among more or less simultaneous advances and of the often accidental or opportunistic character of many advances. The interacting effects tend to be important not only because advances in one area are correlated with or spur advances in other areas, but also because various separate advances often allow for unexpected solutions to problems, or can be fitted together to make new wholes that are greater than the sum of their parts, or lead to other unexpected innovations. Cooperative and interactive effects are called "synergistic," while unexpected discoveries or applications are called "serendipitous."

B. SYNERGISM AND SERENDIPITY

As an example of synergism, let us consider the Polaris missile system. The first Polaris submarine—the *George Washington*—was launched in 1960; the forty-first, and last, was tested in 1967. It would have been almost impossible to argue in the early 1950's, at least before a hard-headed and scientifically knowledgeable audience, that such a system could be produced successfully within a decade. It took at least six technological innovations or breakthroughs, all of which seemed unlikely to be realized soon enough to be reliably useful in an early 1960's weapon system. These were (1) a nuclear propulsion system that would be efficient and reliable enough to be practical; (2) a solid fuel propellant for the missiles that would also be efficient and reliable enough to be practicable; (3) a submarine navigation system (the SINS system) accurate enough for the submarine to locate itself properly in both azimuth and position; (4) a lightweight, reliable, and accurate inertial guidance system to be carried by the missile; (5) small nuclear warheads with sufficient explosive yield to constitute a powerful threat; and (6) successful design, procurement, and assembly of the ten million parts of the system, many of them complex and untested.

In addition, there were at least four problems that might easily have caused major delays in scheduling, or degradation in performance, but which, as it turned out, did not: (1) coordination of eleven thousand contractors—which required another innovation, the development of the PERT programming system (which depended in turn on the development of better computers); (2) development of a survivable communications system (one not destroyable by an enemy first strike); (3) development of adequate life-support systems to enable the submarine to stay under water sixty days and still keep the crew comfortable and efficient; and (4) recruitment of men able and willing to undergo this regime without losing morale, efficiency, and reliability. Many of these innovations and techniques still looked uncertain in the early 1960's, several years after the first submarine had been launched.

Our three lists furnish an inventory of many possibilities for synergism—some perhaps as dramatic as the Polaris submarine. Some combinations will have been almost completely unpredicted, and most will have some surprising aspects about them, that is, there will be many serendipitous developments.

Indeed, many of our advances come out of basic research, which, by definition, tends to produce serendipitous results for applications, since the research is directed not toward specific practical ends, but toward obtaining information and understanding about some important area. Basic research turns out to yield many important applications, but often in most unexpected ways. For example, the current treatment of cancer of the prostate derives from studies of the seasonal change in the size of the prostate gland of hedgehogs; the use of x-rays in medicine resulted from atomic physics research. Serendipity often results from applied research as well: an application is found in a different field than the one intended. The hologram, which, as discussed later, may make practical three-dimensional recording and projection, was invented as a result of an investigation of image magnification; the original objective was not the creation and display of three-dimensional images. In applied technology, serendipity may be no more than playing hunches and experimenting freely.

We can be almost certain that any document written in the year 2000 about the technological advances of the last third of the century will focus attention on serendipitous developments. In some cases, the degree of surprise may be so great as to seem to contradict a law of physics. For example, many applications of lasers appear to contradict the second law of thermodynamics as it was described in old textbooks on optics. These books did not include consideration of what could be done with coherent light. The laser, which makes practical the generation and use of coherent light, appears to be one of the fundamental technologies of the future, and was quite an unexpected breakthrough.

A complex synergistic breakthrough in a modern system may actually be composed of a number of layers of interrelated synergisms, each important in its own right. For example, three interrelated synergisms, illustrated below, are (*a*) the changes in crystallography and chemical technology that made semiconductors possible, (*b*) the combination of semiconductors, thin films, and metallurgical innovations that led to microelectronics and integrated circuits, and (*c*) the combination of propulsion systems, guidance systems, computers based on microelectronics, and composite materials that make advanced aerospace systems feasible.

Some synergisms today will provide new or improved methods of basic scientific research, which will in turn lead to serendipitous and perhaps truly unpredictable innovations. A most important example may be the

FIGURE 1
THREE INTERRELATED SYNERGISMS
(Synergisms Shown in Boxes)

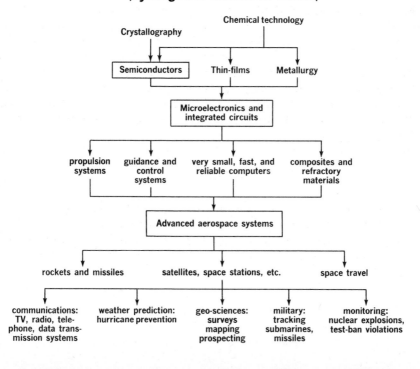

FIGURE 2
A SYNERGISM FOR BASIC MOLECULAR RESEARCH

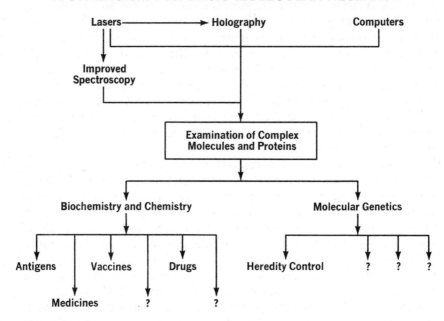

synergism of lasers, holography, and computers that will permit improved spectroscopic and three-dimensional examination of complex molecules and proteins. The resulting advances in understanding of biochemistry, chemistry, and molecular genetics should bring far-reaching improvements in drugs, medicines, vaccines, and antigens, as well as revolutionary effects in hereditary control and other areas that we cannot predict.

In this report we shall not try to explicate and discuss systematically possible synergisms and serendipities. While clearly important, these are, almost by definition, difficult to investigate. We hope that systematic or sophisticated studies can shed some light on the possibilities, at least at the level of speculation and conjecture. For the present, however, we shall confine ourselves to making some isolated comments on some important and already visible possibilities in the six more or less separate areas we have chosen to discuss.

C. NUCLEAR POWER

We shall start our discussion with a very special but important area that illustrates—perhaps all too well—the ambiguous potentialities of many modern technologies. We mentioned in Chapter I that the first twenty-five items in our list of one hundred areas were more or less noncontroversial, while the second twenty-five posed difficult and controversial policy issues. The first two of the controversial areas involve the applications of nuclear fission or fusion. Past programs in both these areas illustrate how easy it is for organizations, such as the United States government, to carry out policies that are at cross-purposes with one another.

When, in 1946, the United States first proposed the Baruch Plan for control of the international operation of nuclear reactors and access to fissionable material, one of the difficulties which dominated the plan was the widespread expectation that we would soon be presented with large and economically justifiable demands for nuclear power. Rather unexpectedly this did not happen for two decades. There had been such large improvements in techniques for generating power by thermal plants that nuclear power was not really competitive with thermal power for these first two postwar decades. One would have thought that the United States government, which was obviously desperately interested in locking up the nuclear genie, or at least in preventing its rapid diffusion, would have sponsored a great deal of research in thermal plants in order to preserve this lead over nuclear power. In fact, of course, the exact opposite occurred. Almost all the research on the improvement of thermal plants (which was, however, unexpectedly successful—at least for a time) was sponsored by private industry. On the other hand, the United States and foreign governments spent many billions of dollars in research on the design of economic nuclear reactors. As a result, nuclear reactors, at least in large installations (say more than five hundred megawatts), are today quite competitive with thermal plants and in many cases very efficient sources of power. In fact almost two-thirds of all new electric generating plants started in the United States in 1966 were nuclear. It is now estimated that the installed power in the European Economic Community will grow by a factor of a hundred from a programmed 3,700 megawatts in 1970 to 370,000 megawatts by the year 2000. It is often said that each five to ten megawatts of electrical capacity can be used to produce enough plutonium each year for one small nuclear weapon. If this estimate is used, one can easily translate these figures for megawatt production into potential capacity for producing small plutonium weapons. (In 1970 the EEC should be able to produce 350 to 700 weapons per year—and in 2000 about 35,000 to 70,000 weapons per year from its peaceful reactors.) Similarly by the mid- or late 1970's the Japanese should have an installed reactor capacity of 5,000 megawatts and thus should, at least theoretically, be able to produce 500 to 1,000 small plutonium weapons a year. We would expect that by the year 2000 even relatively small countries, say of the size and developmental level that Chile or Hungary might have at that time, could easily have a theoretical capacity to produce some hundreds of plutonium weapons a year.

Furthermore most, or all, reactors by the year 2000 are likely to be breeder reactors (the result of another successful program to find out how to use a power generating reactor to generate, at the same time, new fissionable material from ordinary uranium or thorium that is put around a reactor.) Such breeder reactors would generally be operated so that even "nonnuclear" countries could have significant, or even large, stocks of weapons grade plutonium in "storage."

We are not suggesting that the United States-sponsored research program to speed the day when nuclear reactors became economical was necessarily a mistake. There are, after all, important gains to be realized from this development. If very cheap nuclear power can be gained from fast-breeder or fusion reactors, a new stage in the industrial revolution might be initiated. For example, Dr. Alvin M. Weinberg, director of the Oak Ridge National Laboratory,

> . . . talks of atomic power produced at half or even a quarter of present costs. What would we do, he asks, with unlimited power at such a price? . . . Revolutions in industrial chemistry and metallurgy would be possible, he said. Normally in smelting iron ore, coke is required to draw impurities from the metal. Abundant power would obviate this.
>
> Likewise, Dr. Weinberg said, nitrogen-rich fertilizers could be made economically using the nitrogen that is the chief component of air. Above all, he declared, fresh water could be extracted from the oceans in vast quantities.[2]

The last example may be important. About fifteen years ago the cost of desalinated water was $4.00 to $5.00 per thousand gallons. Today a non-atomic one-million-gallon-a-day plant in Guantanamo Bay, Cuba, produces water at a cost of $1.16 per thousand gallons. However, a study by the Bechtel Corporation in 1965 indicated that atomic power plants could reduce the cost of desalinated water to about one-fifth of its present cost, or about 25¢ per thousand gallons. This is competitive with the 25¢ to 40¢ per thousand gallons that is now paid in areas where natural water is plentiful, and much cheaper than the $1.00 or more in watershort areas. It equals the 22¢ rate which Southern California hopes to realize by 1970 from a $2 billion bond project to bring fresh water from inland fresh water supplies. Bechtel proposed a $300 million nuclear-power-and-desalinization plant south of Los Angeles to produce 150 million gallons of water a day, enough for a city of 750,000. It would also produce a power output of 1,800 megawatts, bigger than Hoover Dam, at a price of 4 mills per kilowatt hour, which is competitive with present electricity costs. With fast-breeder reactors, such combination nuclear plants will be even

[2] *New York Times,* January 24, 1965.

more attractive. We suspect that they will be started in the mid-1970's, and widely built in the 1980's and 1990's.

Power from controlled sustained nuclear fusion is also a possibility. Such a technology would permit mankind to tap the deuterium, or heavy hydrogen, widely available from natural water for an effectively unlimited energy source. New developments in creating high temperatures and in containing gaseous plasmas may portend that fusion power may, after all, be within reach.[3]

We do not believe it a foregone conclusion that controlled sustained fusion will be in commercial use by the year 2000, but the odds that it will are often judged about even (which is why it is on our list of twenty-five less probable innovations). These fusion reactions will also probably produce very inexpensive neutrons that will open up all kinds of possibilities for the transmutation of elements—in particular the manufacture of Tritium. Having Tritium widely available, of course, makes it much easier to manufacture small, efficient, lightweight fusion weapons.

It seems clear that the full implications and relationships of these "atoms for peace" programs to other high priority national programs for the prevention of proliferation of nuclear weapons were not carefully and systematically examined. It may well be that even if these issues had been more thoroughly explored the government would not have done things differently; yet one has serious doubts.

Another possible source of nuclear power—the use of peaceful nuclear explosives—has had ambivalent treatment by both the United States and the Soviets. In the 1950's the latter advertised (it now seems inaccurately) that they had done many large engineering projects using nuclear explosives. There has, in the last decade, been a United States program with similar aims, called Project Plowshare, but there has also been much pressure against this project. Indeed there has been an almost excessive awareness by the arms control community and even the general public that nuclear explosives could easily be made into nuclear weapons—at least in contrast to the surprising lack of public controversy about the encouragement of nuclear reactor "atoms for peace" programs. The chief difference seems to be that the Plowshare program makes more explicit—perhaps because it is potentially noisy—its relationship to a weapons program. (While Plowshare explosives are also theoretically weapons they would generally be badly designed for these purposes.) With or without Plowshare, a nation that wanted to acquire nuclear weapons would probably go through a separate program of design for these weapons. While the existence of a Plowshare program would probably be more than marginally useful, it

[3] *New York Times,* July 8, 1965.

probably would not be so much more useful than having a "peaceful" reactor program as public attitudes and discussion seem to assume.

It is interesting to note that while Plowshare is probably, but not certainly, much less important than reactors, it is almost certain that nuclear explosives would still be economic in many mining and excavation situations. Nuclear explosives also seem to be the cheapest source of raw energy in the world, as well as the cheapest source of neutrons and other sorts of radiation, and a unique and inexpensive means of creating a high temperature-high pressure environment. It seems quite plausible that all of these possibilities could be commercially or scientifically exploited.

We shall not discuss here the obvious scenario—in which a very successful Plowshare program creates serious problems of weapons diffusion—except to point out again that Plowshare is probably not much more dangerous in this respect than normal reactors (not to speak of the breeder reactor and nuclear fusion programs).

There are, of course, important new sources of power potentially available from other than nuclear reactions. Thus, commercial recovery of oil could conceivably be among the first of the major new sources of power and fuel in the next thirty-three years. The oil-shale lands in Colorado, Wyoming, and Utah are said to be the world's largest oil reserve: estimates running to two trillion barrels or *five times the world's known reserves* and seventy times the proved reserves in the United States. "The oil is estimated to be worth $5000-billion at current market prices, which would come to about $25,000 for every man, woman and child in the country." [4] The government has just announced proposed regulations for leasing thirty thousand acres, providing for a sliding scale of royalty payments from oil marketed from government-owned lands, which represent 80 per cent of the total. If the extraction process eventually becomes economical enough, the United States might fill not only all of its domestic oil needs but could also become an exporter of oil.

Among other sources of energy are (as a yet unpublished study at the Hudson Institute indicates) numerous low dams on South American rivers. Thus it seems that the Amazon River could be dammed relatively easily. This would not only create an inland "Mediterranean" but could produce about seventy-five million or more kilowatts capacity that could be used to produce electricity at a cost of a few mills per kilowatt hour (or about *one-third* of the *total* current United States capacity at a fraction of the cost).

There may also be changes in the generation of power for the home. Thus

---

[4] *New York Times*, May 7, 1967. But this number is misleading. If much oil were produced in this way, the currently "managed price" of petroleum would clearly drop. However, one basic point is valid: as a result of this new technology the United States is practically independent—at least at current prices—of foreign oil supplies.

such "old" items as solar energy may not only be widely used in household space heaters, and more importantly, to power small generators in power poor areas, but there are other possibilities for becoming less dependent on the power company.[5] One possibility is a charged aerosol generator, which has been developed for the Navy, using a gas, such as helium, sprayed with hot water, to turn heat directly into electricity. The manufacturer asserts that the machine's low cost compactness, and efficiency will make turbo-electric generators obsolete.[6] United States gas companies and Pratt and Whitney are working together to produce a natural gas-powered fuel cell to generate electricity for the home, which would be competitive with a power company's electricity and bring about "all-gas homes." [7]

These items are only a few of several hundred or so that are in the mill for special purpose power sources. We have restricted ourselves here to the nuclear field because this has such important implications for our next section, but the examples indicate some of the many lines of research which could have been followed—in addition to the improvement of various kinds of thermal plants—by a government interested in making nonnuclear power economically more attractive than nuclear power.

D. CENTRAL WAR: TECHNOLOGY AND DOCTRINAL LAGS

The technological revolution in central war [8] illustrates the difficulties and dangers of changing technology in a most dramatic way. In *On Thermonuclear War*,[9] it was argued that every five years or so there is enough of a change in the art of strategic war to make as big an impact on corresponding doctrine as was required between the Civil War and World War I, or between the two World Wars. This was illustrated by considering the kind of central war technology that was available in 1951 and comparing it with what had been available at the end of World War II; similar comparisons were then made for 1956, 1961, and 1965 (the last two were projections). Finally it was argued that the tempo of change would continue at about the same rate. Without going into the argument in detail, Tables I, II, III, and IV below indicate some of the important changes.

---

[5] See Harry Z. Tabor, "Power for Remote Areas," *International Science and Technology,* May 1967, p. 52.

[6] *New York Times,* January 14, 1967.

[7] *Technology Week,* February 13, 1967.

[8] Central war implies a large war between two major powers involving their homelands. It is sometimes called strategic war.

[9] Herman Kahn, *On Thermonuclear War* (Princeton, N.J.: Princeton University Press, 1960), especially Lecture III.

TABLE I

1951 Technology

B-50 and B-36 form backbone of U.S. SAC
Experimental aerial refueling
Initial Production of B-47
First flight of XB-52
Manual Air Defense System started
Air defense has F-80, F-94, F-86, F-84
Production order for Nike-A
Nuclear powered airplane under development
Third- or fourth-generation atomic bombs
Russians have TU-4, MiG-15, and have tested three
   nuclear weapons
Air Research and Development Command, Lincoln
   Laboratory, RAND Corporation, and so on estab-
   lished

Table I above indicates that there were entirely new postwar airplanes available for the United States for both offense and defense and that the weapons to be carried by the offense had been enormously improved over the Nagasaki and Hiroshima bombs. It also indicates that follow-up systems had already been started and that the Soviets were trying to catch up. Finally, and perhaps most important, was the institutionalization—in the United States—of research and innovation in doctrine as well as in technology.

Thus by the early 1950's the United States had modernized and increased its forces substantially but the Russians had scarcely begun to procure intercontinental bombers. They had a rather large force of medium bombers of the TU-4 (similar to the B-29) and Badger (B-47) types, but it now seems clear that both these aircraft were designed and procured for European rather than intercontinental missions—although at the time no one in the United States or Europe seemed to realize this. Although thermonuclear weapons had been tested, the military stockpiles consisted almost wholly of kiloton bombs.

Despite slow means of delivery (bombers) and relatively low-yield warheads, both United States and Soviet forces were almost incredibly vulnerable to surprise attack. At the beginning of the period all United States strategic forces were located at a dozen bases. Hours, perhaps days, would have been required to evacuate them, and days, perhaps weeks of warning, would have been necessary for them to be able to mount effective combat operations. Nuclear weapons were stored in a relatively vulnerable configuration (at first at one site and then at two). In the early part of this period, almost no one seems to have understood the "subtleties" of the problem of vulnerability. Active air defense was deployed to protect cities, Oak Ridge, and Hanford. Strategic Air Command bases were left unguarded (no special radar or other warning system) as well as unprotected (no active defense) on the theory that no one would waste nuclear weapons on military bases. By the middle and end of the period, senior officers in the United States Air Force understood vulnerability very well but did not believe (it now seems correctly) that the Soviets had much actual operational strategic capability for a surprise attack.

TABLE II

1956 Technology

Last B-47E produced
B-52 and KC-135 phased in
B-56, Snark, and XP6M-1 (Martin Seamaster) fly
Regulus 1 in service
Atlas, Titan, and Thor in crash programs
Century series of fighters phased in
Missile Master and SAGE in production
Atomic plane and rocket under development
Atomic powered submarine launched
Inexpensive, flexible atomic bombs
Third generation nuclear bombs
Russians have Badgers, Bears, Bisons, IRBM's, H-bombs

By 1956 not only was the B-50 completely obsolete but its replacement, the B-47, was in its fifth model change. Intercontinental missiles were also coming in. At the same time the replacement for the intercontinental B-36 bomber, the B-52, was being phased in. Air defense was also experiencing a complete generational change in its aircraft.

By the late 1950's, third- and fourth-generation thermonuclear weapons had been procured by the United States and a large spectrum of such weapons was available to the United States forces, from "suitcase" to multimegaton bombs. United States military planners and decision-makers began to think of thermonuclear weapons as relatively inexpensive, if not cheap, but the Soviets still did not. However, the problems of vulnerability were still inadequately understood, and in fact by the end of the period there was much discussion of the existence of a "missile gap." While the United States government conceded the existence of such a gap—and in fact was responsible for disseminating the estimates which gave it plausibility, it simultaneously argued there was no "deterrence gap" since the five hundred missiles which United States intelligence attributed to the Soviet Union would have been unable to do as much damage as the two thousand bombers that the United States possessed. Congressional testimony and other documents disclose that almost none of the top civilian officials and relatively few scholars and journalists understood that these five hundred Soviet missiles, if they existed, could probably have destroyed the two thousand American bombers on the ground in a surprise attack.

TABLE III

1961 Technology

Arms control (techniques and policies)

Controlled response (techniques and policies)

Satellites, such as Vanguard, Pioneer, Discoverer, Tiros, Transit Notus, and Mercury

Soft Atlas and soft IRBM's deployed

25 psi Atlas, 100 psi Titan BMEW's, and Polaris being phased in

Crash program on Minuteman

Guidance breakthrough

B-47E, B-52G, and H, B-58 form bulk of SAC

Bombers operated alert and dispersed

SAGE and Missile Master partially deployed

Bomarc A and Hawk being phased in

Nike-Hercules, F-100, 102, 104 in service

Cheap civil defense

Inexpensive, efficient & versatile nuclear weapons

There are four nuclear countries

Goose, Navajo, Regulus II, F-107, and the like, canceled

By 1961 it was clear to everyone that the arms race had to be controlled and in part as a result of the detente, and in part as a result of unilateral restraint, many policies were adopted to make war less likely, to decrease the cost of defense preparation and to decrease the damage if war actually occurred.

By the early 1960's the United States, at least, was well into the missile era and almost everybody interested in such problems understood the distinction between "first-strike" and "second-strike" tactics, forces, and postures. However, according to the 1963 testimony of Defense Secretary Robert McNamara, the Soviets had not yet hardened and dispersed their missile forces, although it was expected that they would do so by the late

1960's. In the early 1960's some of the doctrinal lags of the late 1950's were revealed. For example, it was disclosed that the most important half of the U.S. Semi-Automatic Ground Environment Air Defense System, that part which was designed to control the air battle defending centers on the American East Coast, West Coast, and the Canadian border, was located on SAC bases and thus was almost certain to be destroyed or disabled in any war in which Soviet missiles were successfully launched at these SAC bases. Similar mistakes in both installations and weapons systems occurred elsewhere. As a result there was tremendous concern about vulnerability and emphasis on such problems as "reciprocal fear of surprise attack" (expressed in terms of "gun duel" models of a strategic confrontation in which the side which gets off a "shot" first may escape all retaliation). By the end of this period the United States had begun to digest not only the preattack implications of two-way deterrence, but also the possibility of intrawar or postattack deterrence, and therefore the need for restraint in the threat and use of force even after hostilities have begun. This resulted in the so-called controlled response doctrine [10] and such policy statements as these: "Principal military objectives in the event of a nuclear war stemming from a major attack *on the Alliance,* should be the destruction of the enemy's military forces, not of his civilian population" (by Defense Secretary McNamara at Ann Arbor, Michigan, June 16, 1962); and the statement of President Johnson in his defense message to the Eighty-Ninth Congress (January 18, 1965): "Our military forces must be so organized and directed that they can be used in a *measured, controlled, and deliberate* way as a versatile instrument to support our foreign policy." (Emphasis added.)

Despite these statements, however, it remains quite clear from other statements that both Secretary McNamara and President Johnson remain doubtful about the feasibility, likelihood, or even possibility of a controlled response in a major war. Moreover, there is little indication that the United States has thoroughly organized its forces (not to speak of the NATO forces) around these concepts.

We are now involved in a new modern era in which there is an incredible menu of weapons systems to choose from, most of which, of course, are not procured—in part because of the competing demands of the ones that are actually procured.

By the mid-1960's it was clear to all who wished to look that some degree of independent nuclear deterrence was—or soon would be—practical in many more countries than the five that already possessed nuclear weapons. It is usually estimated that it would cost a typical "transitional" nation (as defined on pages 58, 60) about fifty million dollars (or less if it had a peaceful reactor program) to achieve a productive capacity of a few nuclear weapons a year. One of the more advanced industrial nations if it has a reasonably

---

[10] Kahn, *On Thermonuclear War,* pp. 171-175.

TABLE IV
1965 Technology

Independent nuclear deterrents practical
"Limits" of bomb technology
Minuteman III and Polaris A_3
Sophisticated satellite program
Navaho missiles, BMEWS-B, Midas-B, SAGE B, Bomarc B and
    C, Nike-Zeus A and B, Hawk B, F-108, B-58B, B-70, nuclear
    powered propulsion and Dynosoar all technologically possible
    but cancelled
Bulk of megaton weapons on "improved" B-52, B-47, and B-58
Protected command and control
Inexpensive, reliable research missile
Super guidance
Bacteriological and chemical warfare
Astronautics

large gross national product (say about fifty billion dollars per year) should be able to procure a sizable Minuteman or Polaris type of missile force. If it spreads its budget over five or ten years, and if it could get missiles at roughly United States costs, such a force should cost about one or two billion dollars a year for five hundred to one thousand deployed missiles. It is an open question whether costs for reasonably effective forces will go up or down in the future. None of this, of course, is likely to put these countries in the same league with the superpowers—in particular their weapons systems are likely to be relatively primitive and the system as a whole to have serious defects—but it does give them capabilities that they may judge to be worth procuring.

The " 'limits' on bomb technology" referred to on the table does not imply that great improvements in nuclear technology are not really possible, but only that, as far as the large weapons are concerned, improvements in a common criterion of efficiency—the explosive power per unit of weight—are beginning to level-off. It is no longer likely that every five years or so we will see an increase by a factor of ten or so in this criterion.

We have not tried in this very brief description to give any real feeling of what the enormous changes in technology meant and how inadequately our doctrine kept up with these changes.[11] We have tried to make clear the plausibility of the claim that every five years or so there has been a real

[11] The interested reader can find a discussion of these issues in Kahn, *On Thermonuclear War*, pp. 417-522, or in an article by Herman Kahn, "Nuclear War" to be published in the forthcoming edition of *The Encyclopedia of Social Sciences* (New York: Macmillan).

revolution in the technology of central war. If this continues there may be about six more such revolutions by the year 2000.

The five-year rule still seems to be a good one for the future. Indeed the rule may now hold for capabilities other than central war. In particular, in the next five years there will be major changes in the art of fighting a counterinsurgency war. There is a great deal of technological development going on in this area—much of it spurred by the Vietnamese conflict. While it is true that much use of modern equipment by the American forces seems to have been contraproductive (being used—at least in the past—as a substitute for such things as night patrolling, administrative reforms, and other important and basic nontechnological measures, rather than to improve the efficiency of such basic measures) this seems to be less true today. As the understanding of this kind of warfare increases, the contraproductive use of technology should, presumably, be even less likely in the future.

It is, of course, possible that guerrillas will also benefit from changes in technology or even from special development efforts. If so, then once again there will presumably be some kind of a measure-countermeasure race. On the counterinsurgent side of this contest such innovations as new methods of creating physical barriers to movement; improving night vision; lighting up large areas; detection devices; booby traps; improved fire power for both air and ground-based vehicles and men; better equipment, food, medicine, and even psychopharmacological chemicals for the individual soldier; better weapons, better transportation, better doctrine, and the like, all seem capable of making a great deal of difference in many situations. Equally important there may be many new techniques to help the indigenous government operate more efficiently and effectively. These may range from the use of computers to help in the control of population to better understood tactics and strategies for economic, social, and political development—that is, the improvements may extend to much more than just police and military operations.

We are not suggesting that insurgency war will be as heavily dependent on technology as local or central war is, or that a technologically superior government will necessarily defeat technologically inferior insurgents. We are pointing out that, as has been true in the past, sufficiently large forces may be able to defeat poorly armed "popular forces" and that "sufficiently large" here may be as much a function of technology and doctrine as of the numbers. Thus, larger forces may in effect be both more purchasable in the open market (or deliverable by an outside supporting power) and may also cost less, at least so long as the insurgents themselves do not also take advantage of new technology.

Let us briefly consider the future of central war technology and other related issues. Table V, below, indicates that the common belief that the United States government, or other governments, automatically acquire any

---

TABLE V

Four Questions That Must Be Answered

1. What will X do that the currently programmed U.S. posture will not do?
2. Why is it worth doing?
3. What is the impact of doing X on the U.S.S.R.; our allies; the "arms race" generally?
4. What is the cost-effectiveness analysis?

---

new weapons system simply because it is available is not true. We have already suggested this by calling attention, in Table IV, to the many cancelled or unprocured systems that were available throughout the 1960's. Indeed it is in fact a major characteristic of the 1960's that there were large numbers of superficially attractive military systems that for various reasons were not procured by the government. Many of these reasons are summarized in the above list of questions that the United States government must ask today in considering a new military system. The questions are roughly in order of priority.

These questions are a rather difficult gauntlet to run. In particular, almost nobody in the United States government is interested in systems which will

FIGURE 3
BUDGETS FOR STRATEGIC FORCES

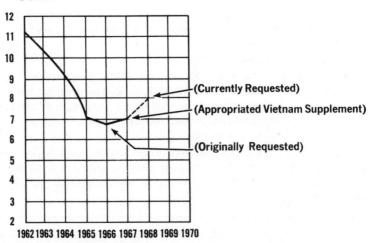

Billions of Dollars

(Currently Requested)

(Appropriated Vietnam Supplement)

(Originally Requested)

1962 1963 1964 1965 1966 1967 1968 1969 1970

FISCAL YEAR

* Statement of Secretary of Defense Robert S. McNamara Before the House Armed Services Committee on the Fiscal Year 1968-72 Defense Program and 1968 Defense Budget, p. 203.

simply kill enemy civilians. There is a strong feeling that we have more than enough capability for what Secretary McNamara calls "assured destruction," or "the capacity to destroy their society as a society." The big issues, therefore, are with regard to special situations and to an alternative mission for strategic forces, termed by Mr. McNamara as "damage limitation." [12]

As shown in Figure 3, one important result on central war forces of asking the above questions is a decline in spending on central war forces. Today we spend about seven billion dollars per year on central war forces; while in the middle and late 1950's we spent about fifteen billion dollars a year. (Thus today's central war expenditures are about 1 per cent of GNP, while ten years ago they were about 4 per cent of GNP.)

Many readers will be surprised by this decline since the defense budget itself has not gone down. Most of the increase, however, has been for conventional and general-purpose forces that are really designed for limited war, such as a conventional or tactical nuclear war in Europe, or counter-insurgency operations, rather than for central war.

The decline seems to be due in equal measure to the fact that central war forces are becoming less expensive and to a diminishing concern about central war.

TABLE VI
Model-T and Model-A Strategic Eras

T	Late 1940's:	Early KT; B-50's and B-36's; little "theory"
	Early 1950's:	Mature KT; B-47's; manual air defense, Nike Ajax; "simple" theory
	Late 1950's:	Mature TN; * B-52's; SAGE, Century fighters; Nike Hercules; B-36 phased out; U-2; Turkish radar; apocalyptic views, first and second-strike issues, reliable go-ahead order
A	Early 1960's:	Alert forces; advanced TN; "invulnerable" Minuteman and Polaris; many R & D cancellations; controlled response; early arms control; civil defense, "acceptance of procurement policies and military doctrines appropriate to a detente"
	Late 1960's:	Further improved TN; sophisticated missiles; more arms control; more cancellations; little perceived threat; some attention to "realistic" scenarios and mobilization bases

* Thermonuclear devices.

---

[12] This is not the place to discuss these issues in detail; Secretary McNamara's annual testimony contains explanations of these concepts.

What about the future of central war technology? Let us introduce some terminology that will be useful in later discussions.

Table VI above suggests that we might call the technology of the late 1940's and the 1950's a Model T technology; we might think of the 1960's as having a Model A technology. (The terminology is deliberately chosen to give a connotation that the technology of the 1950's and 1960's is obsolete but quite usable.) Associated with these technologies are certain kinds of strategic doctrine and views that seem likely to be part of the mental equipment of any nation that owns the corresponding technology, though this last is, of course, by no means certain. It is easily conceivable that Israel, for example, might get a Model T technology yet have some very advanced doctrines and a good understanding of many issues that are relevant to this situation but are usually explicitly confronted only by nations with more advanced technology. (Some Israelis have gone to some effort to acquaint themselves with the nuances of modern strategic thinking.)

Roughly speaking, Model T technology is concerned with "primitive" nuclear weapons, with airplanes for offense and for defense, and with perhaps some relatively simple ground-to-air and air-to-air missiles for defense, and with readily available commercial or research type of missiles adapted for limited strategic purposes. Model A technology is concerned with thermonuclear weapons, relatively advanced military missiles, reasonable solutions of vulnerability problems, some acquaintance with sophisticated arms

---

TABLE VII

The Next Decade or Two

Early 1970's:	Super sophisticated TN weapons and missiles; "early" Ballistic Missile Defense; effective short-range arms control, but West Germany, Japan, and/or others may make preparatory moves to acquire nuclear weapons
Late 1970's:	New aerospace offense and defense systems (perhaps using lasers or nuclear powered vehicles), late 1950 and early 1960 technology diffused, many nth countries and/or mature arms control
Early or Mid-1980's (at least potentially):	France, Germany, Japan, and the like, will have at least a post-Model A technology
	China, Brazil, Mexico, East Germany, Italy, and so on, will have at least a Model A technology
	Improved Model T technology generally available
	U.S. and U.S.S.R. could have massive space capabilities—both defensive and offensive, effective aerospace defense (at least against Model T and A threats), extraordinarily flexible, reliable, and enormously capable logistic systems, and the like

---

control issues, and some consciousness of the subtleties of strategic doctrine. Using this terminology, Table VII above indicates what the technological context of central war is likely to be in the next decade or two. We have left open the issues as to whether or not nuclear diffusion will actually occur, and simply pointed out its potentialities.

TABLE VIII

In the Last Decade or Two of the Twentieth Century

1. Military applications of "100 likely" and "25 possible" areas
2. Some far-out innovations may also occur
3. In any case there will be synergism and serendipity
4. The above will make simple nuclear-armed, long-range vehicles very inexpensive to "intermediate" and perhaps smaller powers
5. Results could also include:
     new kinds of nuclear weapons
     various kinds of death rays
     a menu of techniques for effective chemical and/or biological warfare in various applications
     new techniques for disguised, covert, nonphysical, or anonymous warfare
     well-understood Doomsday machines (or near-Doomsday machines)
     tsunami producers
     climate changers
     earth scorchers
     various forms of psychological, or even direct mental, warfare
     the invention of a "nuclear six-gun" technology—or at least the development of inexpensive and widely available versions of Model T and A (and perhaps more advanced) technologies
6. Depending on the defenses of the large powers and the superpowers (and other "details"), these weapon systems may be "equalizers" of the Gallois * or even of the American Western type and might even be relatively available to private individuals or at least private organizations and extremist political factions
7. Finally there should also be a development of very effective techniques for counterinsurgency warfare—and perhaps insurgency as well

* "Contrary to popular belief, the further we advance into the ballistico-nuclear age, the more possible it becomes to outlaw violence, even if the aggressor nation is stronger and more richly supplied with combat means than the nation it threatens. . . .
  To humanity, it seems assured that the very omnipotence of these new weapons can, at least temporarily, create a form of peace that would be more stable—and more advantageous—than any ever known. . . .
  If this must be the direction of the development, and if the movement is as irreversible as the one which culminated in the generalization of firearms, it would be better for the Western nations to reach an understanding . . . by distributing its weapons among the cooperating states."
—Pierre Gallois (1961)

Another open issue is whether or not the United States and the Soviet Union would try very hard to keep pace with modern technology and particularly whether they will try to defend "adequately" against those with Model T and Model A technology. It is reasonably clear that—barring oversights and mistakes—they can do so if they try, but in doing so they are likely, whether they wish to or not, to spend a lot of money and perhaps engage in a mutual arms race, at least at some moderate speed of "racing"; that is, in protecting themselves against Nth countries they also, to some degree, protect themselves from each other and thus perhaps stimulate mutual competition as a byproduct. This last possibility, of course, could be mitigated by some explicit or implicit understandings.

Finally we come to the last decade or two of the twentieth century. Table VIII sketches some of the possibilities—some of which should arouse anxiety.

Anyone reading Table VIII and thinking through its implications is likely to distrust our statement in Chapter I that the surprise-free projection for the rest of the century is plausible in leaving out large thermonuclear war among the old nations of the world. It seems a more likely conjecture that either the whole nature of international relations will be changed so as to cope with the technology indicated in Table VIII, or else that the system will blow up and international relations will still be changed but by a different mechanism and in a different way. But even those who are most apprehensive for the long run may agree that for the rest of the twentieth century prudential politics may well dominate technology. If so, then even if the technological potentialities are realized, to a greater or lesser degree, it will not necessarily change international relations as much as so many easily assume. This is, of course, an open question and we will discuss it more in Chapter V. Chapter VI considers scenarios that illustrate how this conjecture can go wrong, and Chapter VII discusses what some of the consequences may be like. Changes in the international system itself, including those that military technology might bring about, will be dealt with in Chapter IX.

E. ELECTRONICS, COMPUTERS, AUTOMATION, AND INFORMATION PROCESSING

We turn now to what may be—at least as far as the postindustrial world in the last third of the twentieth century is concerned—the most important, exciting, and salient aspect of modern technology. If the middle third of the twentieth century is known as the nuclear era, and if past times have been known as the age of steam, iron, power, or the automobile, then the next thirty-three years may well be known as the age of electronics, computers, automation, cybernation, data processing, or some related idea.

This whole area is currently about the most dynamic and volatile of our technologies. As a result, when one specialist declares that "the computer gives signs of becoming the contemporary counterpart of the steam engine that brought on the industrial revolution," [13] and another argues that the computer represents "an advance in man's thinking process as radical as the invention of writing," [14] one is not irritated by the grandiosity of the claim, but only by what has become its obviousness. The capacity of the computer ultimately to effect a dramatic extension of man's power over his environment, as well as many other social and economic changes, is by now obvious to all.

1. *Electronics*

Let us consider first the basic electronic technology. In the last decade this has progressed spectacularly, and the changes foreseeable for the next decade—much less the next thirty-three years—are equally impressive.

The pace of change in electronics—and the accelerating tempo—is shown by these dates: vacuum tubes, around 1900; first practical transistor, 1948; transistor use and invention of the integrated circuit, 1958; development of integrated circuits, 1960-1963; and now invention of a fourth generation of change, called large-scale integration or LSI, 1967. LSI is basically an extension of integrated circuit technology involving the wiring of complete circuits on a silicon chip, instead of tying components together. Military systems and commercial applications using LSI techniques should begin to appear in a year or two. Another aspect of LSI devices is that they will not only be used to build better computers, but will also be the product of computers: computers are used to design, interconnect, and produce the circuits.

As a result of these innovations the cost of complex circuits is dropping, from about eighty cents now (compared to three dollars for equivalent transistor circuits) to predictions of a few cents per chip in the next decade. This reduction in cost of about 100 accompanies an increase in reliability of a factor of 100 to 1,000 over what was achieved a decade ago and a 10,000-fold reduction, in the last two decades, in the volume required for a complex electronic package. Present technology permits the manufacture of 100-500 integrated circuits on a silicon wafer an inch in diameter and less than one-hundredth of an inch thick, or complete computer and communications subsystems containing more than 1,000 circuits, each with more than 400 transistors, on half-dollar-size silicon chips less than one-eighth inch thick. The accelerating rate of change in electronics technology makes it almost impossible to say much that is interesting about the electronics technology of the year 2000. Almost all of the possible developments that one can explicitly formulate seem likely to be realized much sooner.

---

[13] From "Information" by John McCarthy, Copyright © 1966 by Scientific American, Inc. All rights reserved. September 1966, p. 65.
[14] Herbert A. Simon, quoted in *Time*, April 2, 1965, p. 88.

2. *Electronic Computers*

Let us first consider the basic computer. Without elaborate input-output devices or sophisticated programs, a computer is really little more than a very large, very fast, and very complex abacus, but even so stripped, it has amazing potentialities. It has also had an amazing record of increase in potentiality over the last fifteen years. If one uses as a standard of measurement the size of the memory space divided by the basic "add time" of the computer (which measures roughly a computer's ability both to hold and to process information), then over the past fifteen years this basic criterion of computer performance has increased by a factor of ten every two or three years (this is a conservative estimate).

While some will argue that we will not duplicate this performance in the future because we are beginning to reach limits set by basic physical constraints, such as the speed of light, this may not be true, especially when one considers new techniques in time-sharing, segmentation of programs to add flexibility, and parallel-processing computers. The experimental parallel-processing ILLIAC IV to be developed for ARPA by Burroughs Corporation, using LSI circuit arrays and extremely high-speed thin-film memory storage, will provide a data processing speed 500-700 times that of existing computer systems and more than 100 times faster than any computer known to be in development.[15] The parallel-processing concept permits various elements of a complex problem to be solved simultaneously, rather than serially as in present systems. Other means of continuing the increase in computer capabilities by a factor of ten every several years may include using basic computational units that operate on the basis of matrices rather than single numbers; large-scale improvement in the present "soft-ware crisis" in programming language, treating complex operations as single units and combining them in both parallel and hierarchical operations, and so on. Thus even excluding the impact of new input-output devices and new concepts for programming and problem formulation, but just considering the basic capacity of the computer as a large and fast abacus has still meant that any doctrine about capabilities and limitations has had to be revised extensively every two or three years. But these exclusions are also important. About nine years ago, a program containing five thousand instructions was considered quite large. Now with the present capacities of computers and new programming languages such as FORTRAN, ALGOL, or MAD for scientific problems, JOVIAL for military applications, or COBOL, LISP or CPL for other problem-solving uses, an individual can handle programs about ten times larger and a team may easily produce a program still larger by a factor of five to ten. These programs that used to take an hour or two to run now take a few seconds.

[15] See *Technology Week* and the *New York Times,* February 11, 1967.

If computer capacities were to continue to increase by a factor of ten every two or three years until the end of the century (a factor between a hundred billion and ten quadrillion), then all current concepts about computer limitations will have to be reconsidered. Even if the trend continues for only the next decade or two, the improvements over current computers would be factors of thousands to millions. If we add the likely enormous improvements in input-output devices, programming and problem formulation, and better understanding of the basic phenomena being studied, manipulated, or simulated, these estimates of improvement may be wildly conservative. And even if the rate of change slows down by several factors, there would still be room in the next thirty-three years for an overall improvement of some five to ten orders of magnitude. Therefore, it is necessary to be skeptical of any sweeping but often meaningless or nonrigorous statements such as "a computer is limited by the designer—it cannot create anything he does not put in," or that "a computer cannot be truly creative or original." By the year 2000, computers are likely to match, simulate, or surpass some of man's most "human-like" intellectual abilities, including perhaps some of his aesthetic and creative capacities, in addition to having some new kinds of capabilities that human beings do not have. These computer capacities are not certain; however, it is an open question what inherent limitations computers have. If it turns out that they cannot duplicate or exceed certain characteristically human capabilities, that will be one of the most important discoveries of the twentieth century.

Existing programs for such near human functions as recognizing analogies between geometric figures, taken from a well-known college-admissions examination, can score at about the tenth-grade level; a second, checker-playing program uses information gained in previous attempts—its experience—to improve its analysis; a third called Student "probably surpasses the average person in its ability to handle algebra problems," using a limited range of ordinary English. "When it runs into difficulty, it asks usually pertinent questions . . . often it resolves the difficulty by referring to the knowledge in its files." [16] If this is where we are now, then the future possibilities—particularly as improvements of many orders of magnitude are realized—may well include something that might reasonably be described as "artificial intelligence"—something much more than just a very fast abacus.

This idea of computer "intelligence" is a sensitive point with many people. The claim is not that computers will resemble the structure of the human brain, but that their functional output will equal or exceed that of the human brain in many functions that we have been used to thinking of as aspects of intelligence, and even as uniquely human. Still a computer will presumably not become "humanoid" and probably will not use similar

[16] From "Artificial Intelligence" by Marvin L. Minsky, Copyright © 1966 by Scientific American, Inc. All rights reserved. September 1966, p. 257.

processes, but it may have properties which are analogous to or operationally indistinguishable from self-generated purposes, ideas, and emotional responses to new inputs or its own productions. In particular, as computers become more self-programming they will increasingly tend to perform activities that amount to "learning" from experience and training. Thus they will eventually evolve subtle methods and processes that may defy the understanding of the human designer.

In addition to this possibility of independent intelligent activities, computers are being used increasingly as a helpful flexible tool for more or less individual needs—at times in such close cooperation that one can speak in terms of a man-machine symbiosis. Eventually there will probably be computer consoles in every home, perhaps linked to public utility computers and permitting each user his private file space in a central computer, for uses such as consulting the Library of Congress, keeping individual records, preparing income tax returns from these records, obtaining consumer information, and so on.

Computers will also presumably be used as teaching aids, with one computer giving simultaneous individual instruction to hundreds of students, each at his own console and topic, at any level from elementary to graduate school; eventually the system will probably be designed to maximize the individuality of the learning process. Presumably there will also be such things as:

1. A single national information file containing all tax, legal, security, credit, educational, medical, employment, and other information about each citizen. (One problem here is the creation of acceptable rules concerning access to such a file, and then as discussed below the later problem of how to prevent erosion of these rules after one or two decades of increased operation have made the concept generally acceptable, as discussed below.)
2. Time-sharing of large computers by research centers in every field, providing national and international pools of knowledge and skill.
3. Use of computers to test trial configurations in scientific work, allowing the experimenter to concentrate on his creativity, judgment, and intuition, while the computer carries out the detailed computation and "horse work." A similar symbiotic relationship will prevail in engineering and other technological design. Using the synergism of newer "problem-oriented" computer language, time-sharing, and new input-output techniques, engineer-designers linked to a large computer complex will use computers as experienced pattern-makers, mathematical analysts of optimum design, sources of catalogs on engineering standards and parts data, and often substitutes for mechanical drawings.

4. Use of real-time large computers for an enormous range of business information and control activity, including most trading and financial transactions; the flow of inventories within companies and between suppliers and users; immediate analysis and display of company information about availability of products, prices, sales statistics, cash flow, credit, bank accounts and interests on funds, market analysis and consumer tastes, advanced projections, and so on.

5. Vast use of computers to reduce and punish crime, including the capacity of police to check immediately the identification and record of any person stopped for questioning.

6. Computerized processes for instantaneous exchange of money, using central computer-bank-and-store-computer networks for debiting and crediting accounts.

In addition, there will be uses of computers for worldwide communications, medical diagnostics, traffic and transportation control, automatic chemical analyses, weather prediction and control, and so on.

The sum of all these uses suggests that the computer utility industry will become as fundamental as the power industry, and that the computer can be viewed as the most basic tool of the last third of the twentieth century. Individual computers (or at least consoles or other remote input devices) will become essential equipment for home, school, business, and profession, and the ability to use a computer skillfully and flexibly may become more widespread than the ability to play bridge or drive a car (and presumably much easier).

3. Automation and Cybernation

We now turn to one of the most widely misunderstood aspects of modern technology. Perhaps it would therefore be best to start with a few simple definitions.

Historically, the first use of mechanization was to increase the usefulness of human or animal muscles in a more or less direct fashion, such as by gaining "mechanical advantage." Thus primitive man learned to use such simple machines as levers in order to lift objects which he could not otherwise lift. The use of an inclined plane is really an advanced form of a lever. A wheelbarrow enables a less primitive man to carry things more conveniently and easier than he could without one. And so on to quite complex machines, such as plows and boats. Later, other sources of energy—principally windmills and waterwheels—were added.

With the impact of industrialization two new things were added: (1) better organization of work—particularly by increased specialization, and (2) the increased mechanization and even automation of production. In the first case, the work is reorganized or broken up into small, specialized pieces, each of which can be done more expeditiously or with less skill. In the second, a sequence of operations was carried out automatically by using simple control devices or more complex machines. The first process is often a forerunner of the second process because simplification or reorganization of the work is often a necessary prerequisite to mechanization and automation.

Very early in this process of the use of complex mechanization and automation there was use of so-called cybernetic techniques. In a cybernetic system there is some method of looking at the output of a system, comparing it with a desired norm and then using this difference to actuate some control mechanism that attempts to adjust the system to the desired norm. A thermostat in a house or a governor on an engine are typical examples of cybernetic systems. Donald Michael has coined the term "cybernation" to describe the situation in which a computer is used to cybernate some automatic system so as basically to eliminate the role of man as a supervisor and use him only as a monitor who can if necessary "override" the system. There is today much concern about the supposedly large, or imminently large, degree of mechanization, automation, and cybernation in the United States.

Thus manufacturers of automation equipment have estimated that automation is eliminating 40,000–50,000 jobs a week, or between 2–2.5 million jobs a year. Limited automation in the steel industry is estimated to have eliminated 80,000 jobs out of a total of 600,000 in the industry between 1953 and 1966, with a minimum of 100,000 more job losses estimated for the next decade. Yet despite the fewer employees needed to turn out increased steel production, mills find it difficult to recruit enough help of the type they need, one reason being that many skilled workers let go in earlier years have moved into other fields.[17] Despite the job losses due to automation, and the influx of about three and a half million young people into the labor market yearly, our present unemployment rate is undeniably low. The economy today is able to supply jobs to replace those lost to automation and to accommodate an expansion of the total working population, with the exception of an official unemployment rate of 4–5 per cent. Moreover, a study by Columbia's Bureau of Applied Social Research found no correlation between mechanizing industries and a better educated work force in 1960, compared to 1950. It concluded that there are "plenty" of jobs in the economy which high school dropouts are capable of handling, even in automated industries, and that the higher unemployment rate among dropouts is probably due to employee selectivity in a too-large labor force. Thus the present problem of automation may not be one of education and retraining, but simply of generating more jobs.

Indeed, as some skeptics are fond of pointing out one has only to go to any construction site, store, or house to see that it is hard to replace the human being in many kinds of relatively lowly labor. In fact, in some ways

[17] *Wall Street Journal,* September 16, 1966.

this low-quality labor with its erratic and sporadic demands is more difficult to replace than some branch of much more skilled labor which, however, has much more predictable demands and requirements. In any case it is important to note that despite all the publicity and controversy there are almost no cybernated industrial plants in the United States today and that even automation has not progressed as far as many publicists, enthusiastics, or viewers with alarm would have us believe. (This is an almost unbelievable statement when one considers all the publicity, but it seems to be true. For this reason more than any other the impact of cybernation and automation, particularly on employment, has been much exaggerated.[18])

This seems to be one of those quite common situations in which early in the innovation period many exaggerated claims are made, then there is disillusionment and a swing to overconservative prediction and a general pessimism and skepticism, then finally when a reasonable degree of development has been obtained and a learning period navigated, many—if not all—of the early "ridiculous" exaggerations and expectations are greatly exceeded. It is particularly clear that if, as suggested in the last section, computers improve by five, ten, or more orders of magnitude over the next thirty-three years this is almost certain to happen.

For the near future, automation and cybernation are likely to create as many jobs as they eliminate, by contributing to the increase of productivity and economic growth. The creation of new jobs is a subtle and undramatic process, and it is difficult to chart how and to what extent increases in productivity causes investment which leads to new jobs, whereas the direct elimination of jobs is both noticeable and dramatic.

The net effects on employment, hours worked, and productivity are difficult to predict, particularly because the rate at which industrial processes are automated may increase and the tradeoff between increased production and leisure that society may choose are both quite uncertain.

Nevertheless it is quite clear that in the next ten years automation will begin to impinge on or to increase its foothold in many areas of activity. Thus to reach its goal of "next day" delivery anywhere in the United States, the Post Office has several companies intensively studying the design of electronic optical scanners to recognize zip code addresses on letters at the rate of six envelopes a second, to be combined with automatic face-cancelers, and letter sorting machines. The twenty-three million dollars to be

---

[18] For a very good discussion of the issues in this section, one might see *The Shape of Automation* by Herbert Simon (New York: Harper and Row, 1965) or *The Myths of Automation* by Charles E. Silberman (New York: Harper and Row, 1966). These are probably the two best popular books on the subject, though they have a difficulty: both authors are so concerned to give a proper perspective on the subject by debunking the exaggerated claims of various enthusiasts and alarmists that the reader may come away with an underestimate of the long-term impact of automation, even if he has achieved a reasonable perspective on the short-term issues.

spent this year by the Post Office on automation equipment is a small part of the investment that will be required to meet the mail "crisis." Other industries will soon have to do much the same thing.

Automation and cybernation may be extended to the home also. The idea of moderately priced robots doing most of the housework by the year 2000 may be difficult to accept at first. According to an enthusiast, Meredith Wooldridge Thring, professor of mechanical engineering at Queen Mary College in London, "within 10 to 20 years' time we could have a robot that will completely eliminate all routine operations around the house and remove the drudgery from human life."

> The great majority of the housewives will wish to be relieved completely from the routine operations of the home such as scrubbing the floors or the bath or the cooker, or washing the clothes or washing up, or dusting or sweeping, or making beds.
>
> By far the most logical step to allow this variety of human homes and still relieve the housewife of routine, is to provide a robot slave which can be trained to the requirements of a particular home and can be programmed to carry out half a dozen or more standard operations (for example, scrubbing, sweeping and dusting, washing-up, laying tables, making beds), when so switched by the housewife. It will be a machine having no more emotions than a car, but having a memory for instructions and a limited degree of instructed or built-in adaptability according to the positions in which it finds various types of objects. It will operate other more specialized machines, for example, the vacuum cleaner or clothes-washing machine.
>
> There are no problems in the production of such a domestic robot to which we do not have already the glimmering of a solution. It is therefore likely that, with a strong programme of research, such a robot could be produced in ten years. If we assume that it also takes ten years before industry and government are sufficiently interested to find the sum required for such development (which is of the order of £1 million), then we could still have it by 1984.[19]

His description of robot household capacities and widespread use seems most reasonable by the year 2000. We shall have to ponder the *double* impact within the next thirty-three years of widespread industrial and household automation.

4. *Information Processing*

The next step in automation is to apply it to information rather than machines. This application is, of course, very closely related to computers as just discussed, but is perhaps best perceived as examining various ways for acquiring, processing, storing, retrieving, and using information.

[19] M. W. Thring, "A Robot in the House," in Nigel Calder (ed.), *The World in 1984* (Baltimore, Md.: Penguin Books, 1964), Vol. 2, p. 38.

The problems of putting something like the Library of Congress conveniently at the fingertips of any user anywhere are dependent on our understanding and simulation of the ways in which people make associations and value judgments. One sticking point is the analysis and comparison of records or documents. Of the stages in information storage, requesting, machine search, retrieval, and print-out, the first two currently require human judgment. Humans must identify those records that deal with a common area of interest, and must analyze each record or document to decide what specific topics it covers, and the other areas with which it should be associated. The process is accomplished by specialization; limiting the records in scope and purpose; analyzing and organizing a collection with great precision in anticipating questions, usually by means of indexing; or permitting a record-by-record search of the whole collection. Technological advances, particularly automatic data-processing equipment in association with computers and new microrecording mediums, are reducing the cost of operating a large information storage and retrieval system, but currently the human labor involved in collecting and analyzing records is still enormous.

However, computers can even now index documents by all the major words in their titles, though they will only select synonymous words for indexing according to their machine language dictionary. The need to improve computer capacities for making associations is therefore critical to real-time search and retrieval of the literature on a subject with many subsidiary facets.

It is impossible to predict how far along we will be by the year 2000 in simulating in computers analytical abilities that require decades and vast amounts of experience for humans to acquire, but thirty-three years of continuing work should be enough to surpass any current expectations that have been seriously and explicitly formulated. We should keep in mind that we have been discussing the most difficult problem of information storage and retrieval. For storage and retrieval of categories of information than can be described in a straightforward way, adequate systems exist now and will continue to grow rapidly.

Fully automatic systems have been developed for detecting index codes of various types (optical film reels, film cards, magnetic cards and paper cards) and for retrieving or displaying records on demand. . . . Records that are already in machine-readable form can be transmitted easily over wires and microwave channels to printing devices, recording devices or computers. Records not in machine-readable form can be scanned by optical-electric devices and then transmitted, to be reconstituted at the receiving end. . . . Second, the capability of controlling the transmitting process . . . can be given to the human or the machine at the receiving end. . . . With such developments, the geographic boundaries of traditional information storage and retrieval systems are beginning to evaporate. In their place are beginning to emerge vast networks of compatible communication devices linking users with many specialized and overlapping collections. Data-transmission costs are still sufficiently high, however, to keep the dissolution of traditional systems from becoming a runaway revolutionary process.[20]

Within about fifteen years, data-transmission costs are likely to be reduced so much that information storage and retrieval will become a runaway revolutionary process.

The current proposal for a National Data Center being debated in Congress, in which the records of some twenty or more government organizations will be amalgamated in one place is an example of things to come. In this case it is proposed that records be kept in the form of individual files so that the information will be as detailed and useful as possible. There is also concern, as we have said, about the possible abuses of such systems. Much of the discussion and debate is focused on methods of preventing such abuse, but almost all agree that the system or one like it will soon be operating.[21]

Similarly, there are likely to be great strides in real-time credit, auditing and banking systems, and in the real-time collection and processing of economic and social information generally.

If all this information is made available to the government, this should give it the ability to assess various current programs and situations, to rapidly initiate new programs or modify old ones, and then to study the short-run results of these actions almost immediately and continuously. Indeed the government might interact with short-term changes in the economic and social system in much the same way as the pilot with a plane, or the driver with an automobile. In terms of research in economics, sociology, medicine, and so on, these detailed personal, social, economic, and biological records should make possible some startling advances. Even with current techniques we should be able to process this information and find out all sorts of subtle correlations or cause and effect relationships as the state of the art of data-processing improves. And as we get some experience in monitoring and manipulating and develop new techniques and theories there should be some most impressive increases in our understanding and control of various aspects of our society.

Of course, the possibility of a serious invasion of privacy by the government (or private individuals) is raised by the rapid progress toward centralized data processing for government, business, and personal record-keeping. This is clearly a serious problem, and while some discussion has involved

[20] Ben-Ami Lipetz, "Information Storage and Retrieval," *Scientific American*, September 1966, p. 238.
[21] See the story on the current IBM study on computer pooling of all files for the city of New Haven, *New York Times*, March 29, 1967.

apocalyptic language, the authors would agree that without adequate safe-guards some of these warnings may prove justified.[22] Indeed it is possible that such problems will be raised not as a by-product of normal commercial and government operations, but because there has been special design and procurement of systems for the surveillance, monitoring, and control of individuals.

Thus a future President of the United States might easily have command and control systems that involve having many television cameras in a future "Vietnam" or domestic trouble spot. Since he would be likely to have multiple screens, he would be able to scan many TV cameras simultaneously. In order to save space, some of the screens would be quite small and would be used only for gross surveillance, while others might be very large, in order to allow examination of detail. Paul Nitze, the present Secretary of the Navy, has made the suggestion that similar capabilities might be made available to the public media or even the public directly. This would certainly be a mixed blessing. Obviously such capability can give a misleading psychological impression of a greater awareness, knowledge, and sensitivity to local conditions and issues than really exists. This in turn could lead to an excessive degree of central control. This last may be an important problem for executives generally.

There are also important possibilities in the field of law enforcement. New York State has already tried an experiment in which the police read the license plates of cars going over a bridge into Manhattan and had a computer check these licenses against its files of scofflaws. The police were able to arrest a number of surprised drivers before they got to the other side of the bridge. (Some of the drivers seemed to feel that this was like shooting quail on the ground.)

Such systems could be made completely automatic. Indeed it would be no trick at all, if the license plates were written in some suitable computer alphabet, to have them read by a television camera that was mounted on an automatic scanner. We can almost assume that toll booths or other convenient spots will be so equipped at some future date. It would then not be difficult to place these records of automobile movements in a computer memory or permanent file as an aid to traffic-flow planning, crime detection, or other investigations (as is done with taxicab trip reports in many cities today). One can even imagine fairly large-scale records of all license plates (or other identification) passing various checkpoints being kept for many streets and routes.

Let us take an even more extreme example. A capability for listening and recording temporarily (or even permanently) can be made very inexpensive. One can imagine the legal or illegal magnetic or other recording of an ap-

[22] See our discussion of Social Control in Chap. VIII, and the related discussion on pp. 389-91.

preciable percentage of the telephone conversations that take place. (For that matter, the same techniques could be applied to "bugged" conversations in bars, restaurants, offices, and so on.) It would then be feasible to scan these conversations rapidly by means of a high speed computer—at least for key phrases—and then record any conversations that meet some criteria for justifying special interest or placement in a more permanent file for further investigation—or just to keep a record. For simple computers, the criteria could be certain words—underworld jargon, obscenities, or words such as "bet," "horserace," "kill," "subvert," "revolution," "infiltrate," "Black Power," "organize," "oppose"—or more sophisticated combinations. Indeed future computers and programs should be able to carry out much more complex operations—possibly responding to nonverbal information, such as an unusually angry or threatening tone in a voice. Such computers may also be able to apply a great deal of inferential logic on their own—they may become a sort of transistorized Sherlock Holmes making hypotheses and investigating leads in a more or less autonomous or self-motivated manner, all the while improving their techniques as they accumulate information about patterns of criminal behavior—or any other kind of behavior that authorities decide ought to be observed. New legal doctrines will need to be developed to regulate these new possibilities for "just looking." [23]

F. LASERS

We pick this area to comment on, in part because it now seems likely that it will be one of the most important of the new areas, and in part to illustrate how rapidly a new area can develop.

The first practical prototype laser was developed in 1960. Within five years there were almost a thousand organizations in the United States and Europe studying lasers. As one reporter put it, "Almost every corporation and every self-respecting university in the nation obtained a laser of some sort." [24] Currently, more than one hundred applications of lasers are being investigated, though only a few applications (including spotwelding of the retina of the eye, piercing diamond dies, precision surveying and alignment, and so on) have actually been tried.

The first major production contract is expected to be granted by the government in 1967 for laser range-finders for the military. The advantages of an electrically scanned laser system over radar are that it can give a far more precise location—pinpointing a rocket within twelve inches of its exact

[23] See the special issue on "Privacy" in *Law and Contemporary Problems*, XXXI, No. 2 (Spring, 1966), for several interesting discussions of problems that have *already* arisen.
[24] *New York Times*, January 15, 1967.

location up to a height of eight miles—and is more accurate in the first few minutes after take-off when the vehicle is too close for radar use. It also has much greater angular resolution and can thus select a very small target area to look at.[25] The last characteristic might be desirable for some missile defense tracking.

Military and civilian applications of lasers are likely to grow rapidly within the next thirty-three years in direct proportion to the increase of laser power for a given weight and volume of generating apparatus. At present, two Massachusetts Institute of Technology students have used Raytheon's 1.1 kilowatt CO_2 gas laser, a giant 20 meters long, to crumble marble and granite after 30 seconds' subjection to an unfocused beam temperature of 2,900° C; the beam produces 11,700° C when focused.[26] The experiments suggest that lasers can weaken rock controllably, permitting convenient-sized pieces to be removed in sequence. If it turns out to be practical, laser rock-crumblers are likely to be used in the near future to make tunnels for highways, railroads, and water distribution, and might make it economical to build tunnels for high-speed, underground intercity transportation. The use of laser beams to blast and vaporize coal may lead to lower costs for acetylene, hydrogen cyanide, and other chemicals.[27] If rock can be weakened, so can men, and possibly tanks and ICBMs, depending on energy radiation levels over distance.[28] Thus the military use of lasers as "death rays" may become feasible in the moderate future.

A technological forecast study of the period 1966–85, conducted by TRW, Inc., in 1966, forecast that tactical weapons using lasers will be introduced before the end of this decade, that laser range-finding and fire-control systems will be operational in 1972, and that as a result highly accurate missiles with two hundred to four hundred mile ranges will become available early in the 1970's.[29]

A combination of this technology with the ILLIAC IV computer mentioned earlier, with a data processing speed "500-700 times that of existing computer systems," could produce a state-of-the-art advance in defense against missiles including multiwarhead and decoy discrimination. The

[25] *Science News,* June 25, 1966.
[26] *Industrial Research,* February 1967.
[27] *Science News,* December 10, 1966.
[28] Two techniques for raising the efficiency of lasers have been developed recently by Technical Operations, Inc., of Burlington, Massachusetts. "One covers a system for coupling lasers in an optical 'antenna' array; the other is for a passive laser Q-switch. The coupling technique links independently-pumped lasers so that the light produced by each is in phase with the others, creating a coherent beam with the characteristics for a single laser. . . . The Q-switch . . . consists of a light-absorbing dye applied to a glass plate; when the plate is placed anywhere in the laser resonator, it momentarily inhibits lasing. A pulse in the multi-megawatt range occurs when the plate is saturated." *Technology Week,* December 19, 1966.
[29] *Ibid.,* March 6, 1967, p. 20.

highly accurate two hundred to four hundred-mile missiles might make close-up nonnuclear kill mechanisms feasible. It is also conceivable in the longer-term that laser-carrying satellites might make a space-based defense system feasible that attacked ICBMs during their early boost phase. Indeed there are many ways lasers may play an important role in making missile defense more effective, and reduce further or even eliminate the cost advantage that the ICBM-penetration aids combination has held over the capacities of missile defense.

Lasers will also have important applications in the field of data storage. IBM has already developed a memory-storage system using an eight-colored laser beam to store as many as one hundred million bits of information on a square inch of photographic film.[30] Even more impressive is the "Data Device" reported by an Air Force scientist, John F. Dove, at Griffiss Air Force Base, Rome, New York. He reports that by using a laser beam to reduce the size of the data signals submitted, an entire library of 20,000 volumes can be stored on a 8-by-10-inch piece of nickel foil, thus storing in one inch what would go on ten miles of magnetic tape. The device measures three by four feet by six inches, was developed for $125,000, and cost about $50,000, some twenty times cheaper than the cost of many storage systems.

Another important application involves the "tuning" of lasers to adjust them to any desired wavelength with great precision, from the shortest wavelengths of ultra-violet to the longest radio wavelengths used for radar. Parallel and somewhat different techniques have been developed at the Bell Telephone Laboratories and in the Soviet Union. Dr. Nicholaas Bloembergen, professor of applied physics at Harvard, has predicted that tuned lasers can "revolutionize" the field of spectroscopy, thereby improving the study of the nature of atoms and molecules:

> Spectroscopy is one of the most basic research techniques of all the physical and biological sciences. It consists of analyzing either the various wave lengths of radiant energy emitted by an object or those wave lengths that are absorbed when such energy is applied to an object. . . . As spectroscopic precision has improved, so has knowledge in countless fields of science. The laser beam that can be tuned represents, in a sense, the ultimate tool in this respect because at any one point in the tuning proc-

[30] The system involves a wavelength selector that singles out colors at the rate of 125,000 color choices a second; a beam deflector "which is so accurate that it can single out more than 130,000 separate spaces in an area the size of a match head"; the use of film emulsions with a mirrored backing to photograph the characteristically different interference patterns for each color of light going and coming through the emulsion, thus permitting bits of information to be stacked on top of one another in the same space; and a decoding device to read the interference patterns. *Science News*, July 23, 1966, p. 51.

ess, it generates only a single wave length. Such a beam, aimed at a tiny specimen—for example, a cell—could be tuned across a broad range of wave lengths. The thousands of lengths at which the specimen absorbs light would indicate, with a precision hitherto beyond reach, the chemical composition of that specimen.

. . . Dr. Rem Khokhlov (of the University of Moscow), believes the method can be used, in photochemistry, to produce new materials and new drugs. Because much of knowledge of matter has been derived from its interaction with radiation (including light), the tunable laser beam should have broad application in basic physics.[31]

Another possible use of high-intensity coherent light in chemical research may be to alter reactions catalyzed by metal surfaces: "Presumably different reactions require light of different frequencies. This opens up the possibility of a new form of selective catalysis, performed by lasers radiating at a number of different frequencies. The operator would merely select the appropriate frequency to enhance any reaction." [32]

A third possibility would be for communications in the near vacuum of outer space. Very low transmission losses of power could be obtained with laser beams, and hence very long-distance transmission of information is feasible. Earth-based lasers and laser-carrying satellites are likely to be the preferred means of precise tracking and communicating with satellites and moon stations. For laser transmission between points on earth, the problem is to overcome the power losses caused by the earth's atmosphere, rain, snow, and fog. The alternatives seem to be between shielding laser transmissions from the atmosphere, or overcoming the atmosphere. In the first case, lenses could be placed in an airtight tube, possibly underground. Shorter spacing between lenses would permit the beam to follow the curves of hills and turns. New gas lenses may eventually be preferable because of their low-power losses. Alternatively, the atmosphere might be overcome by using sufficiently high-powered lasers transmitting from earth to satellite to earth. In 1965 the Air Force was able to photograph a laser beam bounced off a satellite reflector 950 miles high. A beam with a diameter of one-quarter to one-half an inch at the laser source was about four miles wide at the satellite; a small piece of its energy was reflected back and spread to a diameter of about one hundred yards on return. With receivers, amplifers, and laser relays in the satellite, high-powered lasers may eventually be sufficient for earth-satellite-earth transmission.

However, at least potentially, the richest and most important application of the laser probably lies in communications. Because the laser uses frequencies many millions of times higher than the ones used in normal

[31] *New York Times*, March 24, 1967.
[32] *New Scientist*, February 9, 1967.

radio wave communication systems, correspondingly many millions of times more space is available in the frequency spectrum for competing uses or for uses that simply require a broad band.

Thus a millionfold increase in communications capacity would result from switching from current broadband communications (frequencies in the billions of cycles per second) to laser light waves (frequencies in the hundreds of trillions of cycles per second). Although the problems of transmitting information by laser are very substantial in practical application, there are probably more physicists and engineers working on the problem than on any other single project in the field of laser applications.[33] One of the central problems—the development of efficient light modulators to impress signals onto a laser beam—is apparently already on the way to solution.[34]

Such laser beams—transmitted along light pipes—or communicating via satellite (perhaps burning their way through cloud cover) could become the main method of electronic communication by the year 2000.

The enormous increase in information which could be transmitted by such means would cause the cost per communications channel to plummet. Much lower cost would stimulate an immense expansion of data, telephone, holographic TV, and facsimile traffic. With lasers, there would be room for all traffic. It is possible that the combination of computer utilities and widely available computer consoles, laser communications, and abundant information processing—or what is sometimes called the "information-rich" society—will most change the Western style of life by the year 2000.

G. HOLOGRAPHY

We now turn to an area that has been chosen for discussion as much because it is an interesting sort of oddity as because it is important, though it may yet turn out to be *very* important. If we were discussing this area a year or two ago we would have included it in the discussion on lasers because at that time it was thought that lasers were essential to make a holograph work. This no longer seems to be true.

[33] Stewart E. Miller, "Communication by Laser," *Scientific American*, January 1966, p. 19.

[34] In December 1966 Bell Telephone Laboratories announced the development of three light modulators that all require modulating power of less than one watt. Bell states that all three are the most efficient modulators of infrared and visible light to be demonstrated so far. See *Industrial Research*, February 1967; *Technology Week*, January 2, 1967, p. 40; or *Science News*, January 14, 1967. A Georgetown University scientist, William J. Thaler, has announced a frequency modulation technique with which he has transmitted FM music and a voice channel simultaneously over one laser beam. He feels that the technique could be used at present to put fifty thousand messages on a laser beam simultaneously, and five hundred thousand messages in the future with improvements. *Washington Post*, March 4, 1967.

A holograph is a photographic record of an interference pattern between reflected light waves from an object and a second wave of interfering light. The second wave may be from the same light source or from a reflection of the first wave back through the photographic emulsion; in the latter case, the hologram is a record of the interference pattern of light "coming and going." When a hologram—a film with a hodgepodge of specks, blobs, and whorls—is illuminated, the original object is reconstructed in three-dimensional form in a virtual and a real image. This is a "true" three-dimensional image and not an illusion in the sense that if one changes his position then the image changes correspondingly; in particular one can see around and behind objects by such changes in position.

Until this year, it appeared that coherent light, usually from a laser, was necessary at some stage of the holographic process. Color holograms have existed in the last few years that could be illuminated by ordinary light, but lasers were required to make the hologram. The process involved lasers emitting light in the three prime colors; three superimposed holograms, produced by the three colors, were then embedded in the emulsion. When the emulsion was later illuminated by strong white light, holograms in the prime colors were generated and blended to form a fully colored three-dimensional picture.

In order to record outdoor scenes holographically, two new techniques have been developed. Both use ordinary white light at the beginning of the process to illuminate the outdoor scenes and objects. The first, developed by Dr. Robert V. Pole of IBM,[35] makes a multi-imaged picture, called a "holocoder," with ordinary light, and then uses a laser to produce the hologram. A "fly's eye" lens composed of hundreds of individual optical facets is used to produce hundreds of cones producing exposures on a film, each showing the viewed scene at a slightly different angle. A conventional hologram can be made from the multi-imaged picture by passing a laser beam through the film and another multifaceted lens while simultaneously interfering the beam with a reference laser. IBM researchers believe that such an approach could lead to practical three-dimensional holographic photography within a few years. While the images to date have been fuzzy, they believe that such drawbacks could largely be eliminated by better lens arrangement.

The second new technique does not use a laser or coherent light at any point in the making of the hologram. It produces holograms by passing light from the scene through a filter. This allows only one color, or wavelength, to enter the system. The image beam is then split to form two images of the scene. These are brought together at the emulsion in such a way that the light waves from each spot in the scene, being of the same wavelength,

[35] *Technology Week,* February 6, 1967; see also Robert V. Pole, "3-D Imagery and Holograms of Objects Illuminated in White Light," *Applied Physics Letters,* January 1, 1967.

interfere with one another. The result is a multitude of interference patterns, one for each part of the scene. Unfortunately these patterns clash with one another in a manner that, to date, has limited the amount of detail that can be captured.* Thus we have reached the point where the encoding and decoding of a hologram can be accomplished using noncoherent light, although some contrast and detail is presently being sacrificed, as compared to holograms made with lasers. Coarser holograms with low-spatial frequency, made with a laser, can be reconstructed by the illumination of penlights, birthday candles, street lights, the sun, or even the moon, and sixty-watt light bulbs placed fifteen to twenty feet away. Copies can then be reproduced cheaply—twenty-five cents apiece for the first thousand copies—" 'with no noticeable loss of detail' . . . through the fourth generation, that is, a copy of a copy of a copy." [36] This means that, with improvement of the IBM method, multi-imaged "holocoders" can be taken outdoors with ordinary light, made into holograms with lasers, and then illuminated with ordinary light, or with a laser for high-resolution images. Eventually, holograms without use of lasers may give sharp images.

The applications of holography that excite the greatest attention are three-dimensional television and motion pictures. In principle, holograms can be recorded on the photo-sensitive surface of a TV camera, just as on a photographic emulsion, and the holographic data can be transmitted and reconstructed in a TV receiver.[37] For sharp images, a laser might be needed in the TV camera or transmitting equipment to process "holocoders" into holograms; but if the hologram can be transmitted and reproduced in the same detail in the TV receiver, a laser might not be needed within the receiver to illuminate the hologram. However, even if lasers are no longer required for the encoding of holographic TV, they will be needed for transmitting it, since transmission bandwidths exceeding present television bandwidths by factors of several hundred will be required, unless design compromises are made that result in a partial loss of the dramatic results attainable from holograms. Cameras, picture tubes, and associated components will also need to be much better than present-day equipment.

Holography was originally developed as an application of electron microscopy. Theoretically, if holograms made by electron interference patterns were illuminated with ordinary light whose wavelengths are almost a million times greater, there should be a millionfold magnification. Thus eventually the combination of holograms with electron waves or X-rays and improved spectroscopy with tuned lasers will be used to examine the structure of atoms, complex molecules, and proteins. For military uses, holograms will be used for three-dimensional satellite reconnaissance and intelligence photo-

[36] *Science News,* December 31, 1966, and March 11, 1967.
[37] Emmett N. Leiths and Juris Upatnieks, "Photography by Laser," *Scientific American,* June 1965, p. 33.
* *New York Times.* March 19, 1967, p. 60.

graphy, increasing even further the value of strategic intelligence by satellite and the use of satellite reconnaissance in tactical warfare. They will also be useful for side-looking radars and "foolproof" cryptography.

A 1967 estimate includes these likely near-future applications:

> Among the applications of holography proposed in recent months or under development are the following:
> —Radar systems enabling an airport traffic controller to look into a three-dimensional scope and watch all aircraft in the area. . . .
> —Scanners that can map distant planets or enable engineers to see stress patterns in a whirring propeller.
> —Computers that display their solution of engineering problems as three-dimensional images. The object that is displayed can be examined from one side or the other, as if it were really there. . . .
> —Photographs of fog or dust clouds that can be projected into space in three-dimensional form so that each particle can be examined, classified and counted by microscope. . . .
> —Machines that can process hundreds of thousands of pictures, picking out rapidly all patterns that conform to certain criteria. Such devices are already being used to find the signatures of oil-bearing geologic formations from explosion soundings of the earth's interior. The same system can be used to screen electrocardiograms and fingerprint files or search aerial photographs for missile sites. [In other words, the addition of holography to planned uses of high-speed computer evaluation of large volumes of photography, adding increased information capacities from three-dimensional effects.]
> —Side-looking radars that enable aircraft flying offshore to map in detail cloud-covered installations along a coastline.
> —*Microscopes that can display directly the three-dimensional structure of proteins and other complex molecules formed from millions of atoms. Such a capability would revolutionize the development of new drugs.*[38] [Emphasis added.]

Well before the year 2000, almost all of these applications of holography, plus countless others not conceived of today, should be realized.

H. THE BIOLOGICAL MANIPULATION OF MAN

We turn now to a topic that should be of the utmost importance to us: what may be done by medical, chemical, and biological means to affect not only our psychology, vigor, health, and longevity, but the genetic constitution of future human beings and whether or not they should even be born. The prospects in medicine and birth control are exciting, and in genetics and other areas both attractive and a little frightening.[39] The federal gov-

[38] *New York Times,* March 19, 1967.
[39] See our discussion in Chap. VIII.

ernment has put substantial capital behind the National Institutes of Health, the training of medical researchers, and the growth of a large research base, and the results will become very noticeable in the next thirty-three years.[40]

Let us begin with heart attack, the number one killer in the United States, causing 55 per cent of all deaths or 525,000 Americans annually. The emphasis here is likely to be on control and prevention, through education of the population in better diet, exercise, and relaxation. However, there will be emphasis on diagnosis, alleviation, and cure as well. For example, newer diagnostic techniques, such as coronary arteriography, will be used to predict developing trouble. Improved drugs that reduce blood pressure will contribute to an already substantial drop in the last fifteen years in the death rate from both high blood pressure and stroke. More effective heart disease drugs are being developed that reduce fatty deposits that clog blood vessels; two new anticholesterol drugs are awaiting approval by the Food and Drug Administration. Experimental work is being done in clearing coronaries with injections of carbon dioxide. The net result of all this should be a sharp decline in "premature" deaths at ages fifty to sixty.

In the meantime, treatment of heart disease victims is being improved by intensive care, which, by itself, may cut heart-attack deaths in the United States by fifty thousand a year or so. (For example, at Philadelphia's Presbyterian Medical Center, the survival rate of patients admitted after coronaries has increased by a third.) Intensive monitoring of coronary patients is reducing the death toll from arrhythmia—disturbance of the electrical impulses for regulating heartbeats. Damage to the cardiac nerve center, or pacemaker, has been offset by artificial pacemakers installed in the chest and replaceable after three years. (Over fifteen thousand Americans are now walking around with artificial pacemakers.) Future "permanent" pacemakers may use piezoelectric crystals to generate sufficient electrical current from the movement of the diaphragm. They may be designed automatically to change the heart rate to match the amount of work the body is performing. Air-driven pumps to take over part of the work of the left ventricle are expected to be ready for broad use in about five years, and predictions have been made that completely artificial hearts made of silicone or natural rubber, with a synthetic valve system, will become available by about 1980.

Cancer research will probably be dependent on advances in molecular biology and perhaps virology. (Some scientists are becoming more and more convinced that some kinds of cancer may be caused by viruses.) However, reduction of death from cancer in the next thirty-three years will most likely be based on better prevention, early detection, surgery, radia-

[40] For a summary of developments in medicine written for the layman, see J. Bishop and D. M. Davis, *New Horizons in Medicine* (New York: Dow Jones and Co., 1966).

tion, drug therapy, and stimulation of body defenses. The cure rate, currently about one-third of the cases, is expected to double by the close of the century. And this forecast does not take into account the many cases that may be prevented entirely.

Improvements in surgery are developing from new techniques more than from modification of existing methods. Lasers have been used successfully in hundreds of cases to "weld" small tears and defects in the retina. They are also being tried experimentally on malignant melanoma, exploiting the fact that laser light is absorbed more readily by dark tissue, and that separate laser beams can be made to converge on one point. Other disorders may thus be alleviated by the selective creation of lesions within the body. Destruction of tissue by cryosurgery (freezing) is also being used successfully on brain cells to relieve the tremors of Parkinson's disease, and is being tested in surgery on deep brain tumors, bone tumors, the prostate gland, tonsils, and abnormal uterine bleeding. Other new techniques include high-pressure oxygenation in hyperbaric chambers for aiding heart surgery, particularly on infants, and treatment of tetanus, gangrene, severe shock, or blood loss; use of air-pressure devices to treat abdominal bleeding or serve as an inflated splint; use of ultrasonic crystal frequencies to create a decongestant fog for treating pneumonia and cystic fibrosis in babies; improved radiation therapy for leukemia; artificial kidneys and kidney machines; and use of infrared radiation, new isotopes, and ultrasound for locating blood clots and tumors.

Progress will certainly be made in rejoining severed limbs, transplanting tissue and organs, and applying microelectronics and new materials to artificial organs and limbs. Experimentation is being done in rejoining nerves and blood vessels, including new techniques in stapling and gluing artificial membranes to hold blood vessels together. (About fifty thousand people are now using blood vessels made of nylon and dacron.) The groundwork may be laid for eventual transplantation of limbs from dead to live people, assuming, as most researchers do, that a way will be found to overcome the body's resistance to "foreign" tissue. Research in tracking down antigens, which cause the body to reject transplants, may provide new drugs to inhibit the antibody reaction, without leaving the person vulnerable to infection. If so, organ transplantation for damage to the liver, kidneys, or pancreas may become common. Predictions have been made that there will eventually be artificial corneas and lungs; "mechanized artificial limbs as versatile as natural arms, legs and hands"; and "electronic substitutes for all the senses, including sight and touch." It seems reasonable to expect that many or most of these predictions of artificial substitutes for human parts will be realized before the year 2000, particularly after 1975–80 when new materials and success with some artificial organs will stimulate doctors and engineers to become even bolder.

As people live longer, medicine for the aging will claim more attention. Present life expectancies—sixty-seven years for men and seventy-four for women in the United States—will increase somewhat, senility will also be reduced, and arthritis may be eliminated before the year 2000. However, the dominant factor will probably not be a huge increase in life expectancy but rather a decrease in the debilitating effects of aging, such as senility, heart disease, and arthritis—though major extension of life expectancy is also possible.

At the other end of human life, an experimental "artificial womb"—a steel tank containing a solution under pressure so high it drives through the fetus's skin the oxygen that normally would be received via the umbilical cord—is being tried at Stanford University to save the lives of very premature babies. Its goal is to prevent part of the 800,000 to 1,000,000 miscarriages every year in the United States by saving those born as early as the fifth to seventh month of pregnancy.

Medicine for the unborn baby, or fetology, is a rapidly expanding field. More than one thousand different types of birth defects are known, and sixteen major categories cause damage to nearly two hundred and fifty thousand babies a year in the United States. Rhesus haemolytic disease, which may result if the mother is Rh-negative and the father Rh-positive, now can be diagnosed by amniocentesis (examination of fluid drawn off in a needle from the amniotic sac). The disease can be treated by giving the ailing fetus a blood transfusion; about 40 per cent of fetuses are being saved. Thus Rh-factor incompatibility is on the way to being conquered. Other diagnostic techniques include amnioscopy, or analysis of the amniotic fluid, fetal electrocardiograms, and amniography by X-rays and ultrasound. Sampling of fetal cells not only permits determination of the sex of the unborn baby, but also detection of chromosome abnormalities. "As we begin to know more about abnormalities of foetal development, corresponding improvements in techniques of foetal therapy . . . can be expected to follow." [41] What is predicted to follow includes "nanosurgery, 10,000 times times finer than the microsurgery now employed in pediatrics, and dependent on improvements in electron-microscopy and laser instrumentation," intrauterine antibiotic therapy, and finally "genetic engineering"—surgical-engineering, biochemical, and viral processes to bring about genetic modification and manipulation.[42] Finally the drugs themselves will be greatly improved.

Confidence is growing that drugs can be tailor-made to fit specific biochemical pathways. . . . Many of the molecules that if normal make

[41] *New Scientist*, January 26, 1967.
[42] James C. G. Conniff, "The World of the Unborn," in the *New York Times Magazine*, January 8, 1967, pp. 98, 100.

us healthy and if abnormal make us sick—enzymes, for example—come in a number of forms which may differ by only a few atoms. . . . scientists are able to build models that approximate the kind of molecules they hope to influence. They then try to design a drug which will be a close but not exact structural match for a molecule important in the chemistry of a given disease. Technically known as analogs, such drugs may halt an illness in its tracks, or at least slow it down. . . . Careful structural analysis may also produce long-needed antiviral drugs. . . . In order to multiply . . . the virus particle must penetrate into the cell. . . . Working on the theory that prevention of virus penetration into a cell would render it harmless, scientists at [du Pont] were successful in designing cage-shaped drug molecules which did block virus penetration into host cells.[43]

Of the five hundred to six hundred viruses of men and animals that have been identified, about three-quarters have been found to produce disease in man. In a "golden age of virus research" that is about to intensify, vaccines have virtually conquered smallpox, polio, and measles in the United States and Europe, though they remain hazards in other parts of the world. Vaccines against mumps and German measles may be available as early as 1971. Viruses are so changeable and numerous that finding an effective vaccine is still a difficult undertaking. The next thirty-three years will bring a great many new and doubtless quite effective vaccines.

Computers too will make an impact. Currently doctors use computers to review patients' daily records, issue orders to nursing stations, monitor recorders attached to patients, and store and retrieve patients' medical histories. Future applications will include storing current medical knowledge and programs and enabling the doctor to consult this knowledge for alternative diagnoses and prescriptions. Much medical diagnosis and care will be closely related to information processing, and the first computer systems to aid diagnosis have already been built. As a result there should be an enormous increase in the quality and quantity of medical statistics. This should aid—at one end—in improving the use of medical facilities (for example, hospitals will be considered as factories for making healthy people out of sick ones, and their technology, equipment, and processes will be considered in terms of efficiency and output) and—at the other end—should provide an enormous increase in medical knowledge, both theoretical and applied. Indeed it is probable that these computer-kept records will be a major source of new knowledge and of better practice and application.

In addition to what may be thought of as the classic issues, there is now much research on thought processes and genetic constitutions. While these are at an early stage of experiments, the implications will surely become impressive. The problem of the use of scientific developments for good or

[43] Judith Randal, "Molecular Meddling Creates New Drugs," *Think*, March-April 1966, pp. 8 ff.

evil exists in every field, but nowhere so spectacularly as in the potential control of the mind, of genetic makeup, and even of the numbers of human beings. On the first possibility:

Drugs to control [experimental animals'] memory and learning are already available. . . . Another research technique of animal "mind control" . . . is electrophysiology. By implanting tiny electrodes in the brains of chickens, cats, bulls and monkeys, experimenters can send electrical impulses into the brains of an animal and thus regulate his actions . . .

At Berkeley my colleagues and I, working neither with drugs nor with implanted electrodes, have obtained results that the anatomy and chemistry of the brain, as well as the learning ability of the individual, can be improved or crippled by providing a psychologically rich or . . . impoverished environment during the individual's youth. . . .

Just recently (May 24, 1966), Dr. Stanley F. Yolles, Director of the National Institute of Mental Health, predicted to a Senate subcommittee: ". . . the next 5 to 10 years . . . will see a hundredfold increase in the number and types of drugs capable of affecting the mind." . . .

In [the biochemical approach, using molecular biology], we seek to discover how the chemical compounds found in the brain are involved in the brain's work. Once we get answers to this question, we can not only begin to write a step-by-step story of how the brain works when we learn, remember, forget, think and dream, but we can also start a rational search for chemical agents, for drugs, which might control and alleviate the distress of the schizophrenic patient, the forgetfulness of the elderly, and the helplessness of the mentally retarded child—all suffering from minds made sick by malfunctioning brains. . . .

And, inevitably, here as in every field of inquiry, *each major addition to our knowledge brings its corollary: power to control.* In brain research, increased knowledge means increased power to control the mind of man. . . .

To control the mind of man through surgical ablation [cutting] of parts of his brain, or via implantation of electrodes through his skull requires, first, that you catch the man. But, and here is the crucial difference, changing the biochemistry of the brain through drugs or through altering the psychological environment does not always require this prior step. . . .

With the use of chemical brain-control agents, it may become possible to control the individual and the masses, and to do all of this unobtrusively and without the active cooperation of the victims. . . .

[Future possibilities might be the use of a "short-term memory eraser" to wipe out the memory of a painful operation or a horrible accident, or, after forcing criminal suspects or political prisoners to talk, then make them forget that they had done so. Chemicals could be placed in water supplies, food or the air we breathe to work unobtrusively on a mass basis. Drugs helpful for the mentally retarded may lead these individuals to marry and reproduce themselves far more than they do today—unless means to change their defective genes are also developed. A prescribed psychological environment in the very early periods of life might be used to produce inferior brains and people on the one hand, and superior brains and people on the other—thus duplicating *Brave New Worlds* without new drugs and only with more understanding of childhood development. This could create a master group and a subservient group.] The control of the society of the future may very well be won on the psychologically-controlled playing fields of the pre-school nurseries.

. . . Whose *is* the ultimate responsibility when brain research results become applicable to man? . . . The scientist has no corner on wisdom or morality. The men in brain research must recognize that since the concern is a common one, we must draw upon the wisdom of everyone. . . . The scientist must [contribute his special knowledge and skills, and] also sound the first concern, for he is in a position to anticipate the problems that might arise from a successful application of his work. . . . 'How is science with all its new power to be related to our political purpose and values and to our economic and constitutional system?' This is a social problem, not a scientific one.[44]

The problem of responsibility for the uses of science may also become acute in the field of genetics before the year 2000. Prime current objectives are to analyze RNA and DNA, the acid substances which carry, store, and pass on as heredity the "blueprint" for manufacture of proteins by the cell. It is tempting to dismiss some of the more outlandish predictions such as these:

Only 10 or 15 years hence, it could be possible for a housewife to walk into a new kind of commissary, look down a row of packets not unlike flower-seed packages, and pick her baby by label. Each packet would contain a frozen one-day-old embryo, and the label would tell the shopper what color of hair and eyes to expect as well as the probable size and I.Q. of the child. It would also offer assurance of freedom from genetic defects. After making her selection, the lady would take the packet to her doctor and have the embryo implanted in herself, where it would grow for nine months, like any baby of her own.[45]

How will you choose to intervene in the ancient designs of nature for man? Would you like to control the sex of your offspring? It will be as you wish. Would you like your son to be six feet tall—seven feet? Eight feet? What troubles you? Allergy, obesity, arthritic pains? These will be easily handled. For cancer, diabetes, there will be gentle therapy . . . viral and microbial disease will be easily met. Even the timeless patterns of growth and maturity and aging will be subject to our design. We know of no intrinsic limits to the life span. How long would you like to live? [46]

[44] David Krech, "Controlling the Mind Controllers," *Think,* July-August 1966, pp. 3-7.
[45] "Foreseeing the Unforeseeable," *Kaiser Aluminum News,* No. 6, 1966, p. 22.
[46] *Washington Post,* October 31, 1966.

They are merely overdramatic warnings of some of the things which—in all likelihood—will eventually become available. Thus we can soberly note that:

> Dr. Rollin D. Hotchkill, . . . a molecular biologist at Rockefeller University . . . has in his own laboratory already achieved genetic modification in bacteria, with steadily improving ability to direct it along specific lines. He does so by administering altered DNA to replot the genetic codes by which the bacteria reproduce their kind. Some day, he feels, science may be able to effect similarly controlled changes in man by (to name but one method) infecting a pregnant woman with viruses freighted with whatever new genetic information she may wish to have transported to her unborn child.[47]

Anticipating progress to come, geneticists and other scientists have begun sounding the alarm. They warn that future ability to influence human heredity and take a hand in man's own evolution may bring a more profound revolution in human destiny than the first atomic explosion twenty-two years ago. Dr. Philip Abelson, editor of *Science*, wrote in 1965 that "controlled laboratory change of human genetic DNA seems at the moment some distance off. However, the quality of the research talent available makes further dramatic advances inevitable." [48] Professor Theodosius Dobzhansky of Rockefeller University suggests that genetic change will be fostered more by "negative" than "positive" eugenics: people with defective genes will be given appropriate information, and then permitted to decide whether they wish their children to be affected similarly. This is the "negative" technique of attempting to hold down a spread of harmful hereditary traits, as compared to a "positive" eugenics of setting up an ideal human, and then trying to evolve such an "improved" human being within the general population. "Positive eugenics schemes are shipwrecked on attempts to decide what sort of man is the ideal to be striven for." [49]

The implication of genetics research is that men will be able to exercise choice in hereditary factors, though it is hoped that preferences will continue to be very diverse. Similar issues get raised in much more mundane application of science and technology to the problem of begetting children. However, the above are not just oddball or "science fiction" predictions—at least in the long run.

Professor H. Bentley Glass, a biologist at the State University of New York at Stony Brook, stated recently:

> Recent successes in the production of mature ova from cultured mouse ovaries lead me to expect that only persistence by a sufficient number of

[47] *New York Times Magazine,* January 8, 1967.
[48] *Ibid.,* July 17, 1965.
[49] *Washington Evening Star,* December 27, 1966.

skilled scientific workers is needed to attain this goal of [laboratory] cultivation of human reproductive organs, continuous production of eggs and sperms, and formation by fertilization in the laboratory of as many human embryos as may be desired.

I am frequently asked why anyone should wish to pursue this goal. "Aren't the age-old ways of making babies good enough?" . . . Only by studying the development of the human embryo and fetus under continuous observation and under various conditions can medical scientists really learn what factors produce particular kinds of abnormalities and how these may be corrected and avoided.

Moreover, the practice of "prenatal adoption," that is, the implantation of a healthy selected embryo in a foster-mother's womb, appears to have fewer religious and legal objections than the present practice of artificial insemination of woman, with or without the consent of her husband.[50]

For many of us, though, there are great emotional and value objections to artificial human reproduction in the laboratory or choosing our children's characteristics like flower-seed packages. Is it really necessary to breed embryos in the laboratory in order to learn how to correct defective genes? Even if feasible, will we want to go beyond the "negative" eugenics of preventing defects from being passed on,[51] and manipulating genes to reduce disease? Will we move beyond into the "positive" eugenics of improving what are considered today to be average human characteristics? If a great upcoming social problem in biochemical brain research is "who is to control the mind-controllers?" a similar problem will arise in genetics research: Who is to control the genetic engineers, and according to what values?

When Caltech physicist Murray Gell-Mann suggested that "a lot of monkeying around with our genes" simply will not be done because man will recoil from it, biologist [James Bonner, also from Caltech] disagreed.

"It is most unlikely that people will be repulsed by this genetic diddling. It will appear . . . in the guise of genetic improvements first, in the guise of genetic repair, but bit by bit, we shall become accustomed to it."

. . . The need for controlling scientific developments took up much discussion time at the meetings, but no one could agree on the ideal mechanism. Bonner advocated an agency set up specifically for this purpose, while scientist-industrialist Simon Ramo suggested the training of a scientific elite of social engineers specifically educated to deal with such problems. *But when Bonner talked of the way biologists will soon be able to manipulate mankind, Ramo conceded: "I would not want to turn over any of these decisions to any one I know."* [52] (emphasis added)

[50] *New York Times*, February 19, 1967.
[51] The United States Public Health Service estimates that more than two hundred and fifty thousand babies are born with "significant birth defects" each year. *Science News*, December 24, 1966, p. 537.
[52] *Washington Post*, October 31, 1966.

In the now almost completely mundane field of birth control, we are rapidly passing through the "horse-and-buggy" stage of early development. An estimated six to seven million American women out of a total of thirty-nine million in the fertile age groups are currently taking oral contraceptive, and outside the United States, another five million are using pills, with the number rapidly rising. Both Western and Eastern Europe practice birth control by abortion far more than by pills. National preferences in birth control vary greatly, and cannot be entirely explained by income, educational, or religious differences, as is usually supposed. Latin America's two million pill-users probably form a larger group than all the women taking oral contraceptives in Western Europe, Eastern Europe and the Soviet Union, despite Latin America's low income levels and Roman Catholic heritage. In the United States, the use of pills by Catholic women is almost as widespread as that by Protestant or Jewish women.[53] The most popular intra-uterine device (IUD), the Lippes loop, is favored by about one hundred fifty thousand Americans and up to four million women abroad; it is being used mainly in Taiwan, Ceylon, India, and Mexico.

Within about fifteen years, birth control with superior techniques than those today will have become, or will be becoming, a universal phenomenon. We wonder to what extent current predictions of a world population of about 6.9 to 7 billion people by the year 2000—based on the present world rate of increase, averaging more than 2 per cent a year—may be modified by worldwide birth control techniques in the 1980's and 1990's. Those who make demographic predictions for the year 2000 do not make clear what assumptions they are using about the degree of birth control usage in the underdeveloped countries in 1980-2000. As described below, birth control techniques by 1980 are likely to be simple, cheap, and long-lasting. Present experience in the use of pills and IUD's in Mexico, Pakistan, and Taiwan suggests that illiterate and semiliterate women desire and can indeed learn birth control. If the average family in the underdeveloped countries wants to have fewer children by 1980-85, effective birth control techniques will be readily available to them and widely known in their societies. How many will want fewer children is such a complex question of economic, social, and cultural factors that we doubt whether it can be adequately predicted. We have the feeling, though, that the likely extent

[53] *Time,* April 7, 1967, p. 79. According to a 1965 study, of all white American women using birth control, 24 per cent are using pills, including 27 per cent Protestants, 22 per cent Jews, and 18 per cent Catholics. However, the Catholic figure "may be low because some Catholics say they use the pills for reasons other than contraception." Cf. an extended discussion of the situation in the United States in Raymond Gastil and Paul Berry, *Alternative Birth Rate Projections to 1975 for Maternal and Child Health Planning,* Hudson Institute, January 24, 1966.

of birth control usage from 1980 to 2000 is substantially underestimated today, and consequently that the world's population by the year 2000 will almost certainly be less than the seven billion once commonly predicted, perhaps by a billion or two.

Future birth control will probably be extremely cheap to the user, even in underdeveloped countries, both because it will be long-lasting and because it will be subsidized by governments. The United States will begin this year to finance the manufacture and distribution of pills in underdeveloped countries that have voluntary programs, and American subsidies are sure to grow. A second generation of contraceptives that will be marketed within several years will include better IUD's; "minidose" pills taken once a day indefinitely, permitting free ovulation, menstruation, and lactation;[54] and "morning-after" pills. Based on current development work, we can also expect within about four to eight years injections or implantations under the skin that will release minute pellets of a progesterone at a relatively constant rate over a long period. Estimates of the contraceptive lifetime of these implants range from one year at first to an eventual twenty years. Other research is aimed at developing a drug that would alter the estrogenic environment around the female egg, thereby preventing sperm cells from developing the capacity to penetrate the ova. Better understanding of reproduction physiology in the hypothalamus and the pituitary may eventually permit the development of agents to block selectively the release of pituitary hormones that control the ovaries.[55] The long-term goal will probably be to have women infertile all their lives, and to produce fertility for a specific period by a pill or an injection when it is desired.

Medicine for the underdeveloped countries will make great progress in cutting down some diseases, but will be dependent to a great extent on a synergistic interaction with better sanitation and especially alleviation of chronic malnutrition. Vast distribution of cheap, new sources of protein to be developed in the next fifteen years would help condition the reduction of the death rate from diseases that are now preventable or curable and that have been conquered in the United States and Europe, such as tuberculosis, diarrhea, trachoma, and schistosomiasis, a parasitic disease that causes extreme lethargy, and malaria. The progress between now and the year 2000 will probably be directly proportional to the amount of investment in nutritional adequacy, better sanitary practices, and public health clinics. Here is an area limited only by money, and not technology.

[54] *New Scientist*, December 15, 1966, p. 620. (Lactation is extremely important in areas where mother's milk may be the only protein source available to infants.)
[55] *Science News*, April 15, 1967, pp. 349-350.

I. SOME CONCLUDING COMMENTS

Obviously it would be easy to write many more chapters about many other aspects of new technology. For example, we have left out the most glamorous of the new sciences—space and oceanography—as well as such important things as food and agriculture, new nonnuclear power sources, new methods of transportation, new materials, and so on. In other words, we have scarcely started on the exploration of our three lists of Chapter I, and have discussed the material we did discuss in the most superficial fashion. Yet this chapter is overlong as it is.

This is perhaps one of the main reasons why there is not enough study of the application and consequences of new technologies. It is in fact a very difficult and time-consuming job simply to become aware of the many new developments which are underway, and it is clear that it is going to be almost impossible to bring much order out of the confusion caused by the mere richness of new possibilities. In our study, of course, we are more interested in setting up a framework for examining consequences and other implications of technology than in discussing its details.

As for consequences, let us repeat our statement in Chapter I: technology raises issues of "accelerated nuclear proliferation; of loss of privacy; of excessive governmental and/or private power over individuals; of dangerously vulnerable, deceptive and degradable overcentralization; of decisions becoming necessary that are too large, complex, important, uncertain, or comprehensive to be left to mere mortals—whether private or public; of new capabilities that are so inherently dangerous that they are likely to be disastrously abused; of too rapid or cataclysmic change for smooth adjustment, and so on."

As many readers will have noticed, much of our discussion of the technology of the "year 2000" really applies more to the 1970's and the early 1980's. The year 2000 is, in terms of technological development, quite a distance away and there is time enough for even "far-out" predictions to materialize, as well as for many totally new and unexpected developments. Furthermore, the rate at which changes are taking place, both in number and in "intensity," can truly be described as itself increasing—perhaps even exponentially. This raises serious issues, to which we return in later chapters.

Our capacities for and commitment to economic development and control over our external and internal environment and concomitant systematic, technological innovation, application, and diffusion, of these capacities are increasing, seemingly without foreseeable limit. The capacities of our culture and institutions to adapt to so much change in so comparatively short a time may be a major question; the stresses in domestic societies and in

the international system may not be managed sufficiently by meliorist policies. Since the underdeveloped countries are even further removed in industrial and social life from these new technologies than we are, the cultural
shock of their partial adaptation to the new technologies may be even greater
for them. In later chapters we discuss these possibilities and consider issues
raised as technological development increasingly facilitates oppressive social controls. Finally we question whether man's unremitting, Faustian
striving may ultimately remake his natural conditions—environmental, social, and psychobiological—so far as to begin to dehumanize himself or to
degrade his political or ecological situation in some very costly or even irrevocable manner.

CHAPTER III

Some "Surprise-Free" Economic Projections: A Quantitative Scenario

A. INTRODUCTION

1. *The Optimistic Bias*

In this chapter we construct a hypothetical pattern of events in quantitative terms—that is, in terms of measures of productivity, population, growth, work, leisure, and affluence—for the Standard World and its variations. We assume a continuing production of various new technologies of the kind we discussed in the previous chapters. It is difficult to estimate the impact of such technological changes on the average productivity of the labor force. One can, of course, estimate specific increases in productivity by examining applications of innovations in specific industries, but these studies tend to underestimate the total impact—in part because one simply does not know how widely and ingeniously the new techniques may be used. Nor can one predict how efficient the new technique will be after the initial learning period has been exploited. Most important of all, it is almost impossible to form any good estimate of synergistic, let alone serendipitous, effects.

Therefore in this chapter we shall simply postulate that recent rates in such things as increase in productivity will at least be equaled or increased in the future—at least over the long run.[1] More specifically, we shall write a moderately optimistic economic scenario of how things may go, if there are no major wars or depressions, for the next thirty-three years or so.

---

[1] It was one of the main purposes of our discussion in Chapters I and II to make this statement plausible.

What is meant by "optimistic" is illustrated by the following graphs of GNP per capita for the United States and Japan. Here "m" is the medium forecast that would have been arrived at from the steepest possible long-term trend through the data (the long-term trend is not so clear for Japan, because of the interruption in World War II). "L," "M," and "H" are the forecasts shown in the tables of this chapter. The "M" forecasts in such graphs are typically in line with recent short-term trends but exceed the long-term trend.[2] Table I summarizes for ten major countries the GNP per capita growth rate, first along the longest available trend and second as we assume more likely for the next thirty-three years.

One reason for using growth rates higher than those indicated by the long-term trend is that they fit well with the recent experience of most

TABLE I

Comparative Forecasts of GNP Per Capita to Year 2000
Ten Major Countries

	1965 GNP/CAP. 1965 U.S. $	MEDIUM FORECAST GROWTH RATE % PER YEAR	YEAR 2000 GNP/CAP. 1965 U.S. $	FORECAST USING MORE LONG-TERM TREND GROWTH RATE % PER YEAR	YEAR 2000 GNP/CAP. 1965 U.S. $	EARLIEST DATA FOR LONG-TERM TREND
U.S.	3557	3.0	10160	1.8	6750	1869-73
Canada	2464	3.1	7070	1.6	4300	1870-79
France	1964	3.7	6830	1.6	3400	1810-20
W. Germany	1905	4.1	7790	1.8	3600	1860-69
U.K.	1804	3.7	6530	1.5	3000	1860-69
U.S.S.R.	1288	3.7	4650	2.8	3400	1870
Italy	1101	4.1	4450	2.4	2500	1862-68
Japan	857	6.8	8590	3.7	3100	1878-87
India	99	2.9	270	2.1	205	1950
China	98	3.5	321	3.1	285	1933
Unweighted average		4.1		2.3		

SOURCES: Growth rates: computed from GNP per capita 1965 and present medium forecast to 2000 as given in Table XIV, below. Forecasts using long-term trends based on studies of sources reported in Mark Wehle's memorandum, HI-846-RR.

[2] Additional graphs and discussion of sources for the ten major countries have been provided by Mark Wehle in a Hudson Institute paper, HI-846-RR.

FIGURE 1
U.S., GNP PER CAPITA, 1869-2000
(1965 DOLLARS)

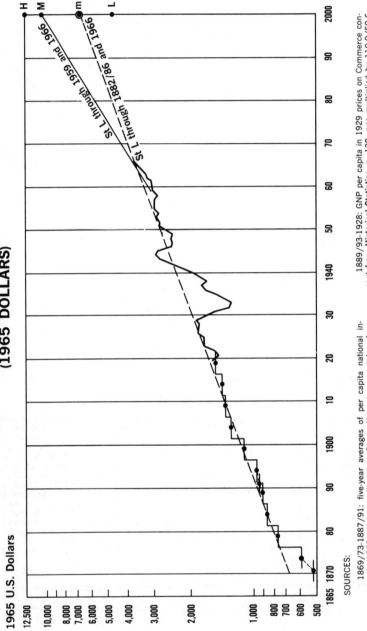

SOURCES:

1869/73-1887/91: five-year averages of per capita national income in 1929 prices, attributed to Simon Kuznets, were taken from U.S. Census Bureau, **Historical Statistics of the U.S.: Colonial Times to 1957** (Washington, D.C., 1960), p. 139, and raised to the level of the Department of Commerce by multiplying by the 1889/93 ratio of Commerce GNP to Kuznets' national income. The raised data were multiplied by 110.9/50.6, the ratio of the implicit price deflator in 1965 to that in 1929, to convert to 1965 prices and further by the ratio 1.016 of 1963-65 GNP from U.N., **Monthly Bulletin of Statistics,** to 1963-65 GNP from U.S. Office of Business Economics, **The National Income and Product Accounts of the United States, 1929-1965** (Washington, D.C., August 1966), p. 3, to put on the U.N. level.

1889/93-1928: GNP per capita in 1929 prices on Commerce concept from **Historical Statistics,** p. 139, was multiplied by 110.9/50.6 and 1.016 as above.

1929-65: GNP per capita in 1958 prices from the O.B.E. publication just cited, p. 156, was multiplied by 1.109 to convert to 1965 prices and 1.016 as above to put on U.N. level.

1966: GNP in 1958 prices from **Survey of Current Business,** April 1967, p. 6, was divided by population including armed forces overseas from U.S. Census Bureau, **Current Population Reports,** series P-25, no. 355, December 16, 1966, and the quotient was converted to 1965 prices and the U.N. level as above.

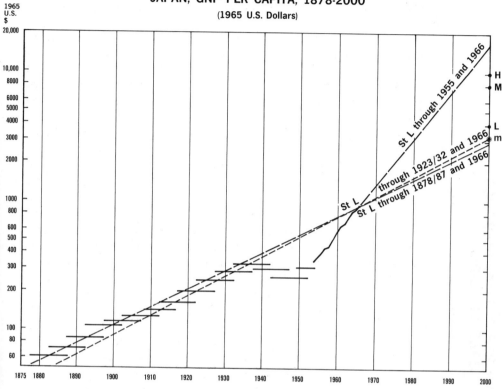

FIGURE 2
JAPAN, GNP PER CAPITA, 1878-2000
(1965 U.S. Dollars)

SOURCES:
Through 1952: Per capita national income in the form of averages from Simon Kuznets, "Quantitative Aspects of the Economic Growth of Nations: I. Level and Variability of Rates of Growth," **Economic Development and Cultural Change,** October 1956, p. 90, was multiplied by the ratio of United Nations GNP in 1960 prices to Kuznets' national income in 1928-32 prices in the overlapping period 1950-54. For this, U.N. GNP 1953-55, fiscal years starting April 1, from U.N., **Yearbook of National Accounts Statistics,** 1961, p. 152, and 1964, p. 163 (1954 figure had to be converted from 1955 prices), was extrapolated back using the year-to-year percentage changes given in Bank of Japan, Foreign Capital Research Society, **Japanese Industry,** 1965, p. 2, and interpolated to calendar years. The products were in turn multiplied by the ratio 1.109 of calendar-year 1956 GNP in 1960 prices from U.N., **Monthly Bulletin of Statistics,** January 1967, p. 180, to the same interpolated between fiscal years 1955 and 1956 from **Yearbook of National Accounts Statisics,** 1964, p. 163 (this assumes the revisions in the **Monthly Bulletin** should be made retroactive); was further multiplied by the 1965 calendar year ratio of GNP or GDP in current prices to that in 1960 prices (implicit price deflator), which had been extrapolated graphically by the consumer price index **(Statistics and Monthly Bulletin);** and finally was divided by the 1965 average of year-end exchange rates **(Monthly Bulletin).**
1954-55: GNP in 1960 prices from **Yearbook of National Accounts Statistics,** 1961, p. 152 (converted from 1955 prices), and 1964, p. 163, was multiplied by 1.109 and by the 1965 implicit price deflator and divided by the 1965 exchange rate as above, then divided by population from **U.N., Demographic Yearbook,** 1965.
1956-64: GNP in 1960 prices from **Monthly Bulletin of Statistics,** January 1967, p. 180, was multiplied by the 1965 price deflator and divided by the 1965 exchange rate and by population as above.
1965: GNP in current prices from **Monthly Bulletin** was divided by the exchange rate and by population from that source.
1966: 1965 figure raised 8.9 per cent (calculated from fiscal-year percentage changes in the **New York Times,** January 20, 1967, p. 48, col. 4, citing Japan Economic Planning Agency), and divided by population from **Monthly Bulletin.**

countries. What is now the comparatively short-term trend may be the future long-term trend. Some of the causes of the recent speeding up of growth are:

1. The contemporary "growth cult" among nations. Economic expansion is national policy around the world, and this policy is accompanied by various national plans as aids to policy implementation. Performance data and comparative statistics are now more readily available, and these assist in providing both guidance and incentive to governments in achieving growth.

2. An *exponentially* growing and "exportable" body of technical knowledge. As is well known, the body of technical knowledge of productive techniques is generally available and growing, and is an "exportable" input from technologically rich areas to those that are deficient. In addition, we place emphasis on the increasingly general application of management science as an important ingredient in raising productivity, with large but perhaps less emphasis on gains in the efficient allocation of resources. (Interesting issues may be raised concerning the availability of knowledge coincident with its lack of use—or even inappropriate use—in many countries.)

3. The moderating of depressions by advanced countries' use of government deficits. Some of the effects such as a higher average percentage of employment (say 96 per cent instead of 94 per cent) should bring about a once-and-for-all increase in per capita GNP. However, this and the moderating of fluctuations should also provide a better environment, financially, for innovation and diffusion of new techniques and technologies.[3]

4. Improvements in world institutional arrangements may be offered as another justification for an optimistic bias, although one cannot be sure to what extent these improvements will continue to be made or precisely what their impact will be. The elimination or reduction of trade barriers, the provision for new sources of international liquidity, the conception of new common markets and the improvement in efficacy of those currently existing, could all improve various growth rates, although it is difficult to say how much. Another institutional benefit would be improvements in the quality of knowledge concerning the theory and execution of growth itself, perhaps especially in respect to development planning techniques and the uses of foreign aid resources by less-developed countries.

Our optimistic projections thus derive from the increased rate at which

---

[3] Angus Maddison argues, for example, that the announced determination of West European governments to maintain full employment by fiscal policy assured the demand for output, so that businessmen were not afraid to modernize, and that this raised the growth rate. *Economic Growth in the West: Comparative Experience in Europe and North America* (New York: Twentieth Century Fund, 1964), pp. 18-19, 38-39, 59.

new technology is being developed, applied and diffused, from the institutionalization of a policy of growth by governments around the world, and from anticipated increases in world productivity. We believe these factors are likely to outweigh important considerations that point in the direction of no increase in the rate of long-term growth in per capita income.

These considerations apply to both the developed and less-developed countries, and although they are generally well known, we ought to mention them here. In the case of the developed nations, such as those of Western Europe and Japan, one can argue that post-World War II growth rates were merely temporary and that, in due course, the long-term more conservative trend will reappear. This position implies that the long-term trend is a depository and expression of fundamental and structural characteristics of particular economies, and that shorter-term "bulges" are caused by unique or once-and-for-all events, which, having had their impact, will subside and put particular economies back to their long-term growth experience.

Among these temporary factors that favorably affect performance are shifts of labor force from agricultural to industrial occupations, with consequent increases in national income; the completion of such a reallocation represents a once-and-for-all benefit. Another is the exhaustion of previously unemployed or underemployed labor resources into productive pursuits as in the United States since 1958.[4] The elimination of a labor supply previously "perfectly elastic" at going wages may result in a lessening of investment, some deterioration of trade balances, and a slowing of growth. Immigration of foreign workers without families was an important component of the dramatic growth in per capita GNP achieved by Western Europe in the postwar period. Western Europe's failure in wartime to assimilate new inventions and to train enough engineers and scientists may have had effects persisting well beyond the making good of wartime destruction and wearing-out.

With respect to the less-developed countries, arguments voiced against their achieving new, higher growth rates include lack of an adequate flow of savings and investment, erratic foreign exchange earnings, insufficient potential economies of scale, lack of labor force skills, inept governmental administration coupled with political malaise, and unabated population pressure. Yet these difficulties do not all seem likely to be permanent.

2. Productivity, Work, Leisure, and GNP

Gross National Product can be approximated by estimating the total number of hours that are worked and the average value of the goods and services that are produced per hour of work. The first quantity depends upon the rate and intensity of participation of the labor force, i.e., upon age-

[4] U.S., *Economic Report of the President*, January 1967, pp. 8, 44, 45.

specific and male-female participation rates and the average number of hours that people work.

For example, in 1967 the United States labor force approximates 74 million persons employed in civilian pursuits. At an average of 2,000 hours of work per person annually, total manhours generated will be about 150 billion. Currently one manhour yields $5.20 of GNP. Thus about $780 billion of GNP should be achieved in 1967.

We have argued that productivity per hour will go up. Before World War II, the increase in productivity per manhour was a little over 2 per cent per year, but since the war, it has averaged about 3 per cent; and a recent report by Secretary of Labor Willard Wirtz indicates that new calculations give 3.8 per cent as the average for the past five years. There is almost a general expectation that the United States ought to average between 2.5 and 3.5 per cent a year or even more over the next thirty-three years. Indeed some expect that as soon as automation reaches its stride it will be 1 or 2 per cent higher than this. Given our optimistic bias (at least for this scenario), based on the four factors listed in the last section, very likely 3 or 3.5 per cent is a good figure on which to focus—though some economists think it is fairly high while others believe it to be low. We shall bound the reasonable possibilities by low and high projections using 2.5 per cent and 4 per cent.

Figure 3 below indicates how the average hours per week have

FIGURE 3
HISTORICAL ANNUAL AVERAGE WORKWEEK 1900-1963

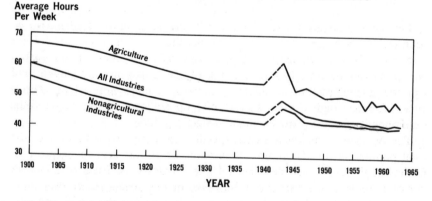

NOTE: Data of 1940-43 are not comparable.

SOURCE: Bureau of Labor Statistics.

decreased in the twentieth century. It should be noted that before World War II a good deal of productivity increase was taken up in decreased hours of work or increased leisure. (A question often debated is what has happened to this increased leisure. Sebastian de Grazia [5] indicates that in the past much of it has been taken up by "moonlighting," commuting, home maintenance, increased standards of child and home care, and the like.)

Since the war, very little of the increased productivity has been taken up in increased leisure. We mentioned that currently the average American who works more or less full-time works an average of 2,000 hours a year. If we extrapolated postwar trends, this should drop to something between 1,700 and 1,900 hours a year by the year 2000. If, as seems probable, there is a renewed tendency to take up the increased productivity in increased leisure, one can imagine the hours dropping substantially below 1,500; possibly even below 1,000 (as explained later).

These, then, are our assumptions and the resulting high and low GNP forecasts to the year 2000:

For both forecasts:
  Year 2000 population: 318 million.
  Per cent employed: 38 per cent
  Work year: 1,600 hours

For low GNP forecast (2.2 trillion 1965 dollars):
  Productivity per manhour rises 2.5 per cent a year

For high GNP forecast (3.6 billion 1965 dollars):
  Productivity per manhour rises 4 per cent a year

The same 2.2 and 3.6 trillion GNP in the year 2000 could have also been yielded by the alternative assumptions shown in Figures 4 and 5. Here three variables are related to the year 2000 GNP: (1) annual hours worked per employed person, (2) percentage of the population employed, and (3) the annual rate of productivity increase. Figure 4 provides various curves for the "high GNP" estimate of $3.6 trillion and Figure 5 reflects requirements for the "low estimate" of $2.2 trillion.

The two sets of curves are each specified in terms of percentages of the total population that is employed. A range of 30 per cent to 43 per cent is shown; these bracket the typical United States experience of about 38 per cent. By selecting a level of GNP, high or low, and a choice of a curve reflecting the proportion of the population that is employed, one may read off the axes of annual hours worked and productivity increase those combinations of hours and productivity required to achieve the designated year 2000 GNP.

[5] *Of Time, Work and Leisure* (Garden City, N.Y.: Doubleday, 1964).

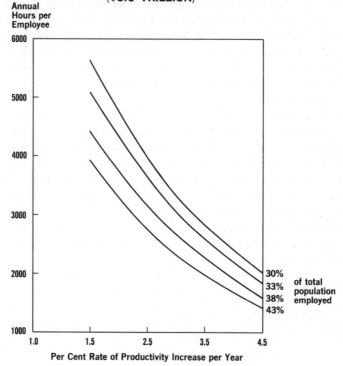

FIGURE 4
YEAR 2000
TO ACHIEVE A HIGH GNP ESTIMATE
($3.6 TRILLION)

Annual
Hours per
Employee

30%
33% of total
38% population
43% employed

Per Cent Rate of Productivity Increase per Year

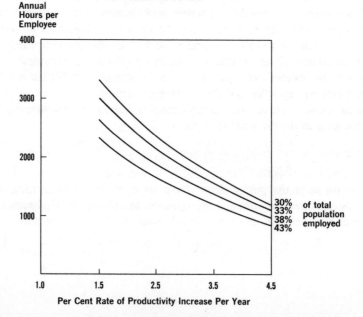

FIGURE 5
YEAR 2000
TO ACHIEVE A LOW GNP ESTIMATE
($2.2 TRILLION)

Annual
Hours per
Employee

30%
33% of total
38% population
43% employed

Per Cent Rate of Productivity Increase Per Year

For example, consider Figure 5, the low GNP estimate of $2.2 trillion. If one assumes that 38 per cent of the total United States population is working, the low estimate may be achieved by any combination of annual hours worked and rate of productivity increase read off the 38 per cent curve. Thus to achieve $2.2 trillion GNP in year 2000 with 38 per cent working, 1,350 hours per worker, 3.5 per cent increase in productivity are required. Alternatively, at 2.5 per cent increase, about 1,880 hours per year must be worked.

These curves may be used in several different ways to depict the conditions for achieving the previously specified high or low GNP. For example, one could select 2,000 hours per year as his expected year 2000 figure with the expectation of achieving the high GNP, $3.6 trillion. Using Figure 4 and reading along the 2,000 hour line, it can be seen that this GNP is achievable with 43 per cent of the population employed in combination with a 3.5 per cent average annual increase in productivity over the 1965-2000 period. Alternatively this GNP may be achieved at the 2,000 hour level by a combination of 3.8 per cent productivity and 38 per cent population working.

Figures 4 and 5 are intended to depict the choices available to the population and the economy with respect to economic growth, attitudes toward work (and, therefore, leisure), and productivity. In terms of conclusions, these two graphs reflect the obvious; namely, that it would be quite surprising not to achieve the low GNP estimate, whereas the high estimate is barely within the surprise-free requirement.

Yet if productivity per hour increases around 3.5 per cent a year, and if current work-oriented, achievement-oriented attitudes are maintained, it should be possible for the United States to reach the high projection—in fact, we could exceed it. In this high projection we can estimate that there would be about one family in twelve with income after federal income tax of at least $50,000 a year. This is the kind of income that we now associate with being a millionaire, and should be compared with the current rate of one family in at least several hundred with such an income.

Later in the chapter we shall give one "scenario" for the United States national income accounts and distribution of income. The reader may wish to glance ahead to section C-4 of this chapter, especially the table on "Distribution of Family Personal Income."

3. Some Additional Justification for the Surprise-Free Economic and Demographic Projection (or Scenario)

In many ways the period from 1952 to 1967 has been similar to "la belle epoque" that occurred from 1901 to 1913. We have already made the point that perhaps the most crucial issue in our study is that current economic trends will continue more or less smoothly through the next thirty-three years and perhaps beyond (and not be rudely interrupted as by the 1908 and 1914 depressions and World War I in the first la belle epoque).

We have called this chapter a "scenario" because we wish to emphasize the possibility that in fact many of the "surprise-free" assumptions of this and the next two chapters may not be realized. On the other hand, as indicated in Chapter I, we tend increasingly to feel that, at least as far as the "old nations" are concerned, the next thirty-three years will not be marked by as many politically and economically surprising and cataclysmic events as the first sixty-six years of this century. This seems to us quite plausible, despite much current anxiety about thermonuclear war generally, and about the current war in Vietnam; or, indeed, much anxiety about many issues, especially those with regard to the relationships between the developed and underdeveloped nations and the possibility of famine in the latter. Despite many obvious places and issues from which instability or chaos might arise, there seems to be a growing consensus that we are entering a period of general political and economic stability, at least so far as the *frontiers and economies* of most of the *old* nations are concerned.

While we shall deal with international aspects of the Standard World in Chapter V, and with many possibilities for instability and disturbance in Chapters VI, VII, and IX, it will be useful to devote a few pages at this point to the general international context in which we make our projections. (The projections, in turn, have influenced our view of the international context.)

There has come to be—in addition to the detente—a better understanding on both sides of the Iron Curtain of the motives, objectives, and style of the opponent (as well as perhaps some wishful thinking). There has been a relative lack of success of Communism in Africa and Latin America, and even in South and Southeast Asia; the strength of this area against Communism is often combined with a relative military and political weakness for offensive actions on its own, which also, by and large, promote stability. There have been a number of technical developments and changes in strategic forces and strategic doctrine that seem to have mitigated many important aspects of the arms competition and reduced the possibilities both of premeditated and accidental war. Most of all there has been an apparent ebbing of political or ideological passion or commitment in the major nations, so that people simply have not been willing to risk war over the issues in international conflict.

An important new factor tending toward stability is the relatively small pressure to territorial expansion in Europe, Japan, Russia, and in North America and South America. A comparison with almost any period in the past four or five hundred years shows a great contrast; the old nations now seem quite satisfied with their current boundaries. (The assumption that frontiers in these areas are generally stable should probably exclude the

German situation, on the assumption that German unification with possible border adjustments might be peacefully or violently accomplished. We should also admit the possibility of Chinese territorial aggressions. There doubtlessly is a probability of frontier changes in parts of Africa and South Asia and Southeast Asia, and of turmoil in the Middle East and elsewhere in the so-called new nations, such as China, which have been recently decolonized or integrated.) While for some of the new nations, boundary disputes, irredentism, and territorial aggrandizement may continue, as throughout history, to create instabilities, the general assessment must be of a condition in which frontier questions are, for most of the older nations of the world, no longer dominating or even serious (immediate or "felt") issues.

One of the main reasons for this is that internal economic development is now widely believed to be the most efficient road to wealth and power. The postwar experience of West Germany and Japan and the postdecolonization experience of other European countries indicates that colonies now are economic liabilities and sources of political and military weakness rather than strength. Doubtless the pendulum of fashion has overshot, but this novel and scarcely explicated attitude has important consequences. In particular we would expect much attention and effort to be placed on maintaining high economic growth rates.

Another current development is of "pluralistic security communities" (on the model of United States-Canadian relations) in which war (or violent change) is actually, or is assumed to be, unthinkable. These partly integrated groupings [6] imply more than a willingness to accept or live with current situations: they require a willingness to live with much deteriorated or strained situations, and yet a determination not to let situations deteriorate too far. Because of this determination to be responsive to the needs of others, a pluralistic security community is an important step forward to political integration or unification. Western Europe is the most notable example, but there is evidence of this development in Latin America too. The twenty years since World War II have demonstrated a peaceful acceptance of existing frontiers in Latin America that has had little or nothing to do with explicit deterrence calculations—nuclear or otherwise. Yet before 1940 many experts would have judged Latin American relations relatively unstable and the probability of war and frontier changes among some nations of the region quite high. Today few would be surprised if the Latin American map in 2000 did not look much the same as today, with the possible addition of some transnational communities—economic and possibly political—which do not destroy or erase the old national frontiers.

Important too is the often neglected fact that trade no longer follows the flag. Thus West Germany and Japan, which hardly possess navies, are the second and fifth largest trading nations in the world today.

[6] Discussed more fully on pp. 372-73.

Indeed most of the old and many of the new nations today enjoy a high degree of security of frontiers and the benefits of access to world trade without much explicit need, if any at all, for a national military capability to enforce their rights and privileges. This probably will continue to be true. Of course, even if world stability persists, military capabilities will remain of importance in international politics. Indeed the military power of the United States and the latent power of such organizations as the O.A.S. and the U.N. provide a major reinforcement of the basic stability—at least against brazen and stark aggression. But in general, so far as the "old nations" are concerned, the uses of military power are likely to be more sophisticated and subtle than in the eighteenth, nineteenth, and early twentieth centuries—when most of our present ideas on the relations between military force and political and economic power were formed.

What will the international hierarchy of the future look like? We suggested in Chapter I that most likely there will be ten "major" powers of which two, the United States and the Soviet Union, will continue to be considered superpowers.[7] Japan, West Germany, France, China, and the United Kingdom are likely to be considered large powers; India, Italy, and Canada intermediate powers; and the next one hundred and twenty nations can be thought of as small powers. The ranking is generally a simple one of estimated GNP in the mid- and late 1970's: the intermediate powers have at least half again the GNP of any of the small powers, the large powers have one-third again the GNP of the intermediate powers, and the superpowers have more than twice the GNP of the large powers; but it should be noted that the grouping is natural.

The foregoing assumes, of course, that the United Kingdom continues to have the same *relatively* poor performance in growth rate of GNP that it has had for more than one hundred years, and that the others continue their performance of the last decade or so;[8] that is, Japan does very well, the West Germans reasonably well, and the Chinese and French moderately well. It should also be noted that this ordering is likely to seem reasonable by other criteria than gross national product. Thus, if one assesses relative potential military power and potential influence on a rather large range of issues in a large range of situations, the result is likely to produce much the same ordering, although for specific issues and specific situations there may be sharp changes.

4. Some Uses of This Chapter

We are to some degree interested in the variables of population growth, gross national product, and GNP per capita for their own sake. Of course we also wish to draw many inferences from these projections. In Chapters

---

[7] Refer to pp. 11 and 17.
[8] See the extrapolations from past performance on p. 30.

IV and V we shall consider some of the political, social, and cultural implications. We would like, however, to make clear even here that we are willing to argue that these variables, particularly the gross national product, are probably rather good indices of what the potential power of many nations or groups of nations might be.[9]

As discussed below, the term power, even though widely used, is an ambiguous one—indeed more difficult to understand and define than many other widely used but ambiguous terms. It is also important to realize that whatever these evolving power potentials may be, they could, if they changed sufficiently from today's balance, eventually create a somewhat different international context than the one that is familiar to us today. But whether or not one wishes to associate these "projections" with the implications we draw, the projections themselves do arise out of widely accepted assumptions or attitudes and thus represent, at least by inference, not only our Standard World, but to some degree an "official" consensus world. They are also reasonably consistent with most of the Canonical Variations described in Chapter VI. Thus, independent of our use of these data, they should be interesting for many other purposes.

Power and influence in international relations are multidimensional concepts that include, among other things, military capabilities, size, wealth, geographic position, and even more vague notions, such as stature, prestige, culture, historical trends and precedents, and so on. To some degree power depends on the estimates of those being influenced. Therefore, in practice, such of these ideas as are easiest to deal with and seem reasonably relevant tend to be dominant—at least in periods of peace. In order to make projections that suggest something quantitative that may often be related to (or an important source of) these characteristics, three simple indices will be used: population, gross national product, and GNP per capita. The first two are proxies for size, and all three are useful to obtain an indication of potential for political importance.[10] These indices are then compared with each other to determine whether the relative position of countries is likely to change, and, against crude absolute standards, to determine the extent to which additional nations may be able to achieve certain capabilities.

The projections to the year 2000 (and in some cases to 2020) have been extrapolated from current data and recent experience, with some modification where recent experience seems specially unlikely to continue. It goes

---

[9] One argument which some people find persuasive is that national power should be strongly influenced by the current and future availability of "useful" adults which is related to, but not identical with, the number of people and the "usable" economic surplus. This last is related to, but not identical with, GNP per capita. One might also, perhaps simplistically, combine population and GNP per capita by multiplying them together and thus get total GNP.

[10] A small GNP per capita is likely to mean that little above subsistence is available for other uses; but this lack of per capita potential could be compensated for by a sufficiently large base.

without saying that such projections involve some reasonably arbitrary decisions as well as more or less sophisticated and well-informed "crystal ball gazing." We have attempted to consider not only the continued current trends to the year 2000, but also the ranges of possible economic and demographic growth rates, using high, medium, and low estimates. There are many variables, such as fertility and mortality rates, population density, rates of productivity, and the like, which are difficult to assess in future contexts. We suggest that the range of projections will afford enough choice to establish what is "reasonable" and "possible" if the underlying assumptions of a Standard World pattern are maintained.

If we took the "projections" of this chapter too seriously—by either taking the indices as the *sine qua non* of power or influence or thinking of the "surprise-free" projections as being more than just "a scenario for a Standard World," it is obvious that we might be subject to valid criticism. GNP per capita is a poor measure of per capita surplus over and above subsistence, since, among other reasons, the "subsistence level" probably rises strongly with income. The presence of a per capita surplus and a large economic base is not a necessary condition for the ability to exert power in international affairs; nor is it a sufficient condition, since the technical, organizational, and political ability to mobilize and use these potentials must also be present. And, even if GNP, population, and GNP per capita were perfect indices of power potential in international affairs, estimates of them are notoriously unreliable [11] and the GNP's have many noncomparable aspects,[12] especially for this purpose.[13]

[11] While in most advanced countries aggregate GNP estimates are believed to be reliable within ± 5 per cent, errors of much larger magnitudes have sometimes been present; and in the bulk of countries, such estimates are probably not reliable within a range of ± 20 per cent. See Paul Studenski, *The Income of Nations* (New York: New York University Press, 1961). Even population figures are sometimes grossly inaccurate. According to an article cited by Oskar Morgenstern, *On the Accuracy of Economic Observations* (Princeton, N.J.: Princeton University Press, 1963), p. 258, the 1950 population census of the United States failed to account for the presence of approximately five million persons, "equivalent to the United States *not* possessing cities of the size of Chicago plus Detroit. . . ."

[12] The most frequent procedure for attempting to achieve comparability between national GNP figures is to translate each of them into United States dollars using official exchange rates. There are well-known and serious difficulties, however. First, exchange rates do not normally reflect comparable purchasing powers: a dollar's work of kroner will not buy the same amount of goods in a Scandinavian country as will that same dollar in the United States. Second, many items entering into GNP are costs of production rather than usable output: in temperate climates more housing, clothing, and heating are required per unit of output; in urbanized societies more police, sewage, and fire protection services are required; and in poorer countries more children must be reared in order that an equivalent number survive to enter the labor force. This list could easily be extended to include a wide variety of other differences between countries which make a comparison of their GNP's less useful for present purposes, such as the extent of leisure time and excess capacity and ability to adapt (mobilize) quickly when the need arises.

[13] Relative internal prices used to weight together the various goods and services

Aside from these difficulties, one could easily criticize the simple extrapolation procedures utilized. But to improve upon these methods substantially is not easy. Despite all the arguments that can be raised against the use of population, GNP, and GNP per capita, it is difficult to find examples of nations that a consensus of experts would consider important in today's world that do not rank high on at least one of these scales, and it is equally difficult, *today,* to think of opposite cases (though in certain instances powerful nations may abstain from exerting their influence). Of course, in the past when the "barbarian problem" was central, and possibly in the future when the technological modernized version or equivalent may exist, GNP and total population may be even more irrelevant. But what other measures of national power would do as well; would they be any more reliable; could they be any less inaccurately projected into the future? In any case, given the limitations upon our resources, we have decided upon the use of GNP and population, and while knowing their shortcomings, we feel it makes little sense for us to invest in substantially more sophisticated forecasting methods at this time.[14] Our purpose is to provide a quick first look at a number of plausible developments that could eventually alter the balance of power in the world, change domestic styles of life or social structures, or cause some other important change. The methods chosen seem adequate and appropriate for this limited goal.

5. *The Achievement of Capabilities*

If one assumed that the same level of income will be required in the future to achieve a certain capability (e.g., a certain military potential) as is required today, then these tables would yield simple comparisons. It is unlikely, however, that it will take the same level of income to achieve a given capability in the future as it does today. Several offsetting forces are at work. On the one side capabilities, especially in the military field, are becoming cheaper, because late-comers do not have to spend as much on

---

entering into GNP differ significantly between countries; it is therefore possible to find two countries with the same level of GNP but with different power potentials because one can produce military goods more cheaply than the other whose comparative advantage lies elsewhere (international trade could, but obviously does not, compensate for such differences, especially where military goods and services are concerned).

[14] Indeed there can be no assurance that more sophisticated techniques would yield better results. Ideally we would like to impose technological, resource, organizational, and cultural constraints on the extrapolations, as well as to introduce checks to insure consistency among the various sets of projections, and in a certain gross and intuitive way we did try to do this. But since there is no adequate way to forecast how such forces will change over time, the assumption that for the most part they will continue changing and influencing GNP and population growth at recent rates has several advantages: (1) it is easy to make the calculations on this basis, (2) it is consistent with our concept of "surprise-free" projections, and (3) it may even turn out to be a reasonably good approximation of reality.

R & D, because of increased knowledge of more efficient means of production, and, most important of all, because of the increasing availability of essential raw materials and manufactured devices. Of course, a late-comer may still have to go through some learning process to achieve economies and efficiency, if not capabilities, but it will become increasingly easy to use generally available and well-understood technology to procure the equivalent of modern (1965) strategic capability. How well such 1965 or even 1975 capabilities will compete with 1985 and 2000 capabilities procured by the large and superpowers is still an open question. In addition, aspirations for a higher standard of living are likely to grow over time, and they are likely to grow most rapidly in nations whose standards of living are currently the lowest, unless the government deliberately takes steps to isolate its population from international demonstration effects. As indicated at the outset, it is the size of the surplus above necessary levels of consumption that is important, and the reader might consider how many and which countries might become able to achieve various levels of technological-military capabilities.

6. *The Relationship of GNP and Population*

Estimates of real per capita GNP for the ten major countries and the nineteen contender countries to 2000 were made by extrapolating a fraction in which the numerator constituted projected GNP and the denominator projected population for the respective countries. Thus the consequent per capita GNP is the arithmetic result of two independently extrapolated variables.

There are legitimate questions concerning the appropriateness of this procedure. Specifically our method seems to imply the independence of aggregate economic activity, the rate of growth of output, and population growth. It is clear that population growth cannot be so neatly divorced from the projected levels of output, and that perhaps specific functional relationships exist between output and population. These possible relationships have been formalized into such problems as the determination of optimum population size for a nation; of the effect of population growth on the growth of per capita output (especially in the less-developed countries); of the implications of the dependency ratio—the proportion of the total population not of labor force age—on growth; and the so-called "population trap" blocking the persistent expansion of per capita GNP in less-developed countries (LDC's).

Unfortunately the links between economic and demographic variables are not clear, especially with respect to LDC's. For example, cogent arguments may be presented both for and against the existence of a large population at a point in time. Favoring substantial populations are factors premised on economies of scale: the possibilities of broad product markets and specialized use of the agents of production. Arrayed against this imposing set of advantages are those counterarguments premised upon classical notions of diminishing returns in output past a certain (optimum) population. Because of its static nature, the resolution of this problem is primarily academic, and, in any event, economists have been unable even to formulate precisely the concept of an "optimum population."

More appropriate is the issue of the effect of the *rate* of population growth on economic development. The majority view (at least with respect to the LDC's) is that rapid population growth impedes economic growth. (We would add that governments able to generate sustained growth in GNP will also have achieved control over the adverse aspects of their specific population difficulties—wisdom in one area will imply wisdom in another.)

For instance, the age distribution within a given population is a significant factor in economic development. A "high" continued birth rate produces a population cross section with a substantial ratio of dependency, stemming from the number of young in the population. Obviously, since these persons are part of the denominator of total population in the reckoning of per capita GNP, then per capita product is reduced. More important is the likely impact on saving and investment of high dependency ratios. The support of a large dependent population implies increased consumption expenditures and a consequent reduction in savings. Further, the composition of investment actually carried out may likewise be affected by the proportion of dependents, since these persons would require educational and health services; to the extent that this occurs, investment will be diverted away from industrial uses.

Another issue faced by developing nations is the "population trap." [15] The trap is a suggested link between the rates of change of income and population in a developing economy, and is used to depict some of the problems faced by less-developed countries in achieving sustained growth in per capita income.

Briefly, developing economies are initially characterized in this analysis by low per capita income, and by almost equal rates of increase in population and product. Thus per capita income is almost constant over time. Next, it is assumed that per capita income increases, as from some sudden gain in exports relative to imports. The "population trap" problem is invoked when, as a result of higher incomes, new public health activities operate to lower mortality rates in the population, population rises, and the previous gain in per capita product is nullified. A proposed resolution of the problem of the trap is for the economy in question to achieve a rather dramatic gain in product, one which is more than sufficient to offset anticipated new population increases, so that increased per capita income is made stable.

Examination of the evidence concerning population and per capita growth in income is not conclusive, but does show that of a selection of less-devel-

[15] For a brief but illuminating discussion of the population trap, see Henry J. Bruton, *Principles of Development Economics* (Englewood Cliffs, N.J.: Prentice-Hall, Inc., 1965), Chapter 14.

TABLE II

*Comparison of Population Growth Rates with
Per Capita Income Growth Rates*

RATE OF POPULATION GROWTH (PER CENT PER YEAR)	RATE OF GROWTH OF REAL PER CAPITA INCOME (PER CENT PER YEAR)							
	TOTAL	LESS THAN ZERO	0 TO 0.9	1.0 TO 1.9	2.0 TO 2.9	3.0 TO 3.9	4.0 TO 4.9	5.0 AND OVER
Total	37	3	4	12	12	2	2	2
3.5 and over	2	1	0	0	0	0	1	0
3.0-3.4	10	0	2	3	4	0	1	0
2.5-2.9	11	1	2	5	1	1	0	1
2.0-2.4	8	0	0	3	5	0	0	0
1.5-1.9	4	1	0	0	2	1	0	0
Less than 1.5	2	0	0	1	0	0	0	1

NOTE: The above is a frequency distribution of developing nations by growth rate of real per capita income cross-classified by growth rate of population, 1957-58 to 1963-64. The countries included are non-Communist ones in Africa, Asia, and Latin America (omitting Israel, Japan, and the Union of South Africa) with populations of around two million or more, for which data were available. Richard A. Easterlin, "Effects of Population Growth on the Economic Development of Developing Countries," in *The Annals of the American Academy of Political and Social Science, World Population*, January 1967, p. 99.

oped countries, only three of thirty-seven have failed to show gains in real per capita income during a recent period. The data in Table II are instructive.

These data do not, as Easterlin points out, reflect significant association between population growth and per capita income growth in LDC's, albeit that the sample used is not comprehensive of LDC's and the period studied short.

Thus, at the risk of oversimplification, product and population were projected independently of each other in our estimates. In general, "high" GNP extrapolations were associated with high population estimates, for both LDC's and developed countries, and low with low. However, in the cases of China and India, the low GNP estimate was associated with high population in the computation of per capita product, and vice versa; this adjustment makes explicit a conclusion that the existence of a large population will work to reduce their level of aggregate product in these two countries.

B. WORLDWIDE PROJECTIONS

Most of the statistical material is divided into two sections: this section deals with worldwide comparisons and Section C is a more detailed projection for the United States alone. While interesting implications can be drawn from these projections, it is clear, as we have been emphasizing repeatedly, that the whole procedure of projection should be taken with several grains of salt. The indices chosen are mechanical and do not adequately reflect subtleties of national affluence, power, quality of life, or other important consequences one might want to infer from them. The growth rates are somewhat arbitrary and the projections from them may easily be wrong. The

FIGURE 6
POPULATION, GNP, AND GNP PER CAPITA BY CONTINENTS, 1965 AND 2000

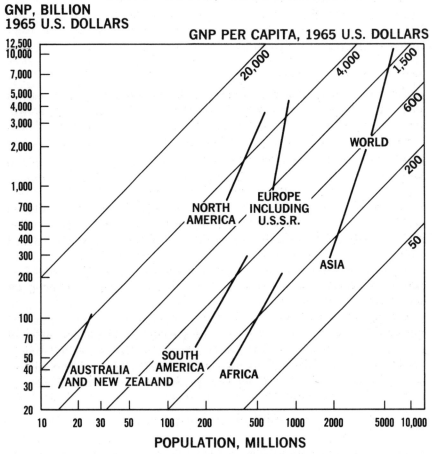

projections are useful to flesh out the Standard World by indicating what would happen *if* all the assumptions, including those on growth rates, were met. While this is an interesting possibility, it is still an unlikely one. Of course all other specific possibilities seem to be still more unlikely.

In the illustrations that follow, the figures for the year 2000 are simply extrapolations on the basis of the assumed rates which are ordinarily shown in the tables. We have usually shown a range of possibilities and selected some "best bet" from within the range; these are indicated by low, high, and medium projections. It should be repeated, however, that we do not really "expect" continuous rates or straight lines, and that wherever we have given some numbers as the "expected result" in the year 2000, that number should be read as representing merely some sort of "central tendency" in a wide distribution of expectations. Similarly the straight lines drawn on some of the figures (e.g., Figure 6) should be viewed as the axes of (rather fuzzy) conic sections and would have been drawn as such except for considerations of legibility.

1. *World and Continents*

Table III shows a year 2000 world population of 6.4 billion persons, 1.9 times the 1965 population of 3.3 billion. The average annual rate of growth implied by this increase is 1.9 per cent. The continents of Africa and South America show the highest population growth rates over the 1965-2000 period, both 2.7 per cent, but the bulk of population, 58 per cent, will continue to be Asian.

An estimate of the Gross National Product summed for all nations, that is, "Gross World Product," is presented in Table III.[16] Gross world product is estimated to increase in some perhaps vague sense by 5.1 times, rising from $2.1 trillion in 1965 to $10.9 trillion in 2000. This increase is the consequence of the fairly high growth rates assumed, averaging 4.8 per cent per year. If the average growth rate were reduced to 3 per cent, gross world product in 2000 would be $6.0 trillion, or only 55 per cent of that found by use of the 4.8 per cent rate.

Per capita world product in 1965 was about $630, about one-sixth of the United States figure. By the year 2000, per capita world product could be $1,700, within a range [17] of $880 to $2,200, depending on the growth rates used to project the GNP's of the individual countries. Thus per capita product could increase its 1965 amount by one-half or by almost four times, a substantial range of uncertainty but still within the dimensions of the Stan-

[16] For obvious reasons, we utterly ignore the incommensurables of the index number problem.

[17] To get this range, the percentages of the low and high projections of GNP per capita below and above the medium for the ten major countries of Table XIV were applied to the $1,700 medium projection here. These ten countries account for three-fifths of world population and three-fourths of world product.

TABLE III
Population, Continents [1]
(Millions)

	1965	1975	1985	2000	2020
Africa	310.7	398	520	779	1,320
Asia	1,889.0	2,343	2,863	3,701	5,100
Europe [2]	674.7	732	792	886	1,040
Oceania	14.0	16	20	25	35
North America	294.2	354	431	578	850
South America	166.2	221	291	420	680
World	3,348.8	4,064	4,917	6,389	9,025

GNP, Continents [1]
(Billion 1965 United States dollars)

	1965	1975	1985	2000	2020
Africa	43.9	69	109	216	537
Asia	287.4	501	883	2,137	7,317
Europe [2]	923.9	1,447	2,271	4,476	11,124
Oceania	28.0	41	60	107	232
North America	774.2	1,203	1,865	3,620	8,740
South America	59.4	91	144	292	761
World	2,116.8	3,352	5,332	10,848	28,711

GNP Per Capita, Continents [1]
(1965 U. S. Dollars)

	1965	1975	1985	2000	2020
Africa	141	174	209	277	407
Asia	152	214	308	577	1,436
Europe [2]	1,369	1,976	2,867	5,055	10,730
Oceania	2,000	2,510	3,080	4,310	6,600
North America	2,632	3,403	4,329	6,255	10,280
South America	357	413	496	695	1,112
World	632	825	1,085	1,700	3,180

[1] With minor omissions. For instance, Oceania is Australia plus New Zealand only, and Europe is European OECD plus Warsaw Pact.

[2] Includes all of U.S.S.R.

SOURCE: Regions and countries of Tables IX-XVII were combined with additional countries outside the tables.

TABLE IV

*Average Annual Rates of Growth of Population, Gross
National Product, and Per Capita GNP, by Continent, 1965-2000*

	POPULATION	GNP	PER CAPITA GNP
Africa	2.7	4.6	2.0
Asia	1.9	5.9	3.9
Europe	0.8	4.6	3.8
Oceania	1.7	3.9	2.2
North America	1.9	4.5	2.5
South America	2.7	4.6	1.9
World	1.8	4.8	2.9

dard Worlds. The distribution of world product by continent is projected to shift in favor of the developing countries, with Europe and North America reducing their relative shares 6 percentage points below 1965 (not shown in the table). This is due in part to the great importance of Japan which, by virtue of its location only, is included in the "developing" continent of Asia.

Asia is projected to achieve highest rates of growth in GNP and per capita GNP, but mainly because of the impressive growth of Japan's economy, coupled with that country's low population growth. Africa is expected to sustain a GNP growth of 4.6 per cent, but this continent will probably experience substantial population expansion. Thus, on a per capita GNP basis, Africa will achieve a relatively low rate of per capita growth, 2.0 per cent. South America is also anticipated to sustain considerable growth in population to year 2000, 2.7 per cent, and this expansion will limit that continent's per capita GNP growth to 1.9 per cent. The data of Tables III and IV are illustrated in Figure 6.

2. A Quantitative Scenario for the World in the Year 2020 [18]

World population in the twenty years ending in 2020 is assumed to grow about as fast as in 1965-2000, to reach 9.0 billion. Over half will live in Asia; only one-fifth will live in Europe and North America as compared with the present three-tenths. In the same period, Gross World Product will rise 5 per cent a year. The share of Asia will reach one-fourth of the total as

---

[18] Extrapolations to the year 2020 were originally made in response to a request from William R. Ewald, Jr., program chairman of the American Institute of Planners' forthcoming symposium "The Next Fifty Years 1967-2017." We would probably not have gone beyond the year 2000 on our own initiative. However, these calculations at least show the impact that twenty more years of cumulative growth at constant rates would have; that such growth would continue without surprises of some sort causing changes becomes more and more doubtful as projections are made to increasingly distant and unpredictable periods.

compared with the present one-eighth share, largely because of the 7.5 per cent GNP growth rate assumed for Japan.

Per capita world output will nearly double in the twenty years ending in 2020, reaching then about five times the world 1965 figure. Japan leads with $33 thousand (compared with only $3.6 thousand for the United States in 1965) (Table XIV, below). The United States and West Germany follow with $19 and $18 thousand, respectively. As in the year 2000, the Soviet Union, with $9.7 thousand, trails the major developed countries.

Presumably, an even greater range of uncertainty pervades the long-range projections for the last two major but less-developed countries, mainland China and India. The area of per capita GNP possibilities is so broad, especially in the case of China, that specific projections become unusually arbitrary. Thus, at best, according to Table XIV, China would exceed only the Soviet Union, and that only if the Soviet Union performs at its low growth rate.

3. The Dichotomized Standard World

As is suggested above, gross world product rises from $2.1 trillion in 1965 to $10.9 trillion in year 2000, with an accompanying increase in world population from 3.4 billion to 6.4 billion. Thus world per capita GNP is projected to rise from about $670 to $1,700 from 1965 to 2000. This increase represents an approximate tripling of per capita GNP and implies a per capita world growth rate of about 3 per cent.

Obviously this growth rate represents a range of disparate rates achieved by various nations and continents. We have assumed that foreign aid programs, tariff agreements, trade patterns, international economic institutions, and the like continue much as they are. As disparities among nations increase, however, changes in these transfers of goods and capital might take place in ways that would affect the relative rates. One such scenario is given in the "Aid-Oriented, More-Integrated World," in Chapter VI, Section A-2.

The disparity in economic performance between the developed and less-developed worlds can be shown by recasting data in Table III into a "Dichotomized Standard World." Most simply, though not most dramatically,[19] this may be done by removing Japan from Asia and including it as part of the industrially developed world of the "Atlantic" West. Then, North America, Oceania, Europe, and Japan may be compared to the remainder of the world—South America, Asia, and Africa.

In 1965 the Less-Developed World, as defined above, contained about 68 per cent of the world population, but produced only 14.5 per cent of its output. By year 2000 the less-developed world will contain three-quarters

[19] The contrast could have been heightened by removing countries such as Albania, Portugal, Mexico, and Central America to the less-developed world, and Venezuela, Argentina, Israel, the Union of South Africa, and some others to the developed.

of world population and will account for about the same proportion of world product as it did in 1965.[20] The growth in output in the less-developed world will exceed population growth, so that there will be an increase in per capita GNP, from $135 to $325 per year, a rate of real growth of 2.8 per cent over the 1965-2000 period.

However, the industrialized continents, plus Japan, will perform remarkably better, with a projected gain in per capita GNP from $1,675 to $5,775, implying an annual growth of about 3.6 per cent in per capita GNP.

Thus, at the beginning of the period, 1965, the per capita product of the industrial world exceeded that of the less developed nations by a factor of about twelve times. By the year 2000 this factor will approach a difference of eighteen times; this means that the "gap" in the dichotomized world will increase by 50 per cent in favor of the developed world by year 2000. At the same time, as we pointed out in Chapter I, the less-developed world is undergoing the disruptions of early industrialization, urbanization, and the rest of the multifold trend, and experiencing simultaneously the awakening of expectations that follows significant economic progress. Whether satisfaction in their absolute progress or envy and resentment of increasing discrepancies between rich and poor will be the dominant reaction of the people of the less-developed world depends, of course, on many economic,

TABLE V
The Dichotomized Standard World
Population
(Millions)

LESS-DEVELOPED WORLD	1965	2000
Africa	310.7	779.0
Asia less Japan	1,791.0	3,578.0
South America	166.2	420.0
Total	2,267.9	4,777.0
DEVELOPED WORLD		
Japan [1]	98.0	123.0
North America	294.2	578.0
Oceania	14.0	25.0
Europe	674.7	886.0
Total	1,080.9	1,612.0
World Total	3,348.8	6,389.0

[1] Japan is taken at its presumed intermediate population growth rate, Table XII.

[20] But as indicated in Table XXII in Chapter I, such countries with about four billion population may be partly developed—at least by 1965 standards.

political, and cultural factors. While the improvement in living standards from those of their parents will be clear to many people, the increasing discrepancies between their lives and those of the industrialized societies will be brought inescapably to the attention of even the most primitive and isolated communities by cheap and improved worldwide communication and transportation.

Tables V-VIII and Figures 7-11 summarize these developments. (Data for these figures come in part from Tables III, XII, and XIII.)

TABLE VI
The Dichotomized Standard World

GNP
(Billions of 1965 U.S. Dollars)

LESS-DEVELOPED WORLD	1965	2000
Africa	43.9	216.0
Asia less Japan	203.4	1,081.0
South America	59.4	292.0
Total	306.7	1,589.0
DEVELOPED WORLD		
Japan [1]	84.0	1,056.0
North America	774.2	3,620.0
Oceania	28.0	107.0
Europe	923.9	4,476.0
Total	1,810.1	9,259.0
World Total	2,116.8	10,848.0

[1] Japan is taken at its intermediate growth rate, Table XIII.

TABLE VII
The Dichotomized Standard World

Per Capita GNP
(1965 U.S. Dollars)

	1965	2000
Less-Developed World	135	325
Developed World	1,675	5,775
World Total	631	1,696

FIGURE 7

THE DICHOTOMIZED STANDARD WORLD
POPULATION (MILLIONS)

Year 1965

Year 2000

Less Developed World

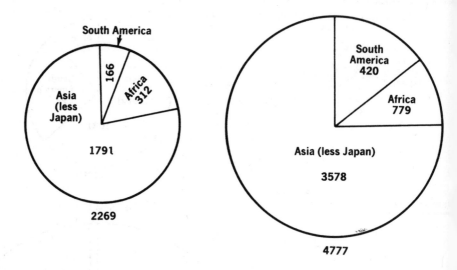

Developed World

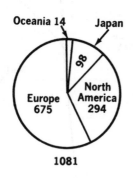

FIGURE 8

THE DICHOTOMIZED STANDARD WORLD
GNP
(BILLIONS OF 1965 U.S. DOLLARS)

ar 1965   Year 2000

ss Developed World

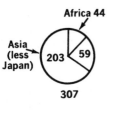

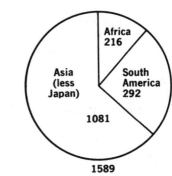

eloped World

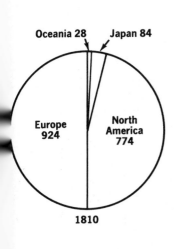

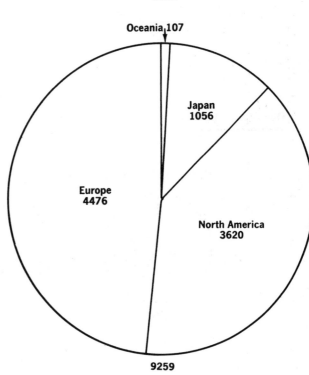

FIGURE 9

POPULATION, GNP, GNP PER CAPITA,
THE DICHOTOMIZED STANDARD WORLD 1965-2000

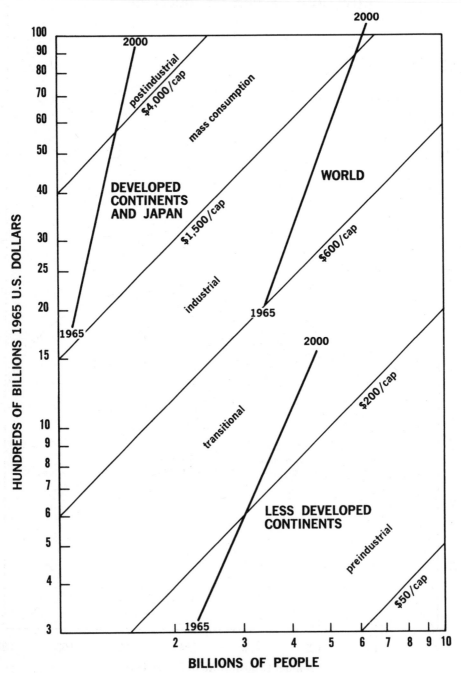

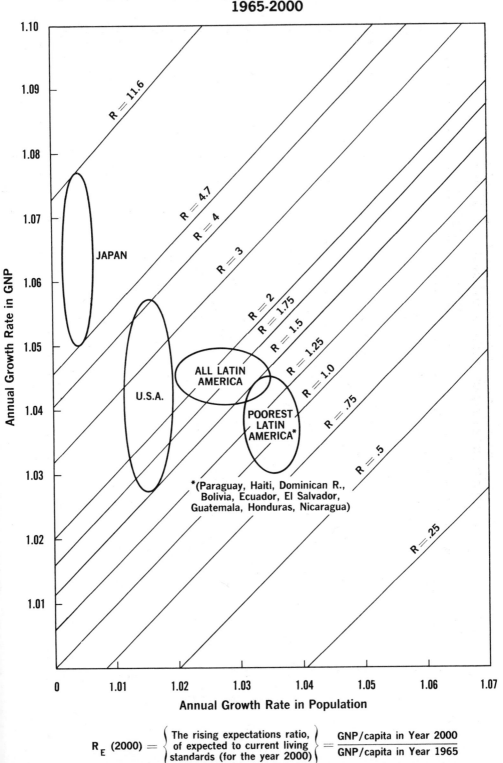

FIGURE 10
THE RISING EXPECTATIONS RATIO:
LIKELY IMPROVEMENTS IN LIVING STANDARDS
1965-2000

$$R_E\ (2000) = \left\{ \begin{array}{l} \text{The rising expectations ratio,} \\ \text{of expected to current living} \\ \text{standards (for the year 2000)} \end{array} \right\} = \frac{\text{GNP/capita in Year 2000}}{\text{GNP/capita in Year 1965}}$$

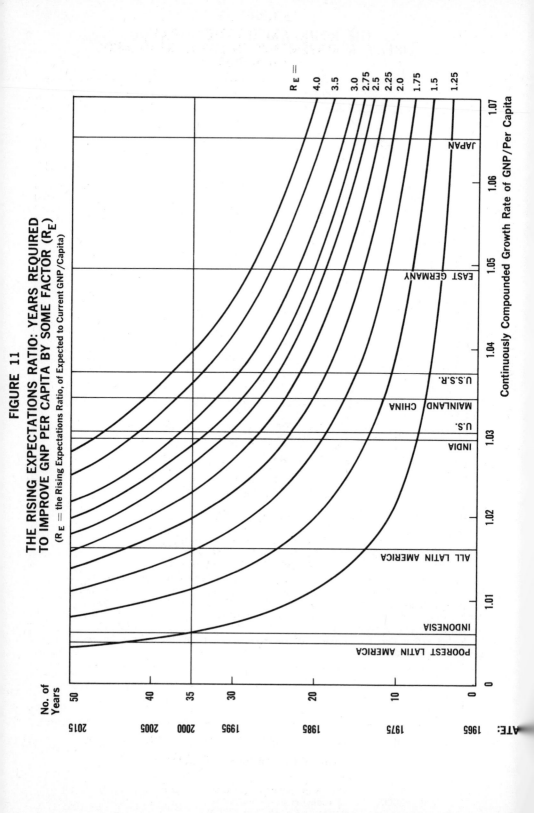

FIGURE 11

THE RISING EXPECTATIONS RATIO: YEARS REQUIRED
TO IMPROVE GNP PER CAPITA BY SOME FACTOR (R_E)

(R_E = the Rising Expectations Ratio, of Expected to Current GNP/Capita)

TABLE VIII
Years Needed to Achieve Current U.S. GNP Per Capita

	1965 GNP PER CAPITA (1965 U.S. $)	NUMBER OF YEARS NEEDED TO REACH $3,600 PER CAPITA [1]
Sweden	$2497	11
Canada	2464	12
West Germany	1905	16
East Germany	1574	17
France	1924	18
United Kingdom	1804	19
Czechoslovakia	1554	20
Japan	857	22
Israel	1334	24
Australia	2009	25
U.S.S.R.	1288	28
Italy	1101	30
Poland	962	34
Romania	757	38
New Zealand	1932	42
Argentina	492	69
Taiwan	221	71
U.A.R.	166	97
Thailand	126	98
China	98	101
S. Africa and S. W. Africa	503	115
India	99	117
Brazil	280	130
Pakistan	91	144
Mexico	455	162
Nigeria	83	339
Colombia	277	358
Indonesia	99	593

[1] The number of years needed to reach $3,600 per capita was calculated on the basis of the 1965 GNP for each country and the "medium" rate we projected for growth of population and GNP. (See Tables XIV and XVII.) The "numbers of years needed" is thus simply a way of looking at the *rate* at which the country's GNP per capita seems likely to approach the current U.S. level in the "standard world"; obviously, to the extent that the "number of years" is large, many factors can be expected to change in the interim.

4. *World Population in 2000*

If substantial population growth is considered as dating from the Agricultural Revolution,[21] then the year 2000 will be the ten thousandth anni-
versary of this phenomenon, which can be summarized simplistically as
follows. From the Agricultural Revolution to the present, world population
has increased from an estimated 10 million [22] in 8000 B.C. to 3.3 billion in
1965, for an average *millennial* rate of growth of about 80 per cent. However, Figure 12 shows that this span divides significantly at about the year
A.D. 1650, the beginning of the modern era. From 8000 B.C. to A.D. 1650,
world population grew at a rate of 50 per cent each thousand years. But,
from 1650 to 1965, the rate of millennial increase was 2,000 per cent. Thus
the rate of population growth per thousand years is 40 times greater in the
modern age than the premodern. (The projection from 1965 to year 2000

[21] "The first great landmark of human history was the development of food production which permitted an enormous multiplication of human numbers, and laid the
basis for the emergence of civilizations. How, when and where hunting and gather-
ing gave way to farming and pastoralism is uncertain. One of the earliest and most
important instances of this transition took place in the Middle East, perhaps between
8500 and 7000 B.C." From W. H. McNeill, *A World History* (New York: Oxford
University Press, 1967), p. 1.
[22] World population: 8000 B.C., 10 million; beginning of Christian Era, 200 to 300
million; A.D. 1650, 500 million. Source: P. M. Hauser, "World Population Problems,"
Headline Series, Foreign Policy Association, No. 174, December 1965.

FIGURE 12
WORLD POPULATION
8000 B.C. – YEAR 2000

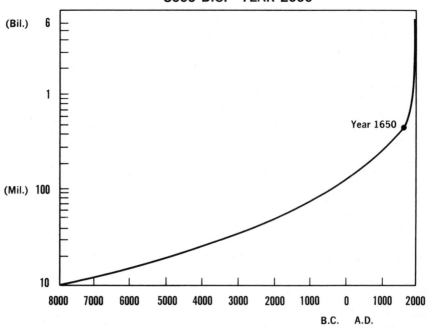

implies almost doubling of world population in 35 years. If the *rate* of increase were to stabilize at the estimated 1965-2000 level, the next thousand-year increase would be 5,600 per cent, for a total of 358 billion, an obvious impossibility.) At some point in the next *few* centuries, presumably population itself would have to stabilize, perhaps at a level somewhere between 10 and 50 billion—though this is extremely uncertain and depends on unknown factors such as food technology.[23]

5. Population and GNP by Region

Forecasts like those shown earlier for continents appear in Tables IX-XI for United Nations regions, for economic and military blocs, and for areas set off by race or culture.

According to the United Nations estimates, which we follow, population growth slows down over the period, even where growth is already slow,

[23] It has been estimated that population will stabilize by about the year 2000, on the basis of the argument that the rate of growth of world population began to drop in 1965, and will continue to do so. See D. J. Bogue, "The End of the Population Explosion," *The Public Interest*, No. 7, Spring 1967. See also our discussion on pp. 363-64.

TABLE IX

Population and Population Growth Rates, Regional Projections
(Millions)

	1965	GROWTH RATE PER CENT	1975	GROWTH RATE PER CENT	1985	GROWTH RATE PER CENT	2000	2020
1. Latin America	233	2.9	313	2.8	417	2.6	615	1,020
2. Middle South Asia, East Asia less Mainland China	820	2.3	1,034	2.2	1,286	1.7	1,666	2,210
3. Southeast Asia	247	2.6	318	2.6	409	2.6	598	1,010
4. Middle East and North Africa	141	2.9	187	2.8	248	2.5	357	580
5. Black Africa	212	2.4	267	2.6	346	2.8	524	910
6. OECD	686	1.0	756	1.0	833	0.9	958	1,160
7. European Members of OECD	342	0.6	362	0.5	379	0.4	403	440
8. WEU	236	0.6	250	0.5	262	0.4	278	300
9. EEC	182	0.7	194	0.5	204	0.5	219	240
10. EFTA	98	0.4	102	0.3	104	0.3	108	115
11. Scandinavia	21	0.6	22	0.3	23	0.4	24	26
12. Warsaw Pact	333	1.1	370	1.1	413	1.0	482	600
13. Eastern Europe	100	0.7	108	0.6	115	0.6	126	140

Line   Composition of region
1   Independent countries formerly ruled by Spain or Portugal.
2   Afghanistan, Bhutan, Ceylon, India, Iran, Maldive Is., Nepal, Pakistan, and Sikkim; Hong Kong, Japan, N. Korea, S. Korea, Macao, Mongolia, Ryukyu Is., and Taiwan.
3   Brunei, Burma, Cambodia, Indonesia, Laos, Malaysia, the Philippines, Portuguese Timor, Thailand, N. Vietnam, S. Vietnam.
4   All Arab states, Cyprus, Israel, and Turkey.
5   Africa south of the Sahara except Rhodesia, South Africa, and Southwest Africa.
6   European OECD, Canada, Japan, Turkey, and U.S.
7   EEC, EFTA, Greece, Iceland, Ireland, Spain, and Yugoslavia.
8   EEC plus U.K.
9   Belgium, France, W. Germany, W. Berlin, Italy, Luxembourg, and the Netherlands.
10   Austria, Denmark, Finland, Norway, Portugal, Sweden, Switzerland, and U.K.
11   Denmark, Finland, Iceland, Norway, and Sweden.
12   Eastern Europe, Albania, and U.S.S.R.
13   Bulgaria, Czechoslovakia, E. Germany, Hungary, Poland, and Romania.

SOURCES:
1965: Tables XII and XV were used for the twenty-nine countries here shown. Bhutan: same source as Pakistan in Table XV. Spanish N. Africa: 1965 forecast in U.N., *World Population Prospects,* 1966, p. 143. All other countries: copied or estimated from U.N., *Monthly Bulletin of Statistics,* various issues, and *World Almanac,* 1963 and 1966.

Growth rates: calculated from population.

1975, 1985, and 2000: Latin America and Black Africa (lines 1 and 5). Medium forecasts for U.N. regions, copied from U.N. *Provisional Report,* 1964, and interpolated to 1985, were combined with those for individual countries. The region forecasts had been adjusted by the U.N. to a uniform assumption about international migration. The country forecasts for 1965-80 were copied from the same source and adjusted to add to the adjusted total for their regions as described for India in Table XII. They were extended to 1985 and 2000 as described for W. Germany in that table. The combined total for the region as defined here was multiplied by the 1965 ratio of actual population to adjusted forecast.

Asia and North Africa (lines 2-4): these regions are coextensive with U.N. regions, so no country forecasts were involved.

OECD and Europe (lines 6-13): combinations of country forecasts, each of which had been corrected for the discrepancy between 1965 actual and forecast. Eight countries are taken from Table XII. For the rest, European forecasts were obtained mostly as for W. Germany in that table, other forecasts as for Canada. E. Germany and W. Berlin were given arbitrary adjustments because populations were declining and stationary 1960-65.

2020: Middle East and North Africa; Black Africa: 1985-2000 growth rate was continued. Other regions: figures for countries in Tables XII and XV were added to similar projections for remaining countries.

---

as for the European OECD (from 0.6 per cent in 1965-75 to 0.4 per cent in 1985-2000). However, the largest area, Middle South Asia and East Asia less mainland China (consisting mostly of India and Pakistan), reduces its growth rate only from 2.3 per cent to 1.7 per cent, and this is the greatest reduction to be achieved by any region. Southeast Asia (about

TABLE X

Regional GNP Projections
(Billion 1965 U.S. Dollars)

	1965	GROWTH RATE PER CENT	1975	GROWTH RATE PER CENT	1985	GROWTH RATE PER CENT 1985-2000	2000	2020
1. Latin America	86.6	4.2	131	4.4	202	4.6	396	973
2. Middle South Asia, East Asia less Mainland China	162.5	6.3	300	6.5	562	6.7	1,481	5,600
3. Southeast Asia	29.2	4.4	45	4.1	67	4.4	128	316
4. Middle East and North Africa	35.2	5.0	57	5.0	93	5.0	194	515
5. Black Africa	20.1	4.5	31	4.5	48	4.5	94	226
6. OECD	1,348.2	4.6	2,122	4.7	3,363	4.8	6,823	18,250
7. European Members of OECD	514.8	4.3	781	4.3	1,186	4.3	2,221	5,139
8. WEU	398.4	4.3	608	4.3	929	4.3	1,759	4,130
9. EEC	299.9	4.4	463	4.4	715	4.4	1,373	3,280
10. EFTA	169.8	4.0	251	4.0	372	4.0	670	1,470
11. Scandinavia	44.8	4.0	66	4.0	98	4.0	177	390
12. Warsaw Pact	409.1	5.0	666	5.0	1,085	5.0	2,256	5,985
13. East Europe	111.3	5.0	181	5.0	295	5.0	614	1,629

NOTE: Composition of regions appears in Table IX.

SOURCES:

1965: the countries of Tables XIII and XVI are combined with unlisted countries. GNP for unlisted countries is computed from the same sources as were used for the listed ones, plus U.S. Arms Control and Disarmament Agency, *World-Wide Defense Expenditures and Selected Economic Data,* Calendar Year 1964, research report 66-1, January 1966, Table I (reprinted in *Bulletin of the Atomic Scientists,* September 1966). Missing countries are assigned the per capita GNP of the rest of their region.

1975-2020: regions 1-3, 6-7, 9-11. Countries from Tables XIII and XVI above and regions here are combined with unlisted countries. Unlisted countries are assumed to grow at the following rates, according to region:

REGION	GROWTH RATE
1	4.0 per cent 1965-75, 4.5 per cent 1975-85, and 5.0 per cent thereafter
2, 3	4.5
6	5.0
7, 9-11	4.0

Regional growth rates are computed from regional GNP.

Regions 4, 5, 12, 13: projected from 1965 at indicated growth rates. Year 2020 figures use 1985-2000 growth rates.

half of it Indonesia and Thailand) will not slow at all and Black Africa will accelerate.

Population may grow faster in the Warsaw Pact area and in East Europe than shown here because the forecasts antedate the recent relaxation of political and economic controls.

Our GNP growth rates (region 4 and 5 excepted) reflect the rates already chosen for component countries below. The apparent speeding up of growth in the OECD and in Middle South Asia and East Asia less mainland China is accounted for by the increasing weight of Japan with its assumed 7.5 per cent medium growth rate. Japan accounts for only half the GNP of the latter region now, but two-thirds of the region's projection to year 2000. The Warsaw Pact countries will pass ahead of the European OECD in economic power, as measured by total GNP, sometime between 1985 and 2000.

Scandinavia is now best off of any region in terms of per capita GNP, followed in the developed world by the other European groupings and then, with a precipitous drop, by Latin America and the areas in Asia and Africa. The comparisons, however, understate true levels of well-being of non-

TABLE XI
GNP Per Capita, Regional Projections
(1965 U.S. Dollars)

	1965	1975	1985	2000
Scandinavia	2,130	2,982	4,281	7,264
OECD	1,966	2,808	4,039	7,120
EFTA	1,736	2,474	3,571	6,187
WEU	1,687	2,428	3,550	6,316
EEC	1,651	2,388	3,503	6,269
European Members of OECD	1,504	2,156	3,129	5,506
Warsaw Pact	1,230	1,800	2,626	4,679
East Europe	1,112	1,687	2,568	4,865
Latin America	371	419	485	643
Middle East and North Africa	249	306	376	543
Middle South Asia, East Asia less Mainland China	198	290	437	889
Southeast Asia	118	141	164	215
Black Africa	95	117	140	179

SOURCE: Regional GNP projections were divided by regional population projections.

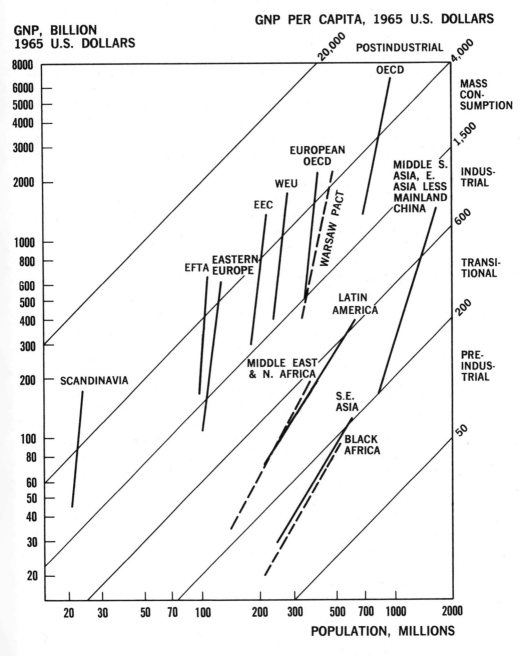

FIGURE 13

**POPULATION, GNP, AND GNP PER CAPITA BY REGIONS
1965 AND 2000**

Communist areas because their currencies are converted to dollars by market rates of exchange. The use of an exchange rate computed from the internal purchasing power of each country's currency compared with that of the United States dollar would give a better comparison; it would also give a higher GNP in United States dollars for the foreign country. The use of market rates of exchange is said to understate the GNP of Canada by 8 per cent, of Western Europe by 13 per cent, of Japan by 36 per cent (another source says 76 per cent) and of the less-developed world by perhaps 20 per cent, as compared with what they would be using purchasing power rates of exchange.[24] The same percentages would hold for GNP per capita. Purchasing power exchange rates are used for Communist countries, so the Warsaw Pact and East Europe groupings are not understated in this way.

The year 2000 GNP per capita projections show less dispersion, proportionately, among developed regions than do the 1965 figures, but more between developed and less-developed (as explained above in section 3). Middle South Asia and East Asia less Mainland China quadruples its per capita GNP to 2000, again because of the increasing weight for Japan with its high GNP growth rate.

Figure 13, like Figure 7 for continents earlier, connects the 1965 and year 2000 population and GNP figures. As to GNP per capita, the less-developed regions, except Black Africa, enter the transitional ($200) and industrial ($600) stages, while the European regions pass beyond $4000 per capita into the post-industrial stage.

6. Population and GNP, Ten Major Countries

Eight of the ten major countries are shown in Table XII as slowing down their population growth between 1965-75 and 1985-2000. The most striking and important cases are China, which slows from 1.8 per cent to 1.3 per cent—indeed, the United Nations estimates that China's growth began to taper off between 1950-60 and 1960-70 [25]—and India, which slows from 2.4 per cent to 1.8 per cent (no sign of this will be visible on the medium projection until after 1980).

The United States and Canada are expected to speed up their population growth slightly on the medium projections.

Comparison of the medium growth rates of GNP, as shown in Table XIII, shows the United States to be almost twice as large in GNP in the year 2000 as the next nation, the Soviet Union. Close to the Soviet Union is Japan, which is assumed to maintain a 7.5 per cent rate of growth of GNP

[24] U.S. State Department, Bureau of Intelligence and Research, *Indicators of Comparative East-West Economic Strength*, 1965, Research Memo. REV 69, October 11, 1966, Table 1, and an unpublished U.S. Government source.

[25] U.N. Department of Economic and Social Affairs. *World Population Prospects as Assessed in 1963*, Population Studies No. 41 (New York, 1966), p. 145.

TABLE XII
Population and Population Growth Rates, Ten Major Countries
(Millions)

	1965	RATES	1975	RATES	1985	RATES 1985-2000	2000	2020
China	700	1.3	793	1.0	872	.9	992	1160
	755	1.8	903	1.5	1052	1.3	1271	1610
	800	2.3	1004	2.1	1240	1.7	1600	2400
India	487	2.2	604	1.9	727	1.5	914	1170
		2.4	616	2.1	761	1.8	988	1280
		2.5	622	2.5	794	2.4	1128	1700
U.S.S.R.	231	1.0	255	1.0	282	.9	316	360
		1.3	260	1.3	296	1.2	352	450
		1.6	273	1.6	320	1.5	402	540
U.S.	195	1.2	219	1.2	246	1.1	290	370
		1.3	222	1.5	256	1.5	318	420
		1.7	230	1.7	274	1.9	362	500
Japan	98	.6	104	.6	111	.3	116	120
		.8	107	.8	116	.4	123	135
		1.1	110	1.1	123	.8	139	165
W. Germany	59	.2	60	.2	61	.0	61	61
(including		.4	61	.4	64	.3	67	72
W. Berlin)		.5	62	.5	65	.5	70	78
U.K.	55	.1	55	.0	55	.0	55	55
		.3	57	.2	58	.2	60	63
		.5	57	.4	60	.5	64	71
Italy	52	.3	53	.1	54	.1	55	57
		.5	54	.3	56	.4	60	65
		.6	55	.4	57	.6	62	70
France	49	.8	53	.5	56	.4	59	64
		1.0	54	.7	58	.7	64	74
		1.1	55	.8	59	.9	68	81
Canada	20	1.7	23	1.6	27	1.6	34	46
		1.8	23	1.9	28	2.0	38	56
		2.2	24	2.1	30	2.4	43	68

SOURCES:

1965

China: medium estimate—U.S. State Department, Bureau of Intelligence and Research, *Indicators of East-West Economic Strength,* 1965 (Research Memo. REV-69, October 11, 1966), Table I. Low estimate—partly allows for a possible 5-15 per cent undercount in the 1953 census. G. E. Pearce, "Mainland China—Geographic Strengths and Weaknesses," *Department of State Bulletin,* August 29, 1966, p. 298. High estimate—exceeds the medium by roughly the margin for the U.N. estimates. U.N., Department of Economic and Social Affairs, *World Population Prospects as Assessed in 1963,* Population Studies No. 41 (New York, 1966), p. 57.

Other Countries: copied or estimated from U.N., *Monthly Bulletin of Statistics,* plus, for India, U.N., *Demographic Yearbook,* 1965, pp. 135-137. India includes Sikkim and Indian-occupied Kashmir-Jammu.

Growth Rates:

China: the overall growth rates implicit in the U.N.'s year 2000 forecasts. U.N., *Provisional Report on World Population Prospects as Assessed in 1963,* ST/SOA/SER.R/7 (New York, 1964), p. 96, were raised 0.2 to 0.4 percentage point on the basis of the U.S. Census Bureau's study (see Pearce, "Mainland China"), which shows a faster growth 1953-65 than the U.N.'s medium estimate. Growth rates to 1975 and 1985 were calculated from population.

India, U.S.S.R., U.S., Japan: calculated from population.

West Germany, U.K., Italy, and France: medium rates were calculated from population. The differences H-M and M-L were computed for N. Europe and W. Europe from U.N., *World Population Prospects,* 1966, pp. 134-136 and were applied to the medium rates for the countries in the region.

Canada: the differences H-M and M-L for U.S. growth rates were applied to medium rates calculated from population.

1975, 1985, and 2000

China: the year 2000 was calculated from the assumed overall growth rates (above) and 1975 and 1985 were interpolated from U.N., *Provisional Report,* 1964, p. 96.

India: medium forecasts for India and Pakistan 1965-2000 were copied from *World Population Prospects,* 1966, p. 67, and adjusted so that with other countries of Middle South Asia (to 1980 from Table A3.8, extrapolated graphically 1980 on) they would add to the U.N. adjusted forecast for the region (Table A3.2). (The U.N.'s regional adjustment reconciles the conflicting migration assumptions of the national forecasts, but is shown only for each region as a whole and not by countries.) For this, the change in the adjusted forecast for the region for each short period was divided among the countries in proportion to the changes over the period in the unadjusted individual country forecasts. The 1965, 1975, 1985, and 2000 forecasts were now multiplied by the ratio of actual population to adjusted forecast for 1965. The U.N.'s high and low forecasts were adjusted equally with the medium.

U.S.S.R. and Japan: U.N. medium forecasts were interpolated to 1985 and multiplied by the ratio of 1965 actual to forecast. Highs and lows were adjusted equally with the medium.

U.S.: the U.N.'s medium forecasts from *Provisional Report,* 1964, were adjusted to add with Canada and other areas to the regional total as described for India. Tentative extensions were made to 1985 and 2000 using *Statistical Abstract of the U.S.,* 1965, p. 6. Medium was taken as two-thirds of the way from the B to the C projection. The extensions were adjusted so that with like extensions for the other areas they would add to the U.N. adjusted forecasts for the region (1985 for the region was interpolated). Here the changes in the adjusted regional forecast 1980-85 and 1980-2000 were divided among the countries in proportion to the changes from the 1980 adjusted forecast to the 1985 and 2000 extensions. The resulting forecasts were multiplied by the 1965 ratio of actual to adjusted forecast.

West Germany, U.K., Italy, and France: medium forecasts to 1980 were adjusted as for India and the U.S. Forecasts to 1985 and 2000 were extrapolated graphically and adjusted as for the U.S. The U.N. figures have been adjusted to allow for a tapering-off of the unforeseen migration 1960-65.

Canada: same as for India and the U.S.

2020

U.S.: medium projection rounded from Table XIX below; high projection assumed to grow 1.6 per cent.

All other projections: figures for 2000 were extended graphically.

TABLE XIII

GNP, Ten Major Countries
(Billion 1965 U.S. Dollars)

	GROWTH RATES	1965	1975	GNP 1985	2000	2020
United States	2.0	692.3 [2]	844	1,028	1,384	2,060
	4.5		1,075	1,669	3,231	7,790
	5.5		1,183	2,020	4,510	13,200
U.S.S.R.	2.0	297.0	362	441	594	883
	5.0		484	788	1,640	4,350
	7.0		584	1,150	3,170	12,300
West Germany	3.0	112.4	151	203	316	571
(including	4.5		175	271	525	1,260
W. Berlin)	5.5		192	328	732	2,140
United Kingdom	2.0	98.5 [2]	120	146	197	293
	4.0		146	216	389	852
	5.0		160	261	543	1,440
France	3.0	94.1	126	170	265	480
	4.5		146	227	439	1,060
	5.5		161	275	613	1,790
Japan	5.0	84.0	137	223	463	1,230
	7.5		173	356	1,056	4,480
	9.0 & 7.5 [1]		199	471	1,393	5,920
China	3.0	60.0	83	113	169	305
	5.0	74.0	121	196	408	1,080
	7.0	90.0	177	348	961	3,720
Italy	3.0	56.8	77	103	160	290
	4.5		88	137	265	639
	5.5		97	166	370	1,080
Canada	3.0	48.3	65	87	136	245
	5.0		79	128	266	707
	6.0		86	155	371	1,190
India	2.0	48.3	59	72	97	134
	5.0		79	128	266	707
	6.0		86	155	371	1,190

[1] Declining population growth rate after 1985 should cause a reduction in maximum GNP growth rate from 9.0 (for 1965-85) to 7.5 per cent.

[2] United Nations definition—see source note below.

NOTE: The 1975 and 1985 lower forecasts for U.K., China, and India have been adjusted to provide a constant rate of change in GNP per capita.

SOURCES:
1965

U.S., W. Germany, France, U.K., Japan, Italy, and Canada: gross national product at market prices times average of year-end exchange rates from U.N., *Monthly Bul-*

letin of Statistics. On their own systems of national accounts, figure for U.S. is $675 billion and for U.K. $87 billion.

U.S.S.R. and China: U. S. State Department, *Indicators of East-West Economic Strength,* 1965, Table I.

India: GNP from U.S. Agency for International Development, *Estimates of Gross National Product: Summary for Non-Communist Countries,* 1965, reports control No. 137, February 6, 1967, was converted to calendar year 1965 rupees by using an implicit price index extrapolated from the cost of living and back to 1965 U.S. dollars by an average of year-end exchange rates (U.N., *Monthly Bulletin of Statistics*).

throughout. West Germany, France, the United Kingdom, and Communist China follow well behind.

In terms of medium projections of per capita GNP, the United States and Japan lead and the Soviet Union, Italy, mainland China, and India trail. Between 1965 and 2000, Japan moves from eighth to second place and West Germany from fourth to third place (Table XIV).

We have already illustrated the projections for the ten major countries in Chapter I, Figure 1.

In these comparisons one should bear in mind the tendency of market rates of exchange to understate the per capita GNP of non-Communist countries, particularly Japan (see discussion of regions, above).

7. Population and GNP, Nineteen Contender Countries

The account of population for the nineteen contender countries (Table XV) resembles that for the majors. In the less-developed world (Section 3 above) Pakistan, Indonesia, Brazil, Mexico, Thailand, the United Arab Republic, Argentina, Taiwan, and Israel are all forecast to reduce their population growth rates between 1965-75 and 1985-2000, but only the last three are estimated, like China, to be doing so between 1950-60 and 1960-70. Nigeria's rate, like Black Africa's above, is projected to rise, though events since the forecast have rendered this less certain. East Germany, the slowest-growing of all majors and contenders, is to be growing only one-fifth of a per cent a year by 1985-2000; however, as pointed out above in Section 5, a relaxation of controls may change this.

Medium growth rates for GNP range from 3 per cent for Indonesia to 6 per cent for the United Arab Republic, Thailand, Israel, and Taiwan (Table XVI). The 1965 GNP of Argentina, shown as $11 billion in the source used here, is shown by A.I.D. as $16 billion.[26] The difference may lie in the exchange rate used.

Sweden has the highest per capita GNP in 2000 as now (Table XVII and Figure 14), exceeding also all the ten major countries but the United

---

[26] U.S., Agency for International Development, *Estimates of Gross National Product,* reports control no. 137, 1965 (February 6, 1967).

TABLE XIV

GNP Per Capita, Ten Major Countries
(1965 U.S. Dollars)

	1965	1975	1985	2000	2020
United States	3,557	3,860	4,180	4,760	5,560
		4,850	6,510	10,160	18,600
		5,140	7,380	12,480	26,300
Canada	2,464	2,800	3,240	4,040	5,330
		3,360	4,550	7,070	12,600
		3,550	5,160	8,670	17,500
France	1,924	2,380	3,050	4,480	7,470
		2,710	3,920	6,830	14,300
		2,950	4,660	9,070	22,100
West Germany	1,905	2,510	3,310	5,150	9,360
(including		2,850	4,230	7,790	17,600
W. Berlin)		3,100	5,030	10,410	27,400
United Kingdom	1,804	2,180	2,650	3,570	5,320
		2,580	3,750	6,530	13,500
		2,790	4,380	8,440	20,300
U.S.S.R.	1,288	1,410	1,560	1,880	2,450
		1,850	2,660	4,650	9,660
		2,130	3,590	7,890	22,700
Italy	1,101	1,450	1,920	2,940	5,070
		1,620	2,440	4,450	9,830
		1,770	2,910	5,930	15,400
Japan	857	1,310	2,010	3,990	10,200
		1,620	3,080	8,590	33,200
		1,810	3,820	10,000	35,900
India	99	95	91	86	79
		128	169	270	552
		143	216	406	1,020
China	75	82	91	106	127
	98	134	186	321	681
	129	223	399	969	3,210

SOURCE: Low GNP was divided by low population, high GNP by high population, except for China and India where low was divided by high and high by low. For these two less-developed countries it was assumed that the magnitude of their population worked against economic growth rather than in favor of economic growth, as in the case of the developed nations. The low forecasts for the U.K., China, and India in 1975 and 1985 were adjusted to make a constant rate of growth in per capita GNP.

TABLE XV

Population and Population Growth Rates, Nineteen Contender Countries
(Millions)

	1965	RATE	1975	RATE	1985	RATE 1985-2000	2000	2020
Pakistan	115.0	3.2	157.2	2.9	209.0	2.2	287.7	410
Indonesia	105.0	2.6	131.0	2.4	168.0	2.4	239.0	380
Brazil	82.2	3.1	112.0	2.9	149.4	2.4	212.1	330
Nigeria	57.5	3.1	78.4	3.2	107.7	3.3	176.4	340
Mexico	42.7	3.4	59.8	3.4	83.9	3.1	133.2	250
Poland	31.5	1.1	35.3	1.1	39.1	1.0	45.4	55
Thailand	30.6	2.9	40.7	2.6	51.9	2.4	73.5	120
U.A.R.	29.6	3.0	39.9	2.9	53.2	2.6	78.5	130
Argentina	22.4	1.4	25.8	1.2	29.0	1.0	33.4	39
Romania	19.0	0.8	20.6	0.8	22.2	0.8	24.6	28
South Africa and								
S. W. Africa	18.4	2.7	24.1	2.8	31.9	2.7	47.7	85
Colombia	18.1	3.2	24.8	3.3	34.2	3.2	54.9	97
East Germany (with								
E. Berlin)	17.0	0.3	17.3	0.3	17.5	0.2	17.7	18
Czechoslovakia	14.2	0.8	15.2	0.6	16.1	0.5	17.2	19
Taiwan	12.4	2.3	15.6	2.2	19.3	1.9	25.2	36
Australia	11.4	1.5	13.2	1.6	15.6	1.5	19.6	27
Sweden	7.7	0.5	8.1	0.4	8.3	0.4	8.8	9.5
New Zealand	2.6	1.9	3.2	2.2	4.0	2.0	5.3	7.8
Israel	2.6	2.0	3.1	1.6	3.7	1.3	4.5	5.7

SOURCES:

1965

Pakistan: Population Reference Bureau, *World Population Data Sheet,* December, 1965 (Washington, D.C.)

Other Countries: U. N., *Monthly Bulletin of Statistics.*

1975, 1985, and 2000

Pakistan: same as for India in Table XII.

Indonesia, Thailand, Argentina: 1975—difference between U.N. unadjusted forecast for the region and forecast adjusted for migration (*World Population Prospects,* 1966) was prorated among countries of region in proportion to unadjusted population. 1985, 2000—1965-80 estimates, obtained as for 1975, were projected ahead graphically. The difference between the sum of the projections for the individual countries and the U.N. adjusted forecast for the region was prorated in proportion to the population read off the graphs.

Taiwan: copied from *World Population Prospects,* 1966, p. 64.

Other Countries: same as for West Germany in Table XII except that no continuation of unforeseen migration 1960-65 was assumed outside of Europe.

2020: figures for 2000 were extended graphically.

Growth Rates: computed from population.

States. Australia and New Zealand drop from second and third place to fifth and eighth, yielding their places to East Germany and Czechoslovakia. Among the less-developed countries, Argentina and Taiwan do well.

TABLE XVI

GNP, Nineteen Contender Countries
(Billion 1965 U.S. Dollars)

	GROWTH RATE	1965	1975	GNP 1985	2000	2020
Poland	3	30.3	41	55	85	154
	5		49	80	167	443
	6		54	97	233	747
East Germany	3	26.8	36	48	75	136
	5		44	71	148	392
	6		48	86	206	661
Brazil	3	23.0	31	42	65	117
	4.5		36	56	107	259
	7		45	89	246	950
Australia	3	22.9	31	41	64	116
	4		34	50	90	198
	5		37	61	126	335
Czechoslovakia	3	22.0	30	40	62	112
	5		36	58	121	322
	6		39	71	169	542
Mexico	3	19.4	26	35	55	99
	4.5		30	47	91	218
	6		35	62	149	478
Sweden	3	19.3	26	35	54	98
	4		29	42	76	167
	5		31	51	106	282
Romania	3	14.4	19	26	40	73
	5		24	38	79	211
	6		26	46	111	355
Argentina	2	11.0	13	16	22	33
	4		16	24	43	95
	5		18	29	61	161
Pakistan	2	10.5	13	16	21	31
	5		17	28	57	154
	6		19	33	80	259
Indonesia	2	10.4	13	15	21	31
	3		14	19	29	53
	6		20	33	80	256

TABLE XVI (*continued*)

	GROWTH RATE	1965	1975	GNP 1985	2000	2020
South Africa and	3	9.26	12	17	26	47
Southwest Africa	4.5		14	22	43	104
	5		15	25	51	136
New Zealand	3	5.10	6.9	9.2	14	26
	3.5		7.2	10.1	17	34
	4		7.5	11.2	20	44
Colombia	3	5.0	6.7	9.0	14	25
	4		7.4	11.0	20	43
	5		8.2	13.3	28	73
U.A.R.	3	4.9	6.6	8.8	14	25
	6		8.8	15.7	38	121
	7		9.6	19.0	52	202
Nigeria	3	4.75	6.4	8.6	13	24
	4.5		7.4	11.5	22	54
	5		7.7	12.6	26	70
Thailand	3	3.85	5.2	7.0	11	20
	6		6.9	12.4	30	95
	7		7.6	14.9	41	159
Israel	4	3.40	5.0	7.5	13	29
	6		6.1	10.9	26	84
	7		6.7	13.2	36	140
Taiwan	4	2.74	4.1	6.0	11	24
	6		4.9	8.8	21	68
	8		5.9	12.8	40	189

SOURCES:

1965

Poland, E. Germany, Brazil, Czechoslovakia, Romania, Argentina, and Colombia: private communications from authoritative sources.

Pakistan, Nigeria: an abbreviation of the method used in Table XIII for India.

Indonesia, U.A.R.: U.S., A.I.D., *Estimates of Gross National Product: Summary for Non-Communist Countries,* 1965, reports control no. 137, February 6, 1967. The U.A.R. figure was raised to put it on a calendar year basis.

Other Countries: GNP at market prices times average of year-end exchange rates from U.N., *Monthly Bulletin of Statistics,* except that Botswana's and Lesotho's GNP (A.I.D., *Estimates of GNP,* 1965) and Swaziland's (assumed the same per capita as Botswana's and Lesotho's) were subtracted from South Africa's GNP (which as reported includes Southwest Africa and these three countries).

TABLE XVII

GNP Per Capita, Nineteen Contender Countries
Medium Estimates
(1965 U.S. Dollars)

	1965	1975	1985	2000
Sweden	2,497	3,535	5,078	8,679
Australia	2,009	2,568	3,218	4,612
New Zealand	1,932	2,250	2,544	3,195
East Germany (including E. Berlin)	1,574	2,529	4,065	8,355
Czechoslovakia	1,554	2,357	3,638	7,046
Israel	1,334	1,949	2,978	5,839
Poland	962	1,396	2,054	3,680
Romania	757	1,143	1,717	3,224
South Africa and Southwest Africa	503	598	699	906
Argentina	492	629	831	1,300
Mexico	455	503	558	680
Brazil	280	319	372	506
Colombia	277	298	322	359
Taiwan	221	314	456	837
U.A.R.	166	221	295	480
Thailand	126	170	239	402
Indonesia	99	107	112	123
Pakistan	91	109	134	200
Nigeria	83	94	107	125

SOURCE: Medium projections of GNP were divided by population.

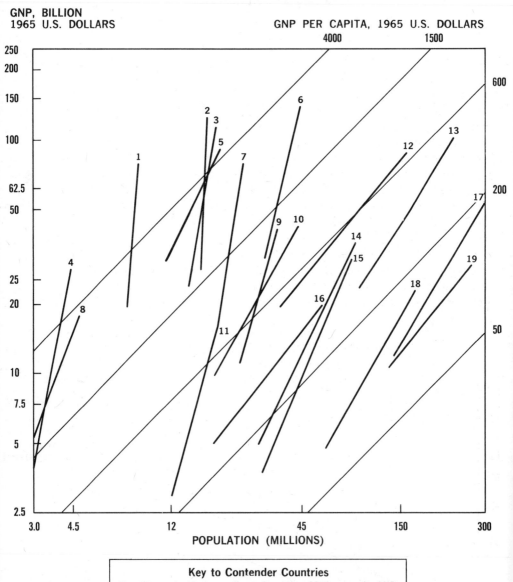

FIGURE 14
POPULATION, GNP, GNP PER CAPITA, 19 CONTENDER COUNTRIES, 1965–2000

GNP, BILLION
1965 U.S. DOLLARS

GNP PER CAPITA, 1965 U.S. DOLLARS

POPULATION (MILLIONS)

Key to Contender Countries
Countries ranked in descending order of Year 2000 per capita GNP:

(1) Sweden	(8) New Zealand	(14) U.A.R.
(2) East Germany	(9) Argentina	(15) Thailand
(3) Czechoslovakia	(10) Union of South Africa	(16) Colombia
(4) Israel	and Southwest Africa	(17) Pakistan
(5) Australia	(11) Taiwan	(18) Nigeria
(6) Poland	(12) Mexico	(19) Indonesia
(7) Romania	(13) Brazil	

C. UNITED STATES PROJECTIONS

1. *Summary of Gross Indices*

The surprise-free United States economic scenario calls for a $1 trillion economy in 1975, 1.5 trillion in 1985, and about $3 trillion in year 2000.

Economic estimates for the United States are premised upon the previously mentioned ingredients of population and labor force, annual hours worked by the labor force, and the productivity (in terms of gross national product per man hour) of that labor force. They focus on the amount of goods and services generated and are stated as high and low aggregate and per capita amounts for each year. This range of economic performance was produced by using two different assumptions of average annual rates of increase in productivity/hour, 2.5 per cent and 4 per cent.

Most of the estimates relate to what is called here the "Standard (U.S.) Society." This is distinguished from the "Leisure-Oriented Society" (see below) by a higher labor force participation rate and longer working hours.

The assumptions used in the projections for the "Standard Society" yield a GNP for year 2000 (in terms of 1965 dollars) of $2.2 to $3.6 trillion; based upon a 1965 GNP of 681 billion, this range implies average annual rates of growth of GNP of 3.4 per cent and 4.9 per cent, respectively. Con-

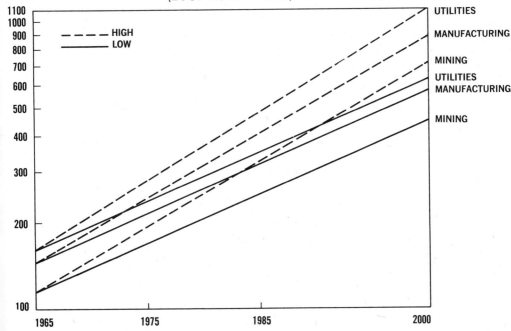

FIGURE 15
INDUSTRIAL PRODUCTION INDICES
(1957-1959 = 100)

sidering a year 2000 population of 318 million, per capita GNP would be slightly more than double the 1965 amount under the assumption of the low rate of productivity increase, and, under the high rate of increase, would be about 3.5 times the 1965 figure. Further, under the "naïve assumption" that personal consumption would retain its relation of being on the order of two-thirds of GNP, then per capita consumption, a partial measure of the standard of living, would also be increased to a level from 2 to about 3.5 times that of 1965.

TABLE XVIII
Summary of Gross Economic Indices
(1965 U.S. Dollars)

	1965 [1]	1975	1985	2000	2020
Population (mil.)	195	222	258	318	421
Households (mil.)	57.3	68.9	82.1	101.3	136.6
GNP (bil.)	681 [2]				
Low		918	1,285	2,177	4,008
High		1,062	1,713	3,628	8,947
Per Capita GNP (dollars)	3,500				
Low		4,150	5,000	6,850	9,550
High		4,800	6,650	11,550	21,250
Index of Output per Man Hour					
(1957-59 = 100)	126				
Low at 2.5 per cent		160	205	296	389
High at 4 per cent		185	274	494	867
Industrial Production Index					
(1957-59 = 100)					
Manufacturing	145				
Low		214	320	570	
High		240	400	890	
Mining	115				
Low		168	248	456	
High		192	323	720	
Utilities	161				
Low		238	352	630	
High		310	580	1,100	

[1] Sources for 1965: Tables XIX, XXVI, and XXIX; U.S. Census Bureau, *Statistical Abstract of the United States*, 1966, p. 36; *Economic Report of the President*, Jan. 1967, pp. 249-50.

[2] U.S. Department of Commerce figure; concept differs from United Nations figure in Table XIII.

2. Population and Labor Force

Estimates for the labor input are, of course, derived initially from projections of the size, sex, and age composition of the population. For year 2000 the estimate of United States total population is 318 million, an amount reflecting a judgment interpolation between the series "B" and "C" projections as contained in the *Statistical Abstract of the United States*.[27] This series and the associated interpolation yield an average annual rate of population growth of about 1.5 per cent per year. This rate of growth is above last year's 1.2 per cent but below other recent years and reflects a forecasted "permanent" reduction in the birth rate. The total population estimate of 318 million thus contrasts with another year 2000 projection, that of the Outdoor Recreation Resources Review Commission,[28] which employs the *Statistical Abstract* series "A," that embodying a higher birth rate, to yield

TABLE XIX
U.S. Population by Age
(ooo)

	1965	2000	2020
Under 5	20,434	32,940	43,000
5-9	20,519	30,380	40,000
10-14	18,956	28,990	38,000
15-19	17,052	28,210	36,000
20-24	13,667	26,430	33,000
25-34	22,358	44,480	60,000
35-44	24,431	41,390	54,000
45-54	22,045	35,140	43,000
55-64	16,966	22,260	36,000
65 and Over	18,156	28,200	38,000
Total All Ages	194,583	318,420	421,000

SOURCES: 1965: U.S. Bureau of the Census, *Current Population Reports*, series P-25, no. 321, 1965, p. 11. Year 2000: two-thirds of the way from the B to the C projection of the Census Bureau in *Statistical Abstract of the United States*, 1965, p. 6. Year 2020: based on projections in U.S. Bureau of the Census, *Current Population Reports*, series P-25, no. 286, 1964, pp. 27, 56-57, 64. Census Bureau projections for population in 2010 were used, and our projection was postulated at two-thirds of the way from their B to their C projection. These figures were then carried ahead using five-year survival rates for 2005-10, age-specific birth rates for 2005-10 two-thirds of the way from the B to the C projected rates, and projected immigration rates.

[27] *Statistical Abstract of the United States*, 1965, p. 6.
[28] U.S.O.R.R.C. *Projection of the Years 1976 and 2000: Economic Growth, Population, Labor Force and Leisure, and Transportation* (1962).

a population of about 350 million. It is believed that such a reduction in birth rates is the more probable case, in part because of the development of the technology of birth control but mostly because of more general acceptance.

By the year 2000, the population age fourteen and over will approximate 232 million; this is the population from which the labor force is recruited. Of this population, about 113 million should be male and 119 million female, and, in terms of broader characterization, this population will be both somewhat older and somewhat younger than is now the case. That is, the proportion of the population in the "middle" grouping of twenty-five to sixty-five will decline. Extrapolations by age groups are shown in the accompanying table and figure.

FIGURE 16
U.S. POPULATION BY AGE (MILLIONS)

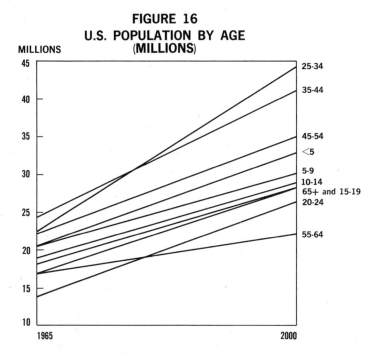

3. Participation Rates, Hours of Work, and Earnings

Of critical importance in the derivation of the labor force size is the labor force participation rate. This rate is a function of many variables, such as attitudes toward work and leisure, requirements for education, retirement policies, and demand for labor. For these reasons the labor force participation rate is difficult to forecast. An "on balance" estimate of this rate has led us to use a labor force participation rate for year 2000 of 59.8 per cent

TABLE XX
Labor Force by Age and Sex
(000)

	1964	1975	1985	2000
Male				
14-17	2,280	2,717	2,762	3,700
18-19	2,026	2,872	2,876	3,990
20-24	5,704	8,331	9,118	11,720
25-34	10,636	14,966	19,275	21,520
35-44	11,559	10,703	14,941	19,920
45-54	10,043	10,810	10,031	16,430
55-64	6,745	7,795	8,236	8,720
65 and Over	2,123	2,087	2,138	2,160
Female				
14-17	1,361	1,711	1,737	3,580
18-19	1,371	2,028	2,020	2,810
20-24	3,220	4,865	5,454	7,050
25-34	4,187	6,124	8,107	9,110
35-44	5,618	5,582	7,913	10,630
45-54	5,682	7,024	6,785	11,010
55-64	3,447	4,826	5,496	5,800
65 and Over	966	1,205	1,473	1,690
Total (Millions)	78	94	108	139

SOURCES: 1964 and 1975, same as for these years in Table XXII. 1985 and 2000, labor force participation rates from Table XXII were applied to population forecasts two-thirds of the way from the B to the C projection in *Statistical Abstract*, 1965, pp. 7-8.

of the population aged fourteen and over, a figure slightly in excess of recent experience and also in excess of other estimates.[29]

The estimated increase in the labor force participation rate derives from an increase in the participation of the female population in the labor force. The female participation rate is projected to approximate 42 per cent in year 2000, as against 1964 experience of 37 per cent.[30] Particularly dramatic are increases in the rates for those in the age group forty-five to sixty-four, and these more than offset a decline in the rate associated with the female population aged fourteen-seventeen.

We estimate there will be an increase in the female participation rate partly because it seems likely there will be an increase in the attractiveness and availability of part-time and intermittent work.

[29] For example, see O.R.R.R.C., *Projections of the Years 1976 and 2000*, p. 137.
[30] *Statistical Abstract of the United States*, 1965, Table 298, p. 217.

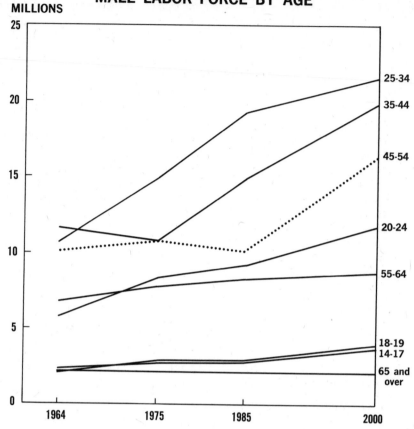

FIGURE 17
MALE LABOR FORCE BY AGE

MILLIONS

25-34
35-44
45-54
20-24
55-64
18-19
14-17
65 and over

1964   1975   1985   2000

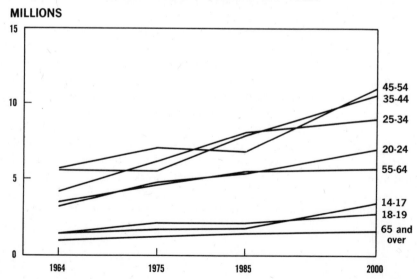

FIGURE 18
FEMALE LABOR FORCE BY AGE

MILLIONS

45-54
35-44
25-34
20-24
55-64
14-17
18-19
65 and over

1964   1975   1985   2000

TABLE XXI
Labor Force, Employment, and Unemployment
1965-2000

	1965 [1]	1975	1985	2000	2020
Population (millions)	195	222	258	318	421
Population 14 and Over	137	162	185	232	307
Labor Force Participation Rate					
(per cent)	56.7	57.8	58.7	59.8	59.0
Labor Force	78	94	108	139	181
Civilian Labor Force	76	91	105	136	179
Civilian Employment	72	87	101	131	172
Unemployment	3.5	3.7	4.2	5.4	7.2
Projected Hours/Employed					
Worker/Yr. (Hrs.)		1,885	1,770	1,600	1,370
GNP (Billion 1965 U.S. Dollars)					
Low		918	1,285	2,177	4,008
High		1,062	1,713	3,628	8,947

[1] SOURCES: Table XIX and *Statistical Abstract*, 1966, pp. 8, 218, and 219.

The participation rate for males is projected at 78.1 per cent.[31] This increase reverses a downward trend in the male rate, even though a significant decline is anticipated in the rate for the age group sixty-five and above because of pension benefits. A decline is also projected in the groups eighteen and nineteen, reflecting the demands of education. Increases are projected for groups thirty-five through fifty-four.

The hazards of estimating the determinants of the labor force participation rate and thus overall employment are well known, and estimates of the

[31] *Ibid.*

TABLE XXII
Labor Force Participation Rates by Age and Sex
(Per Cent)

	1964	1975	1985	2000
Male				
Total	77.2	76.9	77.6	78.1
14-17	31.6	32.1	32.0	31.8
18-19	72.3	69.8	70.2	70.2
20-24	86.6	86.7	87.2	87.5
25-34	96.1	96.2	96.2	96.2
35-44	96.0	96.7	96.7	96.4
45-54	94.4	95.0	95.0	95.0
55-64	84.1	83.9	83.5	83.2
65 and Over	27.1	23.4	20.8	19.0
Female				
Total	37.0	39.9	40.9	42.4
14-17	19.5	20.8	20.9	21.0
18-19	49.9	50.6	51.0	51.3
20-24	49.2	51.5	53.4	54.1
25-34	37.1	39.3	40.6	41.2
35-44	44.8	49.9	50.6	51.3
45-54	51.0	57.6	60.8	61.7
55-64	39.8	45.7	48.2	49.2
65 and Over	9.6	9.8	10.0	10.0
Total	56.5	57.8	58.7	59.8

SOURCE:
1964, 1975: Statistical Abstract of the U.S., 1965, p. 217, citing U.S. Bureau of Labor Statistics, "Labor Force Projections for 1970-80: Special Labor Force Report No. 49," *Monthly Labor Review*, February, 1965, pp. 129-140.
1985, 2000: Extrapolation of 1960-1980 curves derived from that source.

size of the labor force more than three decades hence are at best tentative. However, if a participation rate of 59.8 per cent is accepted for the year 2000, then the total labor force will approximate 139 million.

The level of employment of the civilian labor force has been taken at the conventional full employment proportion of 96 per cent, and a year 2000 employed civilian force of about 131 million was derived. To move further toward the projection of aggregate supply of goods and services, the number of hours worked by this labor force was estimated, premised on an average of hours worked per week of 31. This figure is largely an extrapolation of trends, and serves to reduce total output, although not to the full extent of the reduction in hours. For year 2000, 210 billion man-hours of work are projected.

The productivity adjustment to the aggregate of hours worked was made by assuming the two previously mentioned average annual rates of productivity increase, 2.5 per cent, or "low," and 4 per cent, or "high." These rates were applied over the whole of the time period in question; that is, there was no refinement such as the use of a 3 per cent figure for half the period and 2 per cent for the balance. The productivity measure used was output per man-hour, that is, output per unweighted unit of labor and capital, with no adjustment made for productivity increases which might result from the reduction of the work week. The choice of 2.5 per cent as the "floor" stems from long-term United States performance modified by post-World War II experience; the 4 per cent upper figure is a judgmental rate based upon sanguine interpretations of economic impact of new technology and techniques.

Adjustment of the estimate of hours worked in 2000 by rates of productivity change, and the GNP value per man-hour in 1965 provides the GNP range of $2.2 to $3.6 trillion.

TABLE XXIII
Average Weekly Hours of Work in Selected Industries

	1965 [1]	1975	1985	2000
Manufacturing	41.1	41.5	38.9	32
Contract Construction	37.4	35.6	33.8	31.2
Retail Trade	36.6	35.3	34.0	32.1
Wholesale Trade	40.8	38.6	36.4	32.1
Bituminous Coal Mining	40.1	37.2	34.3	30.1

[1] SOURCE: *Economic Report of the President*, Jan. 1966, Table C-26, p. 240.

FIGURE 20
AVERAGE WEEKLY HOURS OF WORK
IN SELECTED INDUSTRIES

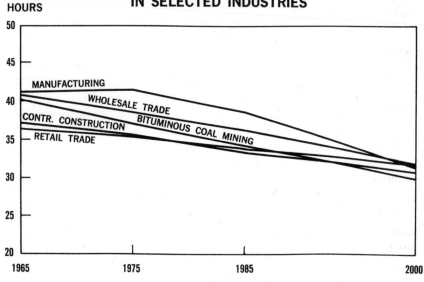

TABLE XXIV

Employees in Nonagricultural Establishments by Industry
(Millions)

	1965 [1]	1975	1985	2000
Mining	0.6	0.6	0.5	0.5
Manufacturing	18.0	19.8	21.3	24.2
Construction (contract)	3.2	3.9	4.9	6.5
Transportation and Utilities	4.0	4.6	5.0	5.9
Trade	12.6	19.8	24.3	35.0
Finance and Real Estate	3.0	3.8	4.6	5.9
Services	8.9	17.5	22.2	34.0
Government	10.1	11.3	12.2	14.6
Total	60.4	81.3	95.0	126.6

[1] SOURCE: *Statistical Abstract*, 1966, p. 221.

4. GNP and Its Major Components

Given the above estimates of the range of aggregate supply of goods and services to the year 2000, the distribution of that product by the expenditures sectors of households, domestic and foreign investment, and govern-

TABLE XXV

*Average Gross Hourly Earnings
in Selected Industries
(Dollars)*

INDUSTRIES	1965 [1]	1975	1985	2000
Manufacturing	2.61	5.15	7.63	11.50
Contract Construction	3.68	5.81	7.94	11.15
Retail Trade	1.82	3.41	4.98	7.40
Wholesale Trade	2.60	4.91	7.22	10.70
Bituminous Coal Mining	3.49	5.98	8.47	12.20
Telephone Communications	2.69	4.78	6.87	10.00
Agriculture	0.95	2.14	3.33	5.10

[1] SOURCE: *Economic Report of the President*, Jan. 1966, p. 241.

ment was projected. The composition of the end use of the supply of goods and services affects or feeds back upon the rate of growth of the economy, as in the case of the level of investment goods production. Thus interactions exist between the growth of supply and the use of that supply, and these are implicit in any long-range projection.

a. Expenditure Sector: Distribution of year 2000 GNP by expenditure sectors follows recent experience with some modifications. In general terms, some increase in the proportion of consumption expenditures is suggested for the year 2000, occurring in coincidence with a decline in the proportion of government purchases of goods and services. The increases in disposable income, leisure time, and in the number of families achieving higher incomes contribute to the projected impressive increase in consumption.

b. Government Spending: Projections for government purchases of goods and services provide for increases in the expenditures of state and local governments relative to those of the federal government. The decline in the proportion of government purchases to GNP coincides with a projected diminution of defense outlays by the end of the century. The impetus for state and local government purchases derives in part from increases in outlays for education.

c. Investment: Dramatic changes in the proportion of investment spending to GNP are not assumed for the "high" projections. Gross private domestic investment is assumed to retain its proportion of the use of total product, at about 15 per cent. Estimates for net foreign investment imply a surplus of exports over imports in 1975 and 1985, with a balance for the year 2000.

TABLE XXVI

GNP and Its Major Components
(Billion 1965 U.S. Dollars)

	1965 [1]	1975	1985	2000	2020
Total GNP (Billions)	681				
Low		918	1,285	2,177	4,008
High		1,062	1,713	3,628	8,947
Personal Consumption Expenditures	432				
Low		583	827	1,452	2,688
High		674	1,098	2,420	5,720
Gross Private Domestic Investment	107				
Low		132	185	313	642
High		154	247	523	1,702
Government Purchases of Goods and Services	136				
Low		193	265	411	651
High		223	348	685	1,423

[1] SOURCE: *Survey of Current Business*, April 1967, p. 6.

Figure 21

GNP AND ITS MAJOR COMPONENTS
(1965 U.S. Dollars)

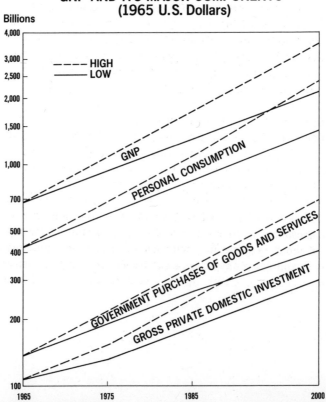

TABLE XXVII

Government Purchases of Goods and Services
(Billion 1965 United States Dollars)

	1965 [1]	1975	1985	2000	2020
Total	$136				
Low		193	265	411	651
High		223	348	685	1,423
Federal	$ 66.8				
Low		81	99	141	
High		91	129	236	
State and Local	$ 69.4				
Low		112	167	270	
High		132	219	450	

[1] SOURCE: *Survey of Current Business*, April 1967, p. 6.

TABLE XXVIII

Gross Private Domestic Investment
(Billion 1965 United States Dollars)

	1965 [1]	1975	1985	2000	2020
Total	$107				
Low		$132	$185	$313	642
High		$154	$247	$523	1,702
Business Investment in					
New Plant and Equipment					
	$52				
Low		$ 75	$105	$165	
High		$ 85	$130	$270	

[1] SOURCE: *Survey of Current Business*, May 1967, p. 4, and *Statistical Abstract*, 1966, p. 499.

d. Per Capita GNP and Disposable Income: The implications of the projection shown on the following pages are discussed in Chapter IV, where we envision great increases in leisure and in alienation from current patterns of work and achievement. As described in that chapter, our economic projections need not be greatly affected by these changes in assumption.

TABLE XXIX

Per Capita GNP and Consumption, 1965-2020
(1965 U.S. Dollars)

	1965	1975	1985	2000	2020
Per Capita GNP	$3,500				
Low		$4,150	$5,000	$ 6,850	$ 9,550
High		$4,800	$6,650	$11,550	$21,250
Per Capita Disposable Income	$2,410				
Low		$2,880	$3,450	$ 4,900	$ 6,800
High		$3,300	$4,600	$ 8,150	$14,550
Per Capita Personal Consumption					
Expenditure	$2,220				
Low		$2,600	$3,150	$ 4,400	$ 6,400
High		$3,000	$4,250	$ 7,000	$13,600

SOURCE: Tables XXI, XXVI and XXX.

Figure 22

PER CAPITA GNP AND PERSONAL CONSUMPTION EXPENDITURES
(1965 U.S. Dollars)

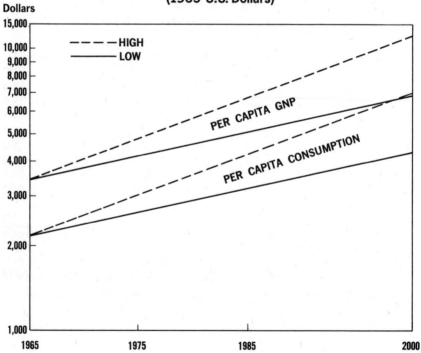

TABLE XXX

Disposition of Personal Income, High and Low Estimates
(Billion 1965 U.S. Dollars)

	1965 [1]	1975	1985	2000	2020
Personal Income	535				
Low		727	1,018	1,713	3,162
High		842	1,357	2,856	7,068
Disposable Personal Income	469				
Low		628	891	1,559	2,864
High		726	1,188	2,598	6,129
Personal Consumption Expenditures	432				
Low		583	827	1,452	2,688
High		674	1,098	2,420	5,720
Personal Savings	25.7				
Low		45	64	107	179
High		52	90	178	406

[1] SOURCE: *Survey of Current Business*, April 1967, p. 8.

TABLE XXXI

Distribution of Family Personal Income before Tax [1]
(1965 U.S. Dollars)

INCOME CLASS ($000)	PER CENT OF CONSUMER UNITS [2] IN INCOME CLASS				
	1965	1975	1985	2000	2020
Under 3	16.2	12.6	9.5	5.6	3.3
3-6	26.2	19.6	12.9	7.0	3.8
6-8	17.7	14.4	11.6	5.2	2.5
8-10	12.7	13.8	11.3	6.6	3.0
10-15	16.3	21.5	24.6	18.0	8.4
15-25	7.9	13.2	20.3	30.4	31.4
25-50	} 3.0	} 4.9	} 9.8	22.2	39.2
50-100					15.1
				} 5.0	
100 and over					3.3
	100.0	100.0	100.0	100.0	100.0
Mean Family Personal Income	$8,380	$10,410	$13,380	$20,980	$34,920

[1] Before federal individual income tax.
[2] Families plus unrelated individuals.

NOTE: The forecast assumes that the top tenth of consumer units goes on receiving the same proportion of family personal income as it received in 1962; likewise for the other tenths.

SOURCES: The 1962 distribution of family personal income published by the U.S. Office of Business Economics was copied from *Statistical Abstract,* 1965, p. 341. A $25,000-and-over income class was added by comparison with the like distribution by the Census Bureau in "Income in 1965 of Families and Persons in the United States," *Current Population Reports,* series P-60, No. 51, January 12, 1967, p. 29.

The ratios of bottom-of-bracket income to mean income (*Statistical Abstract,* 1965, p. 340) for the enlarged 1962 distribution were plotted as in Figure 23. To use this distribution in forecasting, the ratios of family personal income to total personal income and of consumer units to households were computed from U.S. Census Bureau, *Historical Statistics of the United States: Colonial Times to 1957,* 1960, its *Continuation to 1962 with Revisions* (1965), and *Statistical Abstract,* 1965, and were projected to 2020 along their trends. The first ratio was divided by the second, and the quotients multiplied by the forecasts of personal income (average of high and low) per household computed from Tables XXVII and XXX to get 1965-2000 forecasts of mean family personal income per consumer unit. Bottom-of-bracket income was divided by this mean income and the corresponding forecast percentages were read off the 1962 curve (Figure 23) and decumulated.

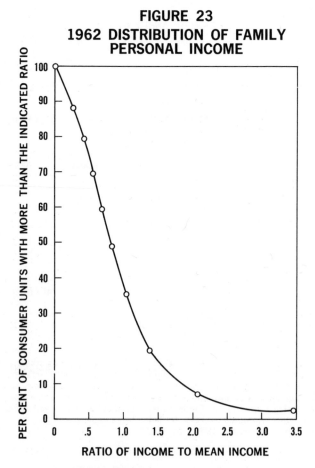

FIGURE 23
1962 DISTRIBUTION OF FAMILY PERSONAL INCOME

RATIO OF INCOME TO MEAN INCOME

PER CENT OF CONSUMER UNITS WITH MORE THAN THE INDICATED RATIO

SOURCE: See Table XXXI.

FIGURE 24

DISTRIBUTION OF FAMILY PERSONAL INCOME AFTER FEDERAL INCOME TAX, USING THREE PROJECTIONS OF PERSONAL INCOME (1965 DOLLARS)

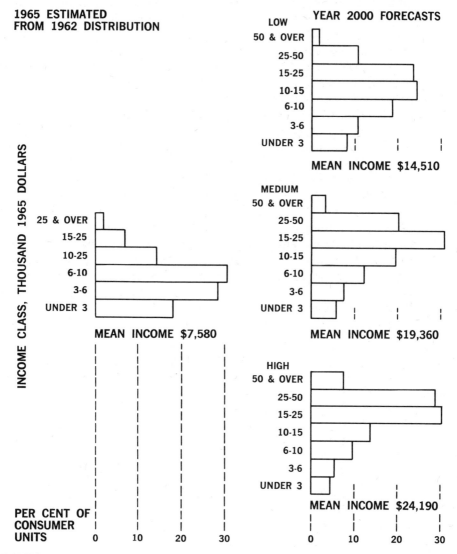

1965 ESTIMATED FROM 1962 DISTRIBUTION

MEAN INCOME $7,580

YEAR 2000 FORECASTS

LOW
MEAN INCOME $14,510

MEDIUM
MEAN INCOME $19,360

HIGH
MEAN INCOME $24,190

INCOME CLASS, THOUSAND 1965 DOLLARS

PER CENT OF CONSUMER UNITS

SOURCES:

Federal individual income tax liability as forecast using past and forecast relations among receipts from the tax, personal income, and Federal and state and local purchases of goods and services. U.S., Office of Business Economics, **The National Income and Product Accounts of the United States, 1929-1965** (Washington, 1966), pp. 33, 52-55, and Tables XXVII and XXX, above. The forecasts were subtracted from those of aggregate family personal income before tax used for or computed as for Table XXXI, and the procedure of that table followed except that income **after** taxes was projected.

5. *Summary of United States in 2020* [32]

United States population was projected at 421 million persons in 2020 with the labor force at 179 million; hours worked per year per employed person were assumed to be 1,370 (Table XXI). GNP was judged to fall between $4 and $8.9 trillion, contingent upon the same alternative rates of annual increase in GNP per man-hour as were used for the period 1965-2000. Growth rates of GNP for 2020 versus 1965 are, respectively, 3.3 per cent and 4.8 per cent.

Personal consumption expenditures would range from $2.7 to $5.7 trillion, in comparison with $432 billion in 1965 (Table XXX). Per capita personal consumption is projected to be from $6,400 to $13,600 in 2020, versus $2,220 in 1965 (Table XXIX). Thus the United States "standard of living" would rise to between three and six times its 1965 level, and this increase would be accompanied by an increase in leisure time.

The distribution of personal income (before income taxes) was depicted in Table XXXI. The distribution is premised on that of 1962; the growth of personal income over the 1965-2020 period is shown by increases in mean family income (from $8,380 to $34,920), and by growth of the percentage of consumer units appearing in higher income classes. By 2000, 27 per cent of all consumer units will attain incomes of $25,000 or over before income taxes; by 2020 this will amount to about 58 per cent (see Figure 24 for distribution after federal income tax).

[32] See footnote 18.

CHAPTER IV

Postindustrial Society
in the Standard World

A. INTRODUCTION

The purpose of this chapter is to continue outlining our Standard World, focusing here on domestic issues for the United States and related socio-economic changes that may also impinge on other advanced societies.

In Chapter I we pointed to a basic, long-term multifold trend which we judged likely to continue during the last third of this century (see Table I, Chapter I). Some of the elements of the trend—especially increasingly Sensate (empirical, this-worldly, secular, humanistic, pragmatic, utilitarian, contractual, epicurean or hedonistic, and the like) cultures; accumulation of scientific and technological knowledge; institutionalization of change, especially research, development, innovation, and diffusion; increasing affluence and (recently) leisure; urbanization and (soon) the growth of megalopolises; decreasing importance of primary (and recently) secondary occupations; and literacy and education—should become especially prominent in the "Visibly Postindustrial" countries projected in Table XXII (Chapter I). These items are likely to become especially conspicuous in the United States, followed perhaps rather closely by Canada, Switzerland, Scandinavia, and, with some cultural differences, Japan. The situation in the rest of Western Europe and the "Early Postindustrial" countries listed on page 60 will probably differ only in degree. Even the projected "Mass Consumption" and "Mature Industrial" economic groups listed on that page are likely to be quite different from their current early industrial conditions, and will probably begin to show "Postindustrial" features in leading sectors of their economies and societies, partly as a result of their own development and partly because of the dominant influence of the most affluent nations both on the world economy and on the styles of life of cosmopolitan elites everywhere. Indeed, even the remaining nations—more than half the world's population, with comparatively rudimentary industrialization and per capita incomes for the most part still below six hundred 1965 dollars—will show the influence, among privileged groups, and in major cities, of postindustrial changes.

B. THE POSTINDUSTRIAL SOCIETY

We introduced Daniel Bell's term "postindustrial society" [1] in Chapter 1, and listed fifteen items, repeated in Table I, below, that seem to us likely to be characteristic of the emerging situation, especially in the United States. (Some of these items are also part of the multifold trend and were discussed in part D of Chapter 1, pp. 34 ff., especially pp. 57-64.)

We shall discuss most of these issues by simply mentioning them, or occasionally conjecturing very briefly on their significance, without attempting to be systematic or exhaustive. Many of the statements will nonetheless be in conclusionary form, mainly because it is easier to focus or provoke discussion in a short paragraph if one states a position than if one attempts to

---

TABLE I

The Postindustrial (or Post-Mass Consumption) Society

1. Per capita income about fifty times the preindustrial
2. Most "economic" activities are tertiary and quaternary (service-oriented) rather than primary or secondary (production-oriented)
3. Business firms no longer the major source of innovation
4. There may be more "consentives" (vs. "marketives")
5. Effective floor on income and welfare
6. "Efficiency" no longer primary
7. Market plays diminished role compared to public sector and "social accounts"
8. Widespread "cybernation"
9. "Small world"
10. Typical "doubling time" between three and thirty years
11. Learning society
12. Rapid improvement in educational institutions and techniques
13. Erosion (in middle class) of work-oriented, achievement-oriented, advancement-oriented values
14. Erosion of "national interest" values?
15. Sensate, secular, humanist, perhaps self-indulgent criteria become central

---

[1] See footnote 9 in Chapter I.

give several alternatives in truncated form. In all cases we tend to "believe in" the position indicated, though perhaps tentatively. These conjectures are no more than our current working hypotheses and are clearly more controversial than most aspects of our Standard World.

It may be useful to compare the shift away from primary and secondary occupations to an earlier transition made in the United States in the mid-nineteenth century. In that predominantly agricultural society, 55 per cent of the labor force were farmers, while today only about 5 per cent of the labor force is engaged in agriculture. One might imagine an average American in 1850, given the information that in one hundred years only 5 per cent of Americans would be engaged in agriculture: he would be very likely to think of these farmers as likely to use their "monopoly powers" to get far more than a proportionate share of power, influence, and resources. He might even assume that the power, prestige, and influence, then held in his day by the 55 per cent of the American people who farmed, would be held by the 5 per cent; or at least that the 5 per cent of the American population who had a monopoly on food production, the most basic of all activities, would be able to exploit their commanding position to overwhelming effect. An American who subscribed to the then widely held Jeffersonian idea that only the freeholder, as opposed to the propertyless laborer, could really participate responsibly in a democracy would have been especially likely to assume that the farmers, or at least the landed gentry, would continue as the most important social group.

While today many believe that farmers have more than their share of government subsidies and political power, especially in unreapportioned legislatures, all would concede that farmers are, by a large margin, not the dominating force in American politics. Furthermore, while continued improvements in agricultural productivity are of great importance, current productivity is so great that so far as the average American is concerned, improvements are routine and of little interest. In the eighteenth or even the nineteenth century, a technical advance in agriculture would have been noted with enthusiasm by the whole community and might have transformed the whole community; today only farmers are likely to be very interested in agricultural innovations.

A similar transformation, though not so extreme, may develop with respect to business activities in a postindustrial society. A smaller percentage of people may be engaged in business, and the very success of private business may make its further successes seem less exciting and dramatic. While businessmen will probably continue to be deeply occupied with their affairs, the issues of finance, investment, production, sales, and distribution that have so long been dominant concerns of so many Americans and Europeans will very likely dwindle in interest. American industry has already been concerned about its declining attractiveness for college graduates, especially for the most intellectually gifted segments of the group, and there may eventually be a general lowering of business morale.

The postindustrial era is likely to be more of a "learning society" than today's. In part this is because of the "information explosion," but mostly because of the rapidity of change. As we mentioned in Chapter 11, the computers of 1967 have about ten times the performance capacity of those of 1964 and 1965, which means that concepts of appropriate computer functions that were perfectly valid for the computers of two or three years ago must be reviewed and sometimes completely changed. In many cases the new concepts that must be devised in order to deal adequately with today's potentialities are very different from those of two or three years ago.

While the computer is a fairly extreme example of rapid change, it is reasonably indicative—though the more likely time for significant change in most areas would be closer to ten or twenty than two or three years. Thus, if the annual per capita increase in income is 4 per cent, then per capita income will double every eighteen years. Such a doubling is clearly a most significant event. Or to take another example, television, which was almost unheard of in private homes in 1946 and 1947, had by 1955 changed American living patterns in a very marked way. In this case, the exact significance of the changes is yet unevaluated. (For example, it is difficult to be sure whether or not it makes a great difference, or how, that large numbers of children and their parents spend an average of several hours every day passively watching a flickering screen.) To give another example, it takes about twenty to fifty years for most countries to double their populations, so there may easily be two or three doublings within one lifetime. Similarly, a country may, within one lifetime, change from being largely or overwhelmingly rural to largely or overwhelmingly urban. Or the number of kilowatts generated per year, the passenger miles in autos or planes, numbers of telephones, and so on may increase by factors of five to a hundred in a decade or two. Any of these changes occurring by themselves could be important. If all of them, and others as well, occur more or less simultaneously, the total rate of change and the need for large adaptions become fantastic. The term future shock has been used to describe the corresponding "acculturation" trauma. These changes seem likely to increase in number, kind, and rate at least for the next three or four decades. The corresponding need for adjustment, adaptation, and control is likely to be one of the most characteristic and central phenomena of the early postindustrial era, although there is some possibility that it will not be either as pervasive or dramatic in a later time period, simply because there may be a deliberate slowing down in order to "take it easier" and to avoid or meliorate consequences of change.

C. CROSS-CULTURAL COMPARISONS

We pointed out in Chapter 1 that in the previous six thousand years of recorded history civilized man, by and large, lived in societies not too dissimilar economically from that of Indonesia today, in which the average income was, give or take a factor of two, the equivalent of about one hundred dollars per capita. (Even the size of the larger societies, e.g., the Roman Empire or the Han Empire, was about the same in population as Indonesia today—about one hundred million people.)

The Industrial Revolution was, in many ways, a more important and more rapid change than any that had preceded. The changes that seem likely in the next thirty-three years also seem likely to lead to some results that are entirely unprecedented. Nevertheless we would suggest that some of the prospects for the year 2000 are, in effect, a return to a sort of new Augustinian age. Conditions (in the superdeveloped countries at least) could then differ from those of the early and mid-twentieth centuries—in some important ways—much as the early Roman Empire differed from the pre-classical world. We are all too familiar with clichés about the decline of the Roman Empire, but for the better part of the first two hundred years the Roman Empire enjoyed almost unparalleled good government, peace and prosperity. And it should be noted that it also began in an "age of anxiety" and apprehension. Arguments are often heard to the effect that the "moral fibre" of the Romans somehow "degenerated" because of a lack of challenge during the period of stability and prosperity. While the issues of cause and effect are complicated and inherently inconclusive, there are some parallels between Roman times and ours. Various analogies, however trite or inaccurate in their usual formulations, ought not be dismissed without some thought, at least as sources for conjectures.

Thus it is interesting to note that when Augustus came to power the free citizens of Rome had 76 holidays a year. When Nero died, not quite a century later, they had 176 holidays a year. In our world, if productivity per hour goes up by 3 or 4 per cent a year (or by a factor of three or four by the year 2000), it is not likely that all of this increased productivity will be used to produce more. As in the Roman Empire, much may be taken up in increased leisure. One can almost imagine that in the next thirty-three years the once populist, bourgeois, conforming Americans become relatively elitist, antibourgeois, and pluralist; significant numbers acquiring attributes that bear comparison to sophists, epicureans, cynics, primitive—or humanist—sensualists, other materialists, and various kinds of dropouts—to mix terminology usually applied to the Hellenistic era with current jargon. As in the Hellenistic and Roman Empires, such groups, while reasonably identifiable, would not necessarily be exclusive or distinct and many individuals might move more or less freely among the various groups. Nevertheless an observer of society might justifiably generalize about the existence of such groups—certainly more justifiably than he could have in traditional America.

What is meant by sensualists, materialists, and dropouts is probably sufficiently clear. Sophists have had a bad press; they are often described as unscrupulous and/or superficial manipulators of words and ideas. While the Greek sophists may have included some like this, very likely most resembled, at least in their philosophic ideas, modern pragmatic positivists or nominalists. The Greek cynics, stoics, and epicureans were all antiwar, indeed, rejected most worldly ambitions and pretensions to an almost escapist degree—in part as a result of their disappointment at what had happened to Greek culture after it had conquered most of the world. The cynics (of whom Diogenes is the best known) went furthest in this direction, scorning established values and aspirations, repudiating accepted codes of behavior, and arguing for a return to poverty and personal independence, and to nature (like "dogs," as the etymology suggests). Unlike the current "hippies," however, they cultivated self-control and asceticism. Most interesting of all to us are the stoic and epicurean reactions—both were basically pessimistic about the "meaning and purpose" of man's efforts (Gilbert Murray's "failure of nerve"), but were still, in their separate ways, philosophies of good and respectable citizens. The stoic, of course, had an almost biblical passion for righteousness and duty, while the epicurean had an almost similar passion "to cultivate his garden and friends." Tables II and III below give capsulated descriptions of these two important reactions.

A modern stoic would correspond to the responsible, duty-minded, hard-working, public-spirited American who feels obligated to do a good job for his government, company, or other institution, and works well without necessarily getting much recognition, supervision, or special reward.

One might distinguish between "Greek" epicureanism, which would

---

TABLE II

The (Roman) Stoic Outlook

1. A passion for virtue and for doing one's duty
2. The four cardinal virtues are wisdom, justice, courage, and temperance
3. But fortitude and indifference to pain and sorrow are also important
4. Only such virtue justifies power
5. But virtue is its own reward
6. Even a slave can be virtuous
7. There is a basic natural law governing mankind
8. Under this natural law all men are basically equal

TABLE III
The Epicurean Outlook

1. Based on emphasizing sensation, emotions, pleasure of the individual soul
2. Criterion of good and evil is sensation, i.e., "pleasure"
3. Power and public life disturb the soul
4. When the body dies, it returns to atoms; when the soul leaves, the body has no "sensations"
5. There should be no fear of death, gods, or natural laws
6. Pleasure is "absence of pain," not active enjoyment (or hedonism)
7. Happiness is the quiet mind, wise and righteous living

correspond to the above, and "modern" epicureanism, which would not emphasize lines 6 and 7 as much. So far as modern epicureanism is concerned, we might wish to distinguish among "wholesome" or "square" epicureanism (e.g., the sophisticated portion of the Southern California "Bar-B-Q" society), the "hip" epicureanism of the "consciousness-expanding," "dropout," "turned-on," and so-called "joy-love" cultures, and hedonistic or aesthetic epicureanism—using these last terms in their current usage.

Finally we can think of the "gentleman" and the "humanist" as being basically interested in self development—the former in acquiring socially approved skills and experiences and having a sense of noblesse oblige to the state, the latter being more interested in idiosyncratic skills and experiences and being committed to more universal values.

The following tables represent one necessarily quite impressionistic (and perhaps somewhat idiosyncratic) attempt to contrast some characteristics that the Americans have in common with the ancient Romans and the Eu-

TABLE IV
Some Differences between Americans and Romans

Characteristic	American Middle Class	Roman Middle/Upper
Human equality	Axiomatic	Absurd
World view	Optimistic	Pessimistic (Stoic or Epicurean)
Dignity	"Putting on airs"	Basic virtue
Poverty	Vice	Basic virtue
National memory	Extremely short	Extremely long
World domination	Still unwilling to accept	Eventually eager to accept

TABLE V
Typical Attitudes of Elites

Characteristic	Romans and Americans	Ancient Greeks and Modern Europeans
Power evokes	Respect	Suspicion
Highest political force	Rule of law	Personality
Most great men receive	Admiration	Denigration
Individualism	Subordinated	Untamed
The primitive masses are	"Citizens"	"Barbarians" or "Helots"
Educated aliens evoke	Slight awe	Amused surprise
Hero Image	Puritan, virtue, stern, conservative, devoted to duty (Cato Sr., George Washington)	Adventurous, unpredictable, conqueror of men and women (Odysseus, Napoleon)
Areas of greatest proficiency	Technical; plumbing, civil and military organization	Theoretical; philosophy, mathematics, pure science, the arts
Greatest weakness	Theoretical knowledge as opposed to applied	Unity, collaboration
Dillettantism	Unappreciated	"Gentlemanly"
Attitude to the other's culture	Indebtedness	Disdain
Leisure	A vice	A goal
The ambition of others	Highly approved, unless it becomes a threat to the Republic	A threat to one's own and therefore disapproved

ropeans with the ancient Greeks, especially the Athenians and other Ionic Greeks. (The Spartans, of course, were much closer to the Romans.) In some ways the Britons of the eighteenth and nineteenth centuries were even more like the Romans than the Americans are (e.g., the aristocratic element, the colonial conquests, the even more stringent supremacy of Law), and the Prussians of the eighteenth century very closely resemble the Spartans; that is, they were much closer to the Romans than to the Athenians.

The first table tries to point out that the analogy is incomplete—even at the "loose generalization" level—by presenting obvious dissimilarities between the democratic Americans and the aristocratic Romans. The second table lists some aspects of the basic analogy that we will occasionally use to make or illustrate some point.

Two points are worth noting about such generalizations. While they are often abused, nevertheless they have some value; while they have some value, they are by no means broadly or strictly applicable. For example, there are many notable exceptions among Romans, Americans, Greeks, and Europeans. The Spartans, the late British ruling class, the Prussians, and the Communists actually partake much more of the characteristics of the Romans in the above list than they do of those listed as typically Greek. This applies also to many members of French elites. There are also many other obvious respects in which the Americans differ from the Romans and in which modern Europeans differ basically from the ancient Greeks. The differences between groups, and within each group, are obvious and substantial. What is less—to the modern reader at least—obvious, and yet perhaps of some interest, is that useful parallels can be discerned at all, and will be acknowledged by many knowledgeable people—though uncomfortably, since we have all learned, quite properly, to distrust "generalizations." The great interest of the analogy is that in many ways Europe and Greece and America and Rome, started from similar points and, most important, something very much like our multifold trend occurred in Hellenistic Greece, the late Roman Republic, and the early Roman Empire.

D. ALIENATION AMIDST AFFLUENCE

In this chapter we are attempting to describe a plausible and culturally consistent projection of a culture, values, and style of life consistent with other features of our Standard World of the year 2000. To test whether such a projection is plausible and consistent is both naïvely simple and insolubly complicated. We can take what we now know about past and current American styles of life together with some current trends—and our knowledge of these is far from complete—and add what we believe or find plausible about the socialization of the child, the development of character, character changes in later life, ways in which social structure and culture change, and so forth, and on this basis try to assess the consequences of some simple, basic trends that are characteristic of our Standard World. These include relatively easy affluence, new technology, absence of absorbing international challenges, and considerable but not disastrous population growth. We must ask, in effect, how these trends might furnish or constrain possibilities for change in the large number of Americans already living who will probably survive into the year 2000, and in those who will be born and "socialized" in the interim.

The first salient factor seems likely to be a vastly increased availability of goods and such services as transportation and communication. A second is a likely increase in leisure and a concomitant reduction of the pressures of work. A third is the likelihood of important technological changes in such areas as psychopharmacology, with possible radical consequences for culture and styles of life. Perhaps the most important is a likely absence of stark "life and death" economic and national security issues.

How can we assess the impact of these changes even on a current situation which itself is imperfectly understood? One of the greatest problems of all psychological and sociological speculation has to do with the dialectical quality of the processes involved. It is difficult to know whether to extrapolate trends or to postulate reactions against the same trends. For example, if work will occupy fewer hours of the average person's life, it is plausible to speculate that for this reason work will become less important. On the other hand, it is at least equally plausible that the change in the role of work may cause work as an issue to come to new prominence. The values surrounding work, which in the developed areas have evolved over centuries, may emerge into a new flux and once again become controversial sources of problems within a society and for many individuals. The ideologies that surround work and give it justification and value, in individual and social terms, may become strengthened in support of what remains of work; on the other hand, they may increasingly come into doubt and become the objects of reaction and rebellion. Indeed both trends may materialize simultaneously in different parts of society and may cause conflicts within many individuals. Clearly one can write many scenarios here, with many different branching points. These quandaries must be resolved ultimately by at least partly intuitive and subjective judgments; the most one can claim for such speculations is that no alternative possibility seems much more likely.

1. Economic Plausibility and Postindustrial Leisure

Let us assume, then, with expanded gross national product, greatly increased per capita income, the work week drastically reduced, retirement earlier (but active life-span longer), and vacations longer, that leisure time and recreation and the values surrounding these acquire a new emphasis. Some substantial percentage of the population is not working at all. There has been a great movement toward the welfare state, especially in the areas of medical care, housing, and subsidies for what previously would have been thought of as poor sectors of the population. Tables VI and VII show one possibility or "year 2000 scenario" for the distribution of work and leisure.

In Chapter III we projected economic indices for the United States in some detail, and indicated how extrapolations to very prosperous levels of personal income were consistent with reasonable assumptions about rates of increase in labor productivity and substantial reduction in hours worked and labor force participation rates. One might construct additional "quanti-

---

TABLE VI

A Leisure-Oriented "Postindustrial" Society
(~1100 Working Hours per Year)

7.5	Hour Working Day
4	Working Days per Week
39	Working Weeks per Year
10	Legal Holidays
3	Day Weekends
13	Weeks per Year Vacation

(Or 147 Working Days and 218 Days Off/Year)

TABLE VII

Thus in a Leisure-Oriented Society One Could Spend:

40 per cent of his days on a vocation
40 per cent of his days on an avocation
20 per cent (or more than 1 day per week) on neither—
that is, just relaxing

---

tative scenarios." For example, a projection for a leisure-oriented society, without alienation, could retain the population of 318 million but cut the work year from 1600 to 1100 hours (1920 hours is now "standard" but somewhat above average) and lower the labor force participation rate to 56 per cent. Under these assumptions, and assuming that the economy has been experiencing the high rate of productivity increase, the leisure-oriented society will still provide for an increase of about 100 per cent in per capita GNP relative to 1965. Table VIII shows this.

TABLE VIII

Year 2000 Economic Scenarios
for U.S. Affluence and Alienation

Population	318 million
Employed Labor Force	122 million
Leisure Oriented Society:	Work year 1100 hours
GNP	$2,321 billion
Per Capita GNP	$7,300

Let us consider in more detail what might happen to the 40 per cent of persons who are normally in the labor force. One possibility for participation rates is set forth in the following table:

TABLE IX

In a "Normal" Postindustrial, Affluent Society of Those (40 Per Cent) Normally in the Labor Force:

50%	Work normal year
20%	Moonlight
10%	"Half-time hobbyists"
5%	Frictional unemployment
5%	Semifrictional unemployment
5%	Revolutionary or passive "dropout"
5%	"Voluntarily" unemployed
100%	

The above is not a very serious conjecture, but it seems not implausible that one-half the people would work in more or less normal fashion, and that one-fifth of the people would work longer hours than normal, either for income or for compulsive or altruistic reasons. Because of the excess contribution of this group, it may be possible to maintain something close to the high GNP projected above, even though some 20 to 30 per cent of the normal labor force contribute little or no labor. The underproducers might be, in effect, hobbyists working a few days a month, or a few months a year, to acquire the income to pursue their hobbies. One can also assume that "normal" frictional unemployment will be somewhat higher than usual, and that there will also be something which might be considered "semi-frictional" unemployment (that is, people who have lost jobs but are taking some time looking for another by using their vacations, or who have unusually high or unrealistic standards of what their jobs should be or who are just lying around living on savings.) There could also be a group, assuming the above conditions, who reject any sort of gainful employment on the ground of principle or preference. And finally, there should be people who are more willing to be on relief than not, if only because they have personal or family problems that make it unwise for them to work if they can survive without; or there may be some who are simply and cynically "on the dole."

The above suggests that in place of the current 20 per cent poor, we may have a similar number, but differently situated, who do not participate normally in the vocational life of the nation.

Consider now the problem of the annual number of hours of work. There could easily be either a four- or five-day week as described in the following two tables:

TABLE X
Some Assumed Five-Day Week Working Patterns

NOMINAL HOURS PER WEEK	LEGAL HOLIDAYS	WEEKS OFF	TOTAL WORK DAYS	TOTAL DAYS OFF	TOTAL HOURS
$5 \times 8 = 40$	10	2	240	124	1920
$5 \times 8 = 40$	10	4	230	134	1840
$5 \times 8 = 40$	10	6	220	144	1760
$5 \times 7.5 = 37.5$	10	5	225	139	1687
$5 \times 7 = 35$	10	4	230	134	1610
$5 \times 7 = 35$	10	6	220	144	1540
$5 \times 7 = 35$	10	8	210	154	1470

TABLE XI
Some Assumed Four-Day Week Working Patterns

NOMINAL HOURS PER WEEK	LEGAL HOLIDAYS	WEEKS OFF	TOTAL WORK DAYS	TOTAL DAYS OFF	TOTAL HOURS
$4 \times 7.5 = 30$	10	4	184	180	1380
$4 \times 7.5 = 30$	10	6	176	188	1320
$4 \times 7.5 = 30$	10	8	168	196	1260
$4 \times 7.5 = 30$	10	10	160	204	1200
$4 \times 7.5 = 30$	10	12	152	212	1140
$4 \times 7.5 = 30$	10	13	144	220	1080
$4 \times 7 = 28$	10	4	184	180	1208
$4 \times 7 = 28$	10	8	168	196	1096
$4 \times 7 = 28$	10	13	144	220	984

It is difficult to guess what patterns will be assumed. It should be noted that if any of the four-day week patterns were adopted the "normal" worker could spend less than 50 per cent of his days on his vocation (but only seven to seven and one-half hours per day), less than 50 per cent of his days on an avocation (possibly working somewhat longer than seven and one-half hours per day), and then still have one or two days off a week for just relaxing. In other words, it would be possible to pursue an avocation as intensely as a vocation and still have a good deal of time for "third-order" pursuits. As we pointed out at the beginning of Chapter III, such patterns can be consistent with continued economic growth at reasonably high rates.

2. Success Breeds Failure: Affluence and the Collapse of Bourgeois [2] Values

John Maynard Keynes addressed himself to this dilemma in one of the earliest and still one of the best short discussions of some of the issues raised by the accumulation of wealth through investment.[3] As he put it,

> . . . the economic problem, the struggle for subsistence, always has been hitherto the primary, most pressing problem of the human race. If the economic problem is solved, mankind will be deprived of its traditional purpose.
>
> Will this be of a benefit? If one believes at all in the real values of life, the prospect at least opens up the possibility of benefit. Yet I think with dread of the readjustment of the habits and instincts of the ordinary man, bred into him for countless generations, which he may be asked to discard within a few decades. . . . thus for the first time since his creation man will be faced with his real, his permanent problem—how to use his freedom from pressing economic cares, how to occupy his leisure, which science and compound interest will have won for him, to live wisely and agreeably and well.

There are those who would argue that with increased freedom from necessity men will be freed for more generous, public-spirited, and humane enterprises. It is a commonplace of the American consensus that it is poverty and ignorance that breed such evils as Communism, revolutions, bigotry, and race hatred. Yet we know better than to expect that the absence of poverty and ignorance will result in a triumph of virtue or even of the benign. On the contrary, it is equally plausible that a decrease in the constraints formerly imposed by harsher aspects of reality will result in large numbers of "spoiled children." At the minimum many may become uninterested in the administration and politics of a society that hands out "goodies" with unfailing and seemingly effortless regularity.

One may choose almost at will from among available hypotheses that may seem to apply to the situation, and one reaches contrary conclusions depending upon the choice that is made; this indeterminancy is perhaps a measure of the inadequacy of contemporary social thought as a basis for generalization, relative to the complexity of human phenomena.

For example, one may take the Dollard et al. [4] frustration-aggression

---

[2] We use this word in the somewhat special sense defined on p. 48.

[3] "Economic Possibilities for our Grandchildren" (1930), reprinted in J. M. Keynes, Essays in Persuasion (New York: W. W. Norton, 1963), quoting from pp. 366-67.

[4] John Dollard et al., Frustration and Aggression (New Haven, Conn.: Yale University Press, 1939).

hypothesis and conclude that aggressiveness will be greatly tranquilized in a society that provides much less external and realistic frustration. This is opposed to the more complex and more psychoanalytically oriented point of view of Freud who points to the role that frustrations imposed by external reality may play in shoring up the defenses of the character structure—defenses that are crucial strengths and that were acquired through learning, with difficulty, as an infant to defer gratification and to mediate among conflicting energies of instinctual impulses, conscience, and the opportunities and dangers of the real world.[5] Research might show, if research could be done on such a subject, that many an infantile and narcissistic personality has matured only when faced with the necessity of earning a living—others only when faced with the necessity for facing up to some personal challenge, such as military service or participation in family responsibility. (The well-known finding that suicide rates drop sharply during wars and economic depressions is subject to diverse interpretation, but it may suggest that such external challenges can serve crucial integrative or compensatory functions for some personalities, and perhaps, less dramatically, for many others.) This is not to say that equally effective or perhaps superior external challenges could not be found to substitute for the working role—or wartime experience—as a maturing or reality-focusing influence. If they are not found, however, while the economy and international and other threats make fewer demands, the decline of the values of work and national service may have some destructive effect.

Thus there may be a great increase in selfishness, a great decline of interest in government and society as a whole, and a rise in the more childish forms of individualism and in the more antisocial forms of concern for self and perhaps immediate family. Thus, paradoxically, the technological, highly productive society, by demanding less of the individual, may decrease his economic frustrations but increase his aggressions against the society. Certainly here would be fertile soil for what has come to be known as alienation.

The word alienation has been used in many different senses, some of them well defined and some in the context of systems of explanation and prescription for the ailment.[6] The young Karl Marx, for example, followed Ludwig

[5] As Freud pointed out, "Laying stress upon importance of work has a greater effect than any other technique of living in the direction of binding the individual more closely to reality; in his work he is at least securely attached to a part of reality, the human community . . . and yet . . . the great majority work only when forced by necessity, and this natural human aversion to work gives rise to the most difficult social problems." *Civilization and Its Discontents* (London: Hogarth Press, 1930), p. 34, note 1.

[6] There is little doubt that this word has been used to refer to too many different phenomena, and too many different hypotheses concerning the causal relations among the phenomena. This is illustrated in the comprehensive but diffuse collection of materials edited by Gerald Sykes, *Alienation, The Cultural Climate of Our Time* (New York: George Braziller, 1964), 2 vols. For an interesting and critical historical

Feuerbach (and to some extent anticipated Freud's *Civilization and its Discontents*) in the belief that alienation resulted from civilized man's "unnatural" repression of his instinctual, especially sexual, nature. Later, however, Marx concluded that alienation resulted from the worker's relationship to labor that had to be done for the profit of another; the cure was to have the worker "own" the means of production; thus alienation could be reduced by shortening the working day,[7] and "the worker therefore feels himself at home only during his leisure." [8]

The alienation that we speculate may result from affluence could have little or nothing to do with whether the society is capitalist or socialist. In either case the control of the decision-making apparatus would be perceived as beyond the reach of and in fact of little interest for the average person. Thus, whatever the economic system, the politics (and even the culture) of plenty could become one not of contentment but of cynicism, emotional distance, and hostility. More and more the good life would be defined in Epicurean or materialistic, rather than Stoic, or bourgeois terms. The enhancement of private values combined with the increased sense of futility about public values would also entail a kind of despair about the long-run future of the whole society. More and more people would act on the aphorism currently attributed to a leader of the new student left: "If you've booked passage on the Titanic, there's no reason to travel steerage."

Thus the classical American middle-class, work-oriented, advancement-oriented, achievement-oriented attitudes might be rejected for the following reasons:

1. Given an income per worker by the year 2000 of well over ten thousand dollars in today's dollars,[9] it may become comparatively easy for intelligent Americans to earn ten to twenty thousand dollars a year without investing very intense energies in their jobs—in effect they will be able to "coast" at that level.
2. It may become comparatively easy for an American to obtain several thousand dollars a year from friends and relatives or other sources, and to subsist without undergoing any real hardship, other than

---

survey, see Lewis Feuer, "What is Alienation? The Career of a Concept," in Stein and Vidich, eds., *Sociology on Trial,* (Englewood Cliffs, N.J.: Prentice-Hall, Inc., 1965). Feuer argues against the term on the ground that: "The career of this concept, from Calvin's depiction of man, the original sinner, alienated from God for all time, to the modern notion of man alienated somehow in every form of social organization, indicates indeed that its dominant overtone is social defeat."

[7] *Capital,* vol. II.

[8] *Economic and Philosophical Manuscripts* (1844), p. 84.

[9] See projections of United States family incomes in Chap. III.

deprivation of luxuries. (Informal polls in the Cambridge, East Village, and Haight Ashbury areas indicate that many "hippies" get along on about ten dollars per week, as do many CORE and SNCC workers.)

3. Welfare services and public facilities will generally probably put a fairly high "floor" under living standards, even in terms of luxuries such as parks, beaches, museums, and so on.

4. With money plentiful, its subjective "marginal utility" would probably tend to diminish, and there would probably be a greatly increased emphasis on things that "money cannot buy."

5. Economic and social pressures to conform may diminish as the affluent society feels increasingly that it can "afford" many kinds of slackness and deviation from the virtues that were needed in earlier times to build an industrial society.

6. If the "Puritan ethic" becomes superfluous for the functioning of the economy, the conscience-dominated character type associated with it would also tend to disappear. Parents would no longer be strongly motivated to inculcate traits such as diligence, punctuality, willingness to postpone or forego satisfaction, and similar virtues no longer relevant to the socioeconomic realities in which children are growing up.

7. Yet the need to "justify" the new patterns may remain, and to the extent that there is any residual guilt about the abandonment of the nineteenth- and early twentieth-century values, there would be exaggerated feelings *against* vocational success and achievement. Many intellectuals and contributors to popular culture would help to make the case against "bourgeois," "managerial," "bureaucratic," "industrial," "Puritanical," and "preaffluent" values. There would then be considerable cultural support for feelings ranging from indifference to outright contempt for any sort of success or achievement that has economic relevance.

Other factors would augment these effects. For example, presumably by the year 2000 much more will be known about mood-affecting drugs, and these drugs will probably be used by many as a means of escape from daily life. At the same time, the young, those without responsibility in the social system, will be increasingly alienated by a society that conspicuously fails to meet what it judges to be minimal standards of social justice and purpose (standards which look impossibly Utopian to decision-makers). Ideological movements would form to rationalize and justify rebellion and renunciation of old "obsolete" values by youth from all classes and strata

of society. Less articulate but equally rebellious young people would contribute to a great rise in crime and delinquency. Other symptoms of social
pathology, such as mental illness, neurosis, divorce, suicide, and the like
would also probably increase. Traditional religious doctrines might either
continue to lose force or continue to be reinterpreted, revised, and secu-
larized so as to pose few obstacles to the current general way of life.

On the other hand, the resources of society for dealing with these problems, perhaps in a (suffocatingly?) paternalistic way, would also have been
greatly augmented. Before discussing the differences that might be made by
social responses to these problems, let us see how they might affect various
social groups.

E. ALIENATION AND THE SOCIAL STRUCTURE

Of course not everyone would suffer equally from the prevalence of
affluence that we have just described. Among the voluntary poor, for example, there would be certain rock-bottom types who would insist on deprivation for reasons that have to do with personal psychopathology. Thus
many skid-row derelicts, alcoholics, drug addicts, ambulatory schizophrenics, and other marginal or self-destructive personalities would insist on living
at a level barely sufficient for survival. Some, indeed, would insist on slow
forms of suicide through starvation, exposure, or malnutrition, as with
some cases of alcoholism.

Most of the relatively poor members of society would, however, be
amply subsidized. They would readily accept welfare as a means of support, and the feeling that the world owes them a living would go largely
unquestioned. Incentives to take unskilled jobs would be minimal, nor
would holding a job—particularly a marginal one—add much to self-
esteem when relief and welfare have so much group approval. Extremist
movements might flourish in the general climate of alienation from the
"power structure." Many whites and middle-class Negroes might view race
riots and acts of destruction with indifference, or even sympathy and approval. The following statement of a well-known poet of Negritude may well
come to reflect the sympathies of a larger segment of both populations:

> Mercy! mercy for our omniscient conquerors
> Hurray for those who never invented anything
> Hurray for those who never explored anything
> Hurray for those who never conquered anything
> Hurray for joy

Hurray for love
Hurray for the pain of incarnate tears.[10]

At the same time, since what Oscar Lewis has described as the "culture of poverty" [11]—with its short-time perspectives and emphasis on immediate survival and pleasure, and the like—would have become, to some degree, also the culture of affluence, the assimilation of the impoverished ghetto-dweller into the larger society would pose less difficult psychological problems. The indolent spectator, the "hipster" and the "swinging cat" would have become in large degree the norm for very wide sectors of the population. Moreover, this group would be receptive to ideologies which welcome the downfall and dissolution of the American postindustrial way of life. These people would tend to be congregated in the major cities that they would probably not control politically but in which they would constitute major pressure groups and could exercise veto rights on many programs. They would probably live in rather uneasy and unstable alliance with the upper middle class, "responsible" people who would continue to control the economic structure and make use of the resources of the city.

The following tables indicate one estimate (from *U.S. News and World Report*) of the likely increase in the concentration of Negroes in major cities. These figures seem to be those that might be reached by a straightforward projection of current trends and probably exaggerate the proportions of the ethnic shift that is in prospect. (Unless these projections assume *all* Negroes have moved to the listed areas, they imply an implausibly high increase in the percentage of Negroes in the total United States population by the year 2000.) Even so, they are an indication of already obvious changes in urban demography that may have great political and economic significance.

It has often been pointed out that current United States racial conflicts involving issues such as housing and education are based as much on issues of poverty and social class as on racism. Although the racism and militancy of the Black Muslims (and the possibility that they may be misused as a group by those who eventually succeed in what seems to be an intermittent power struggle within the movement) may make it difficult for whites to welcome the group, it may be the most active force since the Christian evangelists in recruiting new Negro members into the middle class.

[10] Aimé Césaire, *Cahier D'un Retour Au Pays Natale,* as quoted in Colin Legum. *Pan-Africanism,* rev. ed. (London: Pall Mall Press Ltd.; New York: Frederick A. Praeger, 1965).
[11] Oscar Lewis, *La Vida, A Puerto Rican Family in the Culture of Poverty-San Juan and New York* (New York: Random House, 1966), esp. pp. xlii-lii.

TABLE XII
How Negro Population Will Grow in the Cities

Negroes will make up half or more of the population inside these cities by the year 2000:

	PER CENT NEGRO IN 1960	PER CENT NEGRO IN 2000
Washington, D.C.	53.9	75
Cleveland, Ohio	28.6	67
Newark, N.J.	34.1	63
Baltimore, Md.	34.7	56
Chicago, Ill.	22.9	55
New York City	14.0	50
Philadelphia, Pa.	26.4	50
Detroit, Mich.	28.9	50
St. Louis, Mo.	28.6	50

Negroes will make up one-third to one-half of the population inside these cities:

	PER CENT NEGRO IN 1960	PER CENT NEGRO IN 2000
Atlanta, Ga.	38.3	44
Kansas City, Mo.	17.5	42
Cincinnati, Ohio	21.6	40
San Francisco-Oakland, Calif.	14.3	40
Houston, Tex.	22.9	34
Buffalo, N.Y.	13.3	34
Pittsburgh, Pa.	16.7	34
Paterson-Clifton-Passaic, N.J.	9.3	34

Negroes will make up one-fifth to one-third of the population inside these cities:

	PER CENT NEGRO IN 1960	PER CENT NEGRO IN 2000
Boston, Mass.	9.1	31
Dallas, Tex.	19.0	30
Milwaukee, Wis.	8.4	29
Los Angeles, Calif.	12.2	20

How Negro Population Will Grow in the Suburbs

In suburbs surrounding big cities, Negro population will grow in years ahead —but still will remain less than one-fourth of the total. Here, for some major cities, are the percentages of Negroes in the suburban population:

	PER CENT NEGRO IN 1960	PER CENT NEGRO IN 2000
San Francisco-Oakland, Calif.	4.8	22
Washington, D.C.	6.1	19
Baltimore, Md.	6.7	19

Philadelphia, Pa.	6.1	18
Detroit, Mich.	3.7	13
Houston, Tex.	10.3	12
Cincinnati, Ohio	3.4	12
Cleveland, Ohio	.7	12
Newark, N.J.	6.7	10
Chicago, Ill.	2.9	10
San Diego, Calif.	1.1	10
St. Louis, Mo.	6.1	7
Paterson-Clifton-Passaic, N.J.	1.9	7
Kansas City, Mo.	5.9	6
Atlanta, Ga.	8.5	6
Dallas, Tex.	6.5	5
Pittsburgh, Pa.	3.4	4
Los Angeles, Calif.	3.1	4
Boston, Mass.	.8	2

How Negro Population Will Grow in Total Metropolitan Areas

Including both suburbs and central cities, Negroes by 2000 will make up one-fifth or more of the population in these metropolitan areas:

	PER CENT NEGRO IN 1960	PER CENT NEGRO IN 2000
Baltimore, Md.	21.9	30
Washington, D.C.	24.3	27
Philadelphia, Pa.	15.5	27
New York City	11.5	27
Cleveland, Ohio	14.3	26
Chicago, Ill.	14.3	25
San Francisco-Oakland, Calif. ...	8.6	24
Detroit, Mich.	14.9	20
Atlanta, Ga.	22.8	20
Houston, Tex.	19.8	20

Negroes will make up one-tenth to one-fifth of the population in these metropolitan areas:

	PER CENT NEGRO IN 1960	PER CENT NEGRO IN 2000
Cincinnati, Ohio	12.0	19
Newark, N.J.	13.3	18
St. Louis, Mo.	14.3	17
Kansas City, Mo.	11.2	16
Dallas, Tex.	14.3	13
San Diego, Calif.	3.8	13
Buffalo, N.Y.	6.3	11
Paterson-Clifton-Passaic, N.J.	3.6	10

SOURCE: Census Bureau, 1960; estimates by USN&WR Economic Unit for year 2000, copyright 1966, *U.S. News & World Report,* Inc., from issue of February 21, 1966.

TABLE XIII

The Black Muslims

1. Become legally married
2. Give up alcohol, drugs, and pork
3. Work 8 hours per day—6 days per week
4. Support their families
5. Are strong (even domineering) father figures
6. Dress neatly and conventionally
7. Send their children to school
8. Maintain their dignity and self-respect
9. Save their money
10. Often become small entrepreneurs
11. Hate whites and preach apartheid and violence

Thus, perhaps surprisingly, this group may be the means—over one or two generations—for many who might otherwise have remained in the "culture of poverty" to acquire "father figures," motivation for striving, and ultimately typical American middle-class attitudes and occupations. When this process has been completed, the racism of the Nation of Islam may disappear or diminish, leaving little more "unmelted" in the "pot" than in the typical "successful" American pattern, in which there ordinarily remains some ethnic self-consciousness (and some "intergroup tensions") among mostly assimilated, but still distinct, former immigrant groups.[12]

Returning to the society as a whole: The lower middle classes (who in general will be making between ten and twenty thousand 1965 dollars a year) would enjoy a greatly reduced work week with some emphasis on leisure. While their necessities and basic luxuries would be obtainable without great effort, they might still wish to increase income by moonlighting or by the wife's working. Some, of course, would have little motivation for expending extra effort and for them the problems of occupying leisure time would be a primary concern. Others would want to save money, pursue expensive hobbies, or emulate some aspect of the life patterns of the upper middle classes or even the wealthy. Both groups would provide a tremendous market for all kinds of sports and fads and particularly for various forms of mass entertainment. Year 2000 equivalents for the bowling alley, miniature slot-racing car tracks, and the outboard motor, would be everywhere. The drive-in church, the "museum-o-rama," and comparable manifestations of pressures toward a general degradation and vulgarization of culture would be a likely result of the purchasing decisions of this group. At the

[12] See Nathan Glazer and Daniel Patrick Moynihan, *Beyond the Melting Pot* (Cambridge, Mass.: Massachusetts Institute of Technology Press, 1963).

same time, these people might militate politically against civil rights and against the poor and relatively poor nonworking classes that they must support, and they would likely provide the primary support for both conservative national policies and political jingoism.

The upper middle class (most of whom will have annual income of perhaps twenty to sixty thousand 1965 dollars), by contrast, would, in many ways, be emulating the life-style of the landed gentry of the previous century, such as emphasizing education, travel, cultural values, expensive residences, lavish entertainments, and a mannered and cultivated style of life. For some there would be much effort to amass property and money for personal and family use. Getting away from the cities and from centers of population would be a difficult problem which only large amounts of money will solve. There would probably be some emphasis on "self-improvement" including cultural dilettantism. While among most members of this group we would expect a continuation of current well-to-do suburban patterns, in many cases patterns of life might be increasingly self-indulgent, marriages unstable, children alienated from their parents. Interest in strange and exotic political ideologies, Eastern mysticism, and the like, might flourish, as could a cult of aestheticism and a shrinking from the "grubby" or "crass" aspects of society. Effete attitudes might be combined with contempt for the lower middle class and fear of the poor and of their propensity for violence. There may also be some romanticization of the "noble savage" (or "hippy") who lives outside the values of the society, in voluntary poverty and/or minor or even major criminality.

The very wealthy would be able to buy considerable protection from these exigencies—that is, from all but the cultural confusion and normative conflicts. Because of their social power, many would have responsibility and there might be, in some groups, a sense of noblesse oblige, which would be shared by many in the upper middle class.

Youth could be especially self-indulgent or alienated, as the identity confusion typical of adolescence is exacerbated by the confusion, normlessness, and anomie of the society. Indifference to moral and ethical values and irresponsibility of personal behavior would be combined with feelings of outrage about the vast discrepancies between the wealth of the rich nations and the poor, and an especially painful situation would arise if these young people were drafted for military service in teeming, underdeveloped countries. Combined with pacifism and antipatriotic ideologies would be a strong feeling that American lives are too precious to be spent anywhere else in the world—or indeed to be wasted in America itself. Recruitment into any of the more difficult or demanding professions would be restricted to those (perhaps many) who have adopted Stoic patterns, and to the sons of fathers who are already in those professions and who identify with them. Conformers would—as always—work, aspire to comfortable sinecures, and look forward to early retirement—but now with great confidence. "Bumming around" and hip patterns of life could become increasingly common (though not the norm) in all but the lower middle-class groups. Many would live indefinitely on the resources of friends and relatives and on opportunistic sources of income without doing any sustained work, or in the upper middle-class pattern would cloak themselves in pretentions to artistic creativity. In spite of the prominence of symbols of rebellion and nonconformity, these youths, especially because of their anomie and alienation, would be subject to extreme fads of behavior and political, ethical, and religious ideas.

Of course, it is important to note that the lower middle class, making, say, five to twenty thousand dollars a year, are by 2000 not going to be very different from the lower middle and middle middle classes today. The upper (and middle) middle class in the year 2000 make, say, twenty to one hundred thousand dollars a year and will not necessarily feel independently wealthy. Both groups by and large will probably continue (with some erosion) with current work-oriented, advancement-oriented, achievement-oriented values. The extreme alienation we are talking about is restricted to minorities, which will be important in part because they are likely to be concentrated in the big cities, in part because they appeal to many of the more intellectual members of that ordinarily alienated group—adolescents—and mostly because their members will be literate and articulate and have a large impact on intellectuals and therefore on the culture generally.

It would be useful to make explicit the notions that determine these speculations and to discuss the alternative speculations that might be made. In particular, the evidence that might be found for or against the various alternative hypotheses and speculations should be given; only a small start can be made in this direction here.

F. FUNCTIONS OF WORK

To arrive more precisely at an answer to the question, "What are the consequences of a reduction in the amount of work that needs to be done?" one must ask, "What are the various functions for the individual of the work he performs?" It is easy to make a long list of such benefits at various levels of analysis. For example, people derive from work such benefits as role; status; sense of striving; feeling of productivity, competency, and achievement; and relationships with others and advancement in a hierarchy, whether organizational or professional.

The following table shows some rough characterizations and generalizations about various roles work may play for different kinds of people in the year 2000. Those whose basic attitude toward work is that it is totally abhorrent or reprehensible are not listed, since on the whole they will find it possible to avoid employment entirely.

TABLE XIV

Basic Attitude Toward Work As:	Basic Additional Value Fulfilled by Work
1. Interruption	Short-run income
2. Job	Long-term income—some work-oriented values (one works to live)
3. Occupation	Exercise and mastery of gratifying skills—some satisfaction of achievement-oriented values
4. Career	Participating in an important activity or program. Much satisfaction of work-oriented, achievement-oriented, advancement-oriented values
5. Vocation (calling)	Self-identification and self-fulfillment
6. Mission	Near fanatic or single-minded focus on achievement or advancement (one lives to work)

As discussed later one could easily imagine that many Americans from "normal" (i.e., not deprived) backgrounds will increasingly adopt the first position, that work is an interruption, while many formerly in the lower and economically depressed classes will increasingly shift to the second or third positions which reflect more work-oriented and achievement-oriented values. On the other hand, the man whose missionary zeal for work takes priority over all other values will be looked on as an unfortunate, perhaps even a harmful and destructive neurotic. Even those who find in work a "vocation" are likely to be thought of as selfish, excessively narrow, or compulsive.

Many of the benefits of work could be derived from other forms of activity, provided they were available and, preferably, institutionalized. The model of the cultivated gentlemen, for example, is likely to be available and possibly generally usable in a democratic and upward mobile society like the United States. It may be argued that aristocrats are far more visible in Europe and that it is more respectable for the wealthy to live as landed gentry, rentiers, even as playboys in Europe than in the United States, and that for these reasons the transition to this pattern of life would be easier in Europe. Indeed, historically this has often been the aspiration and achievement (after a generation or two) of the upper middle class and even the lower class nouveaux riches. On the other hand, if it became the ideal it is probably more difficult for a typical European to think of making the social transition to such a status for himself than it would be for the typical American. Of course, the American has seen fewer examples of such lives, and has up to now respected them less. Therefore it seems less likely to be the American ideal.

In the economic structure we are describing, there may be a special problem of the service professions whose productivity per hour may not have gone up. Thus many believe there are probably important limits to the extent to which the efficiency of persons such as teachers, professors, doctors, lawyers, ministers, psychologists, social workers, and so forth can be increased. Others believe that not only can these professions be automated,[13] but that there are huge opportunities for increasing efficiency through better organization, specialization, and the very skilled use of computers. Nevertheless, there are likely to remain irreducible kinds of activities that defy rationalization or improvement, such as those that require face-to-face meeting and conversation. Thus programmed instruction, lectures, and sermons over television are not likely to displace face-to-face human communication, at least not without great loss to those involved. Therefore only part of the current activity in these fields is likely to increase in productivity.

To the extent that recruitment into the service professions is greatly expanded because of the reduced need for people in manufacturing, routine aspects of public administration, and automated administrative and managerial tasks, several problems will arise. One is that it will be perhaps more difficult to recruit people to do difficult and demanding work that either requires long and arduous training or requires working under difficult, dangerous, or frustrating conditions. If the hours of work of people in these professions go down severely, the incentives and psychological functions of membership in the profession may be somewhat diluted. For example, a hospital may have three head nurses if there are three shifts; what happens, however, when there are six or eight shifts? To what extent is authority, expertise, and satisfaction diluted when power, responsibility, and status are so fractionated?

Similar questions should be posed about other kinds of activities. In general, a threefold increase in GNP per capita is far from the equivalent of a threefold increase in productivity per capita in all relevant respects. As real productivity increases dramatically in certain industries, principally in manufacturing and heavily clerical industries, such as banking and insurance and many federal, state, and local governmental functions, which could be very much automated, the price structure would also change dramatically. This would result in enormous increase in the availability, variety, and quality of goods and many standardized services, since these items would become very much cheaper or very much better for the same price. A three-

[13] Thus much legal research can be done most easily through a computerized library. A physician may be able to phone a list of symptoms into a central computer and get back a print-out of suggested diagnostic possibilities. Many laboratory tests might be performable by methods which would present immediate results. Closed circuit television and various kinds of continuously reading tests presented on central display boards could even now make the utilization of hospital personnel also much more efficient. Other possibilities were mentioned in Chapter II.

fold increase in GNP per capita would probably imply a much greater increase in standard of living with respect to these items. Yet, at the same time, skilled, personal services requiring irreducible quantities of human time, training, and talent would become both absolutely and relatively expensive. Thus there would probably still be a very strong demand for, and probably also a much expanded supply of expensive and skilled professionals, managers, entrepreneurs, artisans, technicians and artists—for the most part, the well-educated upper middle class. This group may well be much too busy and well rewarded to be alienated.

Furthermore, even if one imagines the ordinary member of the labor force amply supplied with intricate technology affording innumerable needs and luxuries during his short work week, and even if he can travel anywhere in the less-developed world and easily buy vast quantities of domestic service and other personal attentions during his long vacations, many important consumer items are likely to remain too expensive for him to wish his work week to become *too* short. There will probably still be a class of "luxury items," consisting of such things as vacation houses in extremely exotic places, advanced or "sporty" personal vehicles such as perhaps ground-effect machines, or similar items for the most part well beyond today's technology and prohibitively expensive for ordinary workers by today's standards, that by the year 2000 will be still expensive, but perhaps within reach of the man who is interested in earning enough money—and many, no doubt, will be interested.

G. OTHER FACTORS IN ALIENATION

In discussing alienation, attention ought also to be given to other aspects of cultural change that may contribute to ego-disintegration and feelings of disorientation. Here we meet the difficult problem of diagnosing the malaise of our times. What precisely causes the alienation of adolescents and many others in 1967 is a very controversial matter. Speculation about the year 2000 is, of course, many times more complicated and uncertain. If it sometimes seems to be easier this is presumably mostly because the results are less checkable—though it is possible that there will be clear and predictable tendencies in 2000 that are only ambiguously detectable today. In any case it seems plausible that the "end of ideology" and an inevitable disenchantment with the ideals and expectations of American democracy and free enterprise, coupled with a continued decline in the influence of traditional religion and the absence of any acceptable mass ideologies, have and will continue to contribute to a common spiritual and political rootlessness. As secularization, rationalization, and innovation continue to change the culture in the direction of Sensate and bourgeois norms, the influence of traditional *Weltanschauungen* seems more likely to continue to wane than to undergo any resurgence in the next thirty-three years.

Furthermore some things have happened or are happening that change man's relation to his universe in ways that may be unsettling for many people. For example, the inventions of nuclear weapons and intercontinental delivery systems have probably made human life permanently more precarious, and have introduced into international relations a new level of potential horror that is difficult even to imagine with any precision. At the minimum they provide any who wish for it a good excuse for aimless drifting or horrified resentment; in addition, they are ample reasons for both realistic concern and widespread neurotic anxiety and despair.

Technological change itself may contribute to feelings of estrangement from the new physical world and also from a society strongly affected by continual innovation and disruption. There is a long tradition in American letters of hostility to the machine,[14] and, at least since World War II, an increasing perception that the social consequences of science and technology are, at best, mixed blessings. Machines that perform some functions of the human mind far better than humans can are likely to be even more resented, in spite of their economic benefits, than machines that do the same for human muscles. The human place in the world may be most seriously disturbed by new medical technology. New drugs will raise sharply the questions, what is a real human feeling, and what is a genuine personality? Plastic replacements for hearts and other vital organs raise in new and more difficult form the old problem of defining life and death, and add a new difficulty to the old question, what is a human being?

The exploration of space already under way may also have a somewhat disturbing impact on the imaginations of many people. It is well known, for example, that many schizophrenics are preoccupied with fantasies of space exploration (as well as fantasies involving the immense destructive potential of the H-bomb). Phenomena such as weightlessness, dependence for existence on a wholly artificial and technologically sustained environment, and isolation from familiar objects and human kind may have obvious impact on some minds and more subtle impact on a great many. The unconscious is, as Freud has reminded us, an inveterate punster, and it may not be acci-

---

[14] Leo Marx in *The Machine in the Garden: Technology and the Pastoral Idea in America* (New York: Oxford University Press, 1964), treats this American tradition at some length and with extreme sympathy. Lewis Mumford's *The Myth of the Machine: Technics and Human Development* (New York: Harcourt, Brace and World, 1967), is the latest in his long series of works belonging to this tradition; in particular, it represents a reinterpretation of archaeology and early history intended to show that speech, and not the ability to use tools and technics, was once, and should become again the essential human faculty. See also Eric Hoffer, *The Temper of Our Time* (New York: Harper and Row, 1967), for some caustic comments on this idiosyncrasy of some intellectuals.

dental that phrases such as way out, far gone, out of it, and out of this world are currently used to mean strange or bizarre; and that, moreover, phrases such as way out, dropout, flip-out, freak-out, turned on, tuned in, out of my head, and cool are supposed to refer to desirable conditions.[15] Perhaps the most important alienating influence will be a purely negative thing—the absence of the traditional challenge of work, community approval, and national needs.

H. HUMANISM AND THE VALUE OF TIME

It is possible to suppose that something else might happen. For example, John Adams, our second President, once suggested that: "my sons ought to study mathematics and philosophy, geography, natural history and naval architecture, in order to give their children a *right* to study painting, poetry, music, architecture, statuary, tapestry and porcelain. . . ." (emphasis added).

The passage is peculiarly American; almost no (correspondingly upper-class) European would use the word "right." The most he would have said would be that his sons *ought* to emphasize mathematics, philosophy, geography, and so on, in order that their sons *could* emphasize painting, poetry, music, and the like. He would feel that some interest in painting, poetry, and music was proper and unremarkable. On the other hand for most Americans a man who is deeply preoccupied with porcelain, or any of the fine arts, may still be, even in this less Philistine age, a bit suspect—whether as effeminate or as simply not sufficiently serious and practical. Adams's statement is characteristically American, in that it gives an overwhelming priority to the needs of national security and statemanship and asserts that no one has a *right* to devote his attention to "finer things" for their own sake, until these needs have been adequately met. A contemporary parallel is the American upper middle-class view of the proper relation between work and play. Typically an American businessman or professional man apologizes for taking a vacation by explaining it is only "in order to recharge his batteries"; he justifies rest or play mostly in terms of returning to do a better job. The European by contrast seems to enjoy his vacation as a pleasure in its own right, and does not hesitate to work for the express purpose of being able to afford to play in better style.

We have already suggested that in the postindustrial society that we are describing, in continental Europe the middle and upper classes could, in effect, return to or adopt the manner of the "gentleman." Many Europeans, of course, argue that things are now going the other way, that under the impact of a mass-consumption, materialistic culture the humanistic values that have been so characteristic in Europe are rapidly eroding or disappear-

[15] Freak-out can also refer to a "bad trip."

ing. One can fully concede that this is indeed the current phase and still note that there is likely to be a reaction in the not-too-distant future. Even today many Europeans seem to emphasize nonvocational aspects of their life much more intensely than even the family-oriented Americans do. For example, many Europeans seem to plan intensely, a year ahead, how they will spend their vacations. Once on vacation, they would resent any interruption for work—such as a business phone call—far more than any American would. It is the vacation that, at the time at least, deserves to be taken more seriously—not the work.

While the American has no sense of "staying in his place" and therefore could seek to emulate aristocratic ideals, the issue remains as to what extent the gentleman of leisure will be an ideal. It simply has not been one in the United States in the last one hundred and fifty years. On the other hand, the middle and upper middle class in Europe have often aspired to be gentlemen, and when tradesmen made fortunes they often made the transition, or at least their children did. In the United States, on the contrary, a member of the middle class who makes his fortune, or his descendants, such as those in the Yankee upper class, usually persists in the tradition of hard work and of service of one kind or another.

Thus if the average American had an opportunity to live on the beach for six months a year doing nothing, he might have severe guilt feelings in addition to a sunburn. If an American wishes to be broiled in the sun, he usually must go through a preliminary justification such as the following: "The system is corrupt, I reject it. Its values are not my values. To hell with these puritanical, obsolete concepts." Only at that point can he relax in the sun. If he is more guilty, or articulate, he may proclaim: "All of those robots who are working have sold out to the soulless, inhumane system with its obsolete and grubby, machine-based, materialistic values, and its empty goals of the Bitch-Goddess of monetary success. By refusing to be drawn in, I at least can preserve my humanity, individuality, integrity, dignity, and physical health, as well as my spontaneity, the freshness of my perceptions, the openness of my relating, and my capacity to love." Unless an American has taken an ideological and moralistic stance against the work-oriented value system, he cannot abandon work.

On the other hand, a good many Americans, and typically middle-class Americans, will have a sense of noblesse oblige. Some of the same pressures toward Stoic values that were important in the Roman Empire will be important here as well.

Let it be added that in this "super-affluent" society of year 2000, it is not likely that efficiency (defined by the criteria of maximizing profit or income) will still be primary, though it will doubtless remain important. To some degree this has already occurred and the situation in the United States is today very different from what it was before 1929. For example, it seems to be true that when a middle-class American looked for a job in 1929, he was interested in salary and prospects for advancement. Today, however, the first questions addressed to personnel interviewers are more likely to relate the satisfaction of the applicant's family with the new neighborhood and the quality of the schools. This is, of course, particularly true of professional and managerial workers, but it seems to be more widely spread as well. It is only after the requirements of home and children have been satisfied (and sometimes considerations of pension, vacation, and insurance as well), that salary and advancement are discussed.

We could think of this phenomenon as a shift to humanistic rather than vocational or advancement-oriented values, and conjecture that this tendency will increase over the next thirty-three years. Indeed, unless there is a surprising interruption in the exponential progress of prosperity, sensate-humanist and epicurean values almost surely will come to dominate older bourgeois virtues, and may even return, in some respects, to criteria that antedated the "bourgeois" element of the multifold trend, which has been a driving force for more than five centuries. Thus Keynes—here the "reactionary"—returns to the Sermon on the Mount:

> I see us free, therefore, to return to some of the most sure and certain principles of religion and traditional virtue—that avarice is a vice, that the exaction of usury is a misdemeanour, and the love of money is detestable, that those walk most truly in the paths of virtue and sane wisdom who take least thought for the morrow. We shall once more value ends above means and prefer the good to the useful. We shall honour those who can teach us how to pluck the hour and the day virtuously and well, the delightful people who are capable of taking direct enjoyment in things, the lilies of the field who toil not, neither do they spin.
>
> But beware! The time for all this is not yet. For at least another hundred years we must pretend to ourselves and to every one that fair is foul and foul is fair; for foul is useful and fair is not. Avarice and usury and precaution must be our gods for a little longer still. For only they can lead us out of the tunnel of economic necessity into daylight.[16]

The new values could not only be premature, they could also be wrong. The year 2000 conditions we have sketched could produce a situation in which illusion, wishful thinking, even obviously irrational behavior could exist to a degree unheard of today. Such irrational and self-indulgent behavior is quite likely in a situation in which an individual is overprotected and has no systematic or objective contact with reality. For example, there are probably many people for whom work is the primary touch with reality. If work is removed, or if important functions are taken from work, the contact these people have with reality will be to some degree impaired. The

[16] J. M. Keynes, "Economic Possibilities for Our Grandchildren," *Essays in Persuasion,* pp. 371-72. Compare Matthew 6:19-34.

results—minor or widespread—may become apparent in forms such as political disruption, disturbed families, and personal tragedies—or in the pursuit of some "humanistic" values that many would think of as frivolous or even irrational.

Humanistic values are, of course, a question of definition. While some may judge certain ideologies that invoke humanistic language as better described as sentimental, self-indulgent, or rationalizations of quite irrational feelings of rebelliousness and selfishness, others will accept the ideology. (While this is, of course, more or less a value question, facts and analysis have some relevance to it.)

Consider this question of humanistic versus irrational or indulgent behavior. In 1926 the British economist Arthur Redford said, in describing the adjustment of British yeomen to industrialization: "In the course of a generation or two it becomes quite 'natural' . . . for a fixed number of hours each day, regulating their exertions constantly . . . there may be some temporary restlessness among the 'hands,' but the routine soon reestablishes itself as part of the ordinary discipline of life." While this may be a rather callous observation, "progress" and other conditions predominantly made the adjustment a necessary one.

In the post affluent, seemingly very secure world of the year 2000, we will not likely, and presumably should not, be willing to ask people to make sacrifices of this order. However, new issues will arise. Consider the following two statements put forth by Berkeley students on signs they were carrying while picketing and later on a BBC television broadcast:

> I am a human being; please do not fold, spindle, or mutilate.

> Life here is a living hell.

One can only agree with the first, assuming we understand precisely in what way the students believe they are not treated as well as IBM cards. Thus it was widely believed, especially in the 1930's and 1940's, by people who thought they were "psychologically sophisticated," that any kind of discipline for children causes undesirable repression, inhibits creativity, and creates neuroses; that almost completely permissive upbringing is necessary for a parent not to "fold, spindle, or mutilate." Today psychoanalysts are emphasizing that a reasonable level of benevolent but firm discipline is very much needed by a child, and that excessive permissiveness is more likely to result in a child marred by guilty wilfulness, irresponsibility, and inadequacy.

Of course, the students would argue that they do not mean anything so extreme, but just that they ought to be treated better than items processed by machines. One can only sympathize with their lack of ability to communicate with a seemingly unfeeling, bureaucratic administration choosing to enforce computer decisions. But to argue that the idiosyncrasies of a computer that allows ten minutes between classes which require fifteen minutes to reach, or that assigns art classes to basements and engineering classes to top-floor rooms with windows, creates difficulties for students, is rather different from arguing that life is a "living hell." The most that students could reasonably say was that the administration made life unnecessarily complicated and frustrating, and had occasionally overstepped its proper bounds. Yet they chose to state (and no doubt felt) these issues in moralistic, politicized, ideological, and emotionally extreme terms. Similarly, increasing numbers of Americans are likely not only to reject currently held work-oriented, achievement-oriented, advancement-oriented attitudes, but are likely to adopt the kind of "spoiled child" attitudes that seem to have characterized at least some of the Berkeley protesters.

I. WHAT IS A STABLE STATE FOR THE ALIENATED-AFFLUENT SOCIETY?

Nevertheless such a society—affluent, humanistic, leisure-oriented, and partly alienated—might be quite stable. It might, in fact, bear some resemblance to some aspects of Greek society (though of course Greek society did not develop primarily because of affluence). We can imagine a situation in which, say, 70 or 80 per cent of people become gentlemen and put a great deal of effort into various types of self-development, though not necessarily the activities which some futurists find most important for a humanistic culture. But one could imagine, for example, a very serious emphasis on sports, on competitive "partner" games (chess, bridge), on music, art, languages, or serious travel, or on the study of science, philosophy, and so on. The crucial point here is that a large majority of the population may feel it important to develop skills, activities, arts, and knowledge to meet very high minimum absolute standards, and a large minority more or less compete to be an elite of elites. One issue is whether or not people who are not well rounded in a number of areas simultaneously, more or less as a gentleman should be, will be considered seriously inferior, or whether it will be sufficient for a person to fulfill himself even if he wishes to do it very narrowly. In both cases, however, there are likely to be at least subtle social pressures for such self-development. In the absence of such social pressures, then, we would still expect much of the same kind of activity but now more in the range of 20 or 30 per cent of the population than 70 or 80 per cent.

Thus there is a very large difference between merely having community acceptance of the right for an individual to spend a lot of time and money on improving himself in this way, and community "demand" that he do so in order to be considered a reasonable or full member of the community, or an educated man. It is hard to believe that in the long run we are not going to get something on the order of the latter in the affluent, postindustrial society. That is, people who are behaving in the new modes will simply look down on those who are not. Indeed there are now such pressures on families in middle-class communities, where there is great emphasis on giving the children dancing lessons, music lessons, and fostering nonutilitarian skills which improve their ability to enjoy themselves and, most important, to be more socially desirable. In other words, middle-class children in the United States are now being treated in a manner not too dissimilar from the way aristocrats treated their children some years ago, except that there is little emphasis on being hard and tough, having a sense of noblesse oblige, and there are somewhat less demanding standards of performance. But while contemporary American parents are in many ways very soft on children, and certainly demand much less in the way of help with chores or housework than they did several generations ago, when it comes to socially important achievements in school, dancing, music, athletics, and so on, they tend to be rather startlingly demanding. While it is true that in many cases the children enjoy these activities and do not resent having their schedules so filled, there are many cases in which they do, in fact, feel overburdened by their demanding routine and still feel real pressures to maintain it.[17]

J. A NOTE ON THE PROBLEM OF MAINTENANCE

Many people have been concerned with the possibility that our high future standard of consumption may be negatively affected by the difficulty of maintaining the various vehicles, appliances, and other gadgets involved in personal life, not to speak of the various buildings or personal services. It is clear that there will indeed be a problem. Even today we find that people are

---

[17] One example of the new pressures on children is the "swimming club," which allows earlier, longer, and more vigorous training. As a result old speed records are easily broken; the old records are now almost trivial. This sort of emphasis, which requires an extreme dedication to a (noneconomic) activity from very young children, is also likely to be quite common. Even more likely, of course, will be somewhat less emphasis on any one activity but almost as much emphasis on a set of activities with, of course, lower standards. Fashions for extraordinary achievement of one sort or another may sweep the country. This is, of course, one way in which one can imagine leisure being used in an affluent society. It is difficult to imagine any other that seems plausible that is also satisfactory, in that it does not result in large numbers of people who have a sense of meaninglessness and purposelessness about their lives.

throwing out toasters and inexpensive appliances rather than repairing them. Thus, if one compares the United States with a country like Colombia, to take an extreme example, one finds that Americans junk cars many, many years before they would be junked in Colombia. In Colombia, because there is a shortage of foreign exchange, they do not allow the easy importation of cars. Therefore Colombian mechanics—many of whom are illiterate—have become extraordinarily skilled in keeping old cars running, even manufacturing spare parts. This example gives us a clue to one of the things that might happen. We may import mechanics in the same way we today import resident physicians and interns (in many hospitals 70 to 80 per cent in the United States today come from less-developed nations). One can also easily imagine that as far as moving parts are concerned, the relative cost of repairing could become more and more expensive and the typical solution—both in home and business—may be much like the solution now adopted by the Air Force and many industries: complete replacement of modular units. Thus moving parts such as motors and cleaning elements that are likely to wear out will be built to be maintenance free, and if they fail they will be pulled out and replaced as a unit, the old unit then rebuilt, destroyed, or (as suggested earlier) sent to a less-developed nation for salvage. As for maintenance that cannot be done this way, it is probable that large maintenance organizations will be created that will contract such service for many people (but perhaps not the majority of homeowners, who may prefer to do much of it themselves as a hobby and as a method of "investing" their leisure time). This contract maintenance could be staffed by several kinds of persons. First, there would be Americans who happen to have grown up in a way that leaves them motivated to work, but whose gifts do not enable them to achieve in the more managerial, bureaucratic, intellectual pursuits favored by those who continue to work in this new society. Second, there is likely to be a good deal of import of labor from places like Latin America where competent mechanics will exist who cannot earn very much. (It is easy to imagine that in the year 2000 a mechanic who might be lucky to make two or three thousand dollars a year in Latin America could make ten to twenty thousand a year in the United States.) This import of labor could be via normal immigration, or through special contract labor routes, as in the EEC today.

In view of this potential combination of new designs, new organizations, and useful tasks profitable for an imported class of foreigners, it seems unlikely that the problem of in-place maintenance cannot be solved. For very skilled maintenance, as with expensive watches, one would expect either that repairing will be an extremely valued skill reimbursed proportionately, that there will be imported contract labor, or that the watch or other item will be sent to a foreign country for repair.

K. SOCIAL RESPONSE TO NEW DIFFICULTIES

The most serious issue raised by these speculations (in addition to their validity, of course) is whether they are not just modern manifestations of traditional "aberrant" behavior, or whether they represent a reasonable adjustment or transition state to new traditions and mores. There is also the question of to what degree society will be self-correcting and self-adjusting. Doubtless, however, there will be much room and need for improved social policies. Just as it seems likely that societies have learned to handle routine economic problems sufficiently well to avoid serious depressions, it may be that we have begun to understand social and psychological problems well enough to avoid the partial passivity and failure implicit in these speculations.

While few would now believe that the mere multiplication of productive powers is likely to bring mankind into Utopia, or into anything resembling it, it would be ironic (but not unprecedented) if this multiplication of resources were to create problems too serious for the solutions that those very resources should make feasible. Efforts will doubtlessly be needed to invent and implement ways of coping with the new and unfamiliar problems that will certainly arise. (What these will and should be is beyond the scope of this report, which is intended, of course, to raise such issues rather than to evaluate and settle them.) Yet, despite best efforts, social policies frequently go wrong; in the final chapter we explore some of the ways this can happen and some of the things that might help to anticipate difficulties early enough to cope with them.

CHAPTER V

International Politics in the Standard World

A. INTRODUCTION

We shall examine in this chapter, but with more freedom and selective detail, some international aspects of the Standard World described in Chapter III. For the most part, we shall be making explicit assumptions that make plausible "surprise-free" extrapolations of current international trends. Of course, what is relatively unsurprising to us—and to several of our colleagues at Hudson Institute—may seem quite startling to some other opinion. On the whole, however, we believe we are reflecting much of informed, current opinion. We will leave out discussions of such issues as the future and likely role of NATO, France, and so on, because there seems to be so little consensus on these issues.

The Standard World, with our projections of existing trends, is probably relatively familiar and acceptable to most readers. Its elements are for the most part those with which we live today; its problems are to some degree the problems of today, though often either intensified or given a new dimension. The Canonical Variations, discussed in the next chapter, are in many ways more interesting because they incorporate significant, yet not completely implausible, deviations from the standard trends (though on the whole they could still be classified as surprise-free); from this point of view, even more interesting are those future potentialities (noted in Chapter VII) which challenge the surprise-free and standard projections and radically alter the terms of the world we know today.

We will not write a detailed scenario for arriving at the Standard World but we will indicate some of the ways current international issues are tending and some of the arguments for our beliefs. Perhaps the most important assumption of the international aspects of the Standard World is that the physical territories of most or all of the old nations of the world are likely to be free of invasion and even relatively free of domestic violence. That is, we assume, as explained in Section A of Chapter III, that the world's situation today is not very different from that of Europe in 1815, a period when Europe had been through a quarter century of intense ideological conflict and when many expected to see still more such conflict in the following twenty-five or fifty years. While there were serious revolutionary disturbances in 1830 and 1848, they were not as intense as many had feared and they were relatively easily contained or limited. When a serious change in the balance of power did occur, in 1866 and 1871, it came from a more or less unexpected source (Prussia); and the Great War that ended an era of almost one hundred years of relative peace and stability grew directly out of that unexpected change in the balance of power.

We will not, in this chapter, speculate about a change in the current balance of power that would be equivalent to the nineteenth-century rise of Prussia or what the equivalent of 1914 might be. As a result the Standard World, as described, will have a certain static and even unreal appearance, but it is difficult to pick out any such salient "new" possibility that could reasonably be included in the Standard World.

B. A CLASSIC PARALLEL TO THE PROJECTED SITUATION

In Chapters I and IV we pointed out several points of comparison between the current (and even more, the projected year 2000) situation and that in the classical period.

A different aspect of this parallel emphasizes international issues. Here America once again plays the part of Rome, Europe of Greece, and the Soviet Union (or China) of Parthia or Persia. We have already noted that there are important similarities in attitudes toward work, leisure, duty, public affairs, culture, and the like, between the Greeks and the Europeans on the one hand, and the Romans and the Americans on the other. Amaury de Riencourt and others have made much of such parallels. They are indeed suggestive, though of course they predict nothing for certain.

The international history also presents analogies. Greece eagerly seized the opportunity for world empire, but failed. The Romans—more or less against their will—were forced three times to intervene in the Greek world to prevent its domination by a single power. The first two times they withdrew after accomplishing this mission. The third time they stayed. Indeed, in order to protect weak powers (apparently a genuine motive) the Romans found it necessary to take over and administer about half of the area that had previously been conquered by the Greeks, leaving the other half to the Parthians, with whom they had an uneasy coexistence.

Greece colonized the Mediterranean and Black Sea coasts and islands from Marseilles to the Caucasus (if Hellenistic Macedon is included, one might say as far as India), but could not hold this empire together: it fell apart long before the impact of the Romans. Similarly the European powers colonized the underdeveloped world so that by 1914 they dominated every country except the United States (a former colony), some Latin American countries, and Japan. Even nominally independent countries, like China and Egypt, were *de facto* puppets of the Western European powers. Today all except the least developed countries are independent from Western Europe and in some instances hostile to it.

The relationship between Rome and Parthia was like a cold war dotted with "hot" campaigns. Neither side was able to win a decision and uneasy coexistence continued for centuries. Islam finally conquered both.

Rome was much less willing than Greece to colonize the world; its policy was similar to the "balance of power" policy followed by Britain with respect to the continent of Europe from four hundred years ago until 1945: to prevent the rise of a single large power sufficiently strong to represent a threat to it. To achieve this aim, the Romans, like the Americans today and the Britons of the last three centuries, worked through a system of alliances. Throughout the first half of the second century B.C., the announced reason for intervening in the Hellenistic area was in each case an alleged threat, or affront, to their allies. Thus, they fought two successful campaigns against Macedon, and one victorious campaign against Syria. The end came when a pretender to the throne of Macedon (by now partitioned into four separate republics) had some local successes against Roman forces of occupation. The Greek cities, notably Thebes, Athens, and Corinth, thought that moment opportune to join forces with the pretender. They were quickly and decisively punished. In 146 B.C., shortly after the sack of Carthage that same year, the Greeks were defeated and Corinth demolished. Greece and Macedon ceased to be independent states. Added to the Asian colonies taken earlier from Syria, most of the Hellenistic area thus became part of the Roman Empire.

Having tasted the fruits of victory after the second Punic War, the Romans became aggresively imperialistic in the first half of the second century B.C.

The United States fought two wars in Europe in this century and became the world's preeminent power without developing anywhere near as much a taste for aggressive imperialism. Much more than the Romans, the United States showed itself generous not only to its allies but to its defeated foes. But if the United States were to find it necessary to intervene in a major

European war once more in this century, and if it then found, as the Romans did, supposed allies more or less openly on the side of the enemy, it seems plausible that permanent steps might be taken to try to prevent World War IV, even if it meant permanent occupation or other domination of Europe.

If the United States pacified the European zone by some form of permanent occupation, the form this would take would undoubtedly be quite different from the Roman take-over of the Hellenistic area. There is little in recent American history or the current international scene to suggest the likelihood of such an outcome. Certainly it is not part of our Standard World. All that should be pointed out here is that there are interesting parallels in the historical situation and, as we said in Chapter IV, in some of the national characteristics—some relevant and some less so.

The potential of this situation seems very likely to go unrealized and even to wane as the century proceeds, as the following pages indicate.

C. SOME (AGREED) INTERNATIONAL ASPECTS OF THE STANDARD WORLD

1. *Coexistence and Detente*

Perhaps the most crucial political aspect of the Standard World is that it assumes both a continuation of and a decreasing interest in competitive coexistence and detente. The concept of coexistence gained prominence in the late 1950's as an alternative to the Marxist concept of the inevitability of war between Communist and Capitalist states. It implies the presence not only of forces that tend to bring about mutually advantageous cooperation and toleration but also of forces that tend to produce situations of competitive conflict and confrontation. Thus, if divisive forces become predominant, coexistence can degenerate into almost pure conflict, while, if tensions steadily diminish or common interests grow, coexistence evolves into some combination of indifference, complete toleration, cooperation, or *entente*. It is the ever present threat that existing hostilities will lead to an even more dangerous degree of hostility that distinguishes "coexistence" from the normal give and take of competition, indifference, or cooperation. Thus divisive and cohesive forces being more or less evenly balanced, "coexistence under conditions of peaceful competition" becomes a state of equilibrium. We will assume that this tension between divisive and cohesive forces continues with diminishing strength. Thus the United States-Soviet relationship remains a detente and does not become an *entente* (which would lead to one of the More-Integrated Worlds—one of the Canonical Variations of Chapter VI— rather than the Standard World). Another initial, and at this writing arguable, assumption of the Standard World of this chapter is that the Vietnam war will not prove an important turning point in events—but in the next chapter we consider some possibilities in which it is a turning point.

a. The Concept of Military Superiority. Despite ideological and political conflicts, the United States and the Soviet Union have adopted attitudes of coexistence in a mutual effort to avoid an armed clash and to advance other interests. That is, although the major common interest linking these antagonists is their fear of a nuclear exchange (and, thus, of any confrontation that might lead to appreciable risk of such an exchange), they also have other possibilities for advantageous cooperation. However, if either of these nations *believed* that it had gained an overwhelming military superiority over the other (and was willing to rely on this belief), an important factor of mutual restraint would be removed, and the other elements of coexistence perhaps undermined. Under likely future conditions such a degree of superiority is probably not attainable (and, more important, confidence in that superiority is even less attainable), at least in the absence of an almost incredible degree of incompetence or indifference by one side or the other. A lesser level of superiority and confidence—even if militarily and politically significant—is, given the uncertainties, not likely, by itself, to have a great effect on the balance of terror or on coexistence generally. But intense crises or other political developments may occur in which even a qualified and uncertain superiority can have important effects. The mere possibility of such a development can have important if limited effects on current relations and normal levels of tension. In addition, the situation may not be symmetric. A degree of superiority which might not be significant if held by A, may be very significant if held by B. However, fully conceding all of this, it is difficult to imagine (in 1967) either side's gaining a degree of superiority that would by itself make a great difference, so long as surprises of the sort listed on page 24 do not occur.[1]

In part because of the relative political ineffectiveness of having a limited military superiority, much of the competition under coexistence has emphasized efforts to maintain or improve "images"—images that are affected by the size of each participant's industrial base, the rate of economic growth and technological development, current or likely future "public" military strength or displayed weapons technology, successes and failures in diplomatic and military forays, grandiose projects such as space exploration, displayed attitudes of domestic populations, relations with allies, underdeveloped and other countries, and competition for "prestige" as well as for political and ideological leadership. Despite the intense competition in these areas, factors such as these are not likely to be decisive in upsetting the present balance—unless the leadership in almost all of them shifts in the same direction, or unless some especially potent combination of gains is

[1] But see Richard J. Whalen, "The Shifting Equation of Nuclear Defense," *Fortune*, June 1, 1967, pp. 85-87, 175-178, 183, for a contrary view.

unexpectedly scored by one side or the other. The situation is likely to remain stable so long as neither the United States nor the Soviet Union suffers such an overwhelming (and unlikely) loss of prestige or strength that either it feels it must recoup this loss or the other side tries to "cash in" on its advantage. Thus, at least in the Standard World, it seems reasonable to project into the future a continuation, confirmation, or even an habituation to an effective balance between the United States and the Soviet Union, which could, of course, then be upset if this attitude led to excessive complacency by either side.

b. *The United States-Soviet Arms Competition.* We assume that in the Standard World the Soviets and Americans continue an essentially stable arms procurement and research and development competition with first one side and then the other getting ahead—the United States program being somewhat more broadly based than the Soviets' but never sufficiently so as to put the Soviets seriously behind. Both countries will probably procure (in the late 1960's or early 1970's) a light cover of ballistic missile defenses with both area and local defense capabilities,[2] but neither country is likely to try (or perhaps to be able) to pursue the program so vigorously or effectively that it succeeds in upsetting the balance of terror between the two countries or even touches off very much of an offense-defense arms race. There is some belief that these BMD programs and their improved follow-ups might negate (at least in the 1970's and 1980's), to some extent, the British, French, and Chinese nuclear missile forces. But, except possibly for the United States anti-Chinese capability, no decision-maker is likely to have so much confidence in these complex and uncertain defense systems that he would be willing to risk a major confrontation that he would be unwilling to risk in the absence of BMD.

By the end of the century there may be effective space defense systems that (if asymmetrically deployed) could raise again the question of "overwhelming military superiority," but we believe it is valid to exclude such breakthroughs from any Standard World—or at least not to let them play any role early in the era being considered.

The preceding discussion does not imply that differences in military postures and tactics might not make a great deal of difference to the outcome if deterrence actually failed and there were a large-scale war. Under such circumstances seemingly minor differences, such as a factor of two in the accuracy of missiles, the discrimination capability of a ballistic missile defense radar or the efficiency of the warheads in an interceptor missile, could make a large difference in the casualties or other outcomes of such war. It is conceivable, of course, that some very intense crisis could occur in which

---

[2] Of course, the United States is currently trying to negotiate a bilateral moratorium on the procurement of BMD, but at this writing it seems most unlikely that it will succeed.

the fact that a decision-maker felt he risked casualties of between five and ten million rather than between thirty and one hundred million might make a great difference in his decisions. Moreover, large wars are unlikely, but not impossible, and if one occurred, the details of military systems could have profound consequences for the number of survivors and their prospects for recuperation. But from the point of view of "surprise-free" projection, rather than from that of a prudential and responsible government, such differences in the military establishment are not likely to have any significant consequences—that is, consequences at the day-to-day political level or even in the kinds of crises that may occur.

Of course, the Soviets have during the past twenty years become accustomed to having substantial military inferiority in the central war area. This has doubtless reinforced their normally conservative attitudes toward risk. If the Soviets were to become equal or superior to the United States in the central war area, they might become more willing to take risks under certain circumstances. Thus in a future "Cuban missile crisis" it might be that the Soviets would not be deterred from involving the equivalent of Berlin or Turkey in the crisis, that is, that they would feel, "If we expand the crisis in this way, it is the Americans who will eventually have to back down and not we." (This assumes that one major effect of United States strategic superiority in the Cuban missile crisis was to discourage the Soviets from escalation of this kind.) Such a development could result from a self-defeating prophecy. The United States, secure in its expectations of prudent and conservative Soviet behavior and anxious to stabilize or limit the arms race, might allow the Soviets to achieve equality (or even an advantage) so that their inhibitions toward risk-taking behavior are reduced. Whether or not this particular self-defeating prophecy is a realistic one, the issue of self-defeating prophecies is an important one in the Standard World.

c. The European Balance. The three major European nations (the United Kingdom, West Germany, and France) seem to be about ten to fifteen years behind the United States in central war technology. Thus, as indicated in Chapter II, any one of them could, without United States help, attain something like United States 1960 technological capabilities in central war forces even by the early or mid-1970's. Such technological capabilities would include being able to procure, deploy, and operate current Minuteman-type missiles for something less than two million dollars a year per missile (spread over five years) and seagoing Polaris-type missiles for something less than twice that sum per missile. This implies that for a billion dollars a year, or one-fifth of their current defense budgets, any one of these nations should be able to procure and operate anywhere from five hundred to one thosuand Minutemen and between two hundred and fifty to five hundred seagoing missiles, and to have a significant portion of these missiles initially deployed and operating by the early or mid-1970's—completing the force by the middle or late 1970's. Of course if the Soviets deployed even a primitive ballistic missile defense system, the problem of penetration aids would become important, and European abilities in this area are uncertain. Other major uncertainties would revolve around such issues as guidance, command and control, reliability, operating costs, and the efficiency of the nuclear warheads. With help from the United States all of the above uncertainties could be decreased or eliminated. Indeed, with sufficient help, Europe could better this timetable appreciably.

Assuming that the Soviets do not deploy elaborate active and passive defenses and given all the uncertainties of nuclear war, these kinds of European forces presumably would give any European nation reasonably adequate deterrence against deliberate Soviet nuclear attack. ("Adequate deterrence" might mean a reasonably credible ability to damage severely Moscow and Leningrad and a possibility of causing major destruction to the next largest twenty to fifty Soviet cities.) If the Soviets do build elaborate active and passive defenses, war-fighting capabilities of these forces may be diminished significantly. This would depend upon the vulnerability of the missiles, the command and control arrangements, penetration capabilities, warhead size, and so on. Given the inevitable uncertainties and the likely political situations in Western and Eastern Europe, it seems that these calculations would not affect prewar deterrence very much for most plausible scenarios. Further, the European nations, by themselves, could acquire conventional (and eventually tactical nuclear) forces which—with reasonable cooperation—would probably be adequate to deter and possibly even defeat a large ground attack by the Soviets—at least the kind of ground attack likely to arise from a mutually undesired crisis rather than one preceded by an extended national mobilization.

None of these nations, however, seems likely to be able to have the kind of forces (or "resolve") that would enable them to use nuclear power for much extended deterrence; for example, to protect West Berlin by threat of escalation (though even this last is to some degree controversial). And it would take a common effort by these nations to have a really adequate, conventional or tactical nuclear defense against a maximum conventional or tactcail nuclear attack by the Soviets.

Given a situation in which the Soviets seem effectively deterred (and uninterested) in attacking Western Europe and the relatively good prospects for the larger European nations to acquire independent defenses, more countries than France may decide to pursue independent policies. Even more than France, they would be able to protect their lines of retreat. (The French today are careful to make the point that they have not dropped out of NATO but have simply withdrawn from integration. They clearly wish to enjoy NATO guarantees. If the situation ever became dangerous they would probably immediately attempt to reintegrate with NATO forces; but they feel, probably reasonably, that they would have time to restore integration if the international situation deteriorated.)

Thus while West Germany is likely to be interested in preserving a strong United States alliance and strengthening its French connections, it is also likely to feel that Germany can do this and still pursue a much more independent policy than in the past. (It seems clear, for example, that even a year ago it would have been impossible for the Christian Democrats to have chosen an ex-Nazi to lead them. Today they are perfectly willing to place domestic considerations over fear of foreign reactions.) This growth of moderate nationalism is as likely to be healthy as it is to be dangerous, but it introduces new elements into the situation. Obviously it is likely to lead to much more independent and assertive West German military and alliance policies.

The European Economic Community may achieve some sort of political unity, but probably more or less along the lines of the Fouchet plan (modeled on Switzerland rather than the United States), in which the Community would be run by a Council of Ministers who have authority to make community-wide decisions; Italy, France, and West Germany (at least) would each have veto rights (and probably any two of the Benelux countries). England may enter the market; if it does not, it is likely either to achieve associate status that will enable it to participate while maintaining many of its links with the Commonwealth, or to turn even more closely to the United States.

d. Avenues for Coexistence. While past exchanges promoting coexistence have largely been a matter of trading American technology for displays of Russian arts, economic exchanges have grown in importance. Europe has also facilitated coexistence by supplying machinery and technology in exchange for Soviet oil, gold, and other products. The role of Europe in what has been previously considered an essentially bilateral coexistence relationship obviously will grow in importance in the years to come. But opportunities for international trade between Russia and the United States will also present an increasingly broad range of future possibilities. United States nonmilitary exports to the Soviet Union in 1965 were less than 0.2 per cent of total United States nonmilitary exports, and our imports from the Soviet Union were at a comparably low level. Here, as in the past, the most important single factor affecting such trade will be the degree to which it is believed to be compatible with various political interests.

In addition to avoiding war, many expect other common interests to become important in the Standard World. These possibilities range from slowing the spread of nuclear weapons to common efforts by the United States and the Soviet Union to improve or stabilize the international system or to otherwise promote common goals (a tendency which is much increased in the More-Integrated Worlds). It is also equally likely—and not incompatible with the above—that the United States and the Soviet Union might not find themselves in very intimate contact and that, in effect, a mutual withdrawal occurs (a tendency which is much increased in the Inward-Looking Worlds).

2. Some Principal Actors and Variables

a. Communist China. Until quite recently there were four kinds of typical, and widely held, though perhaps much exaggerated estimates with regard to the prospects of Communist China. While there has been some correction, many still have:

(1) A tendency to overestimate the political, military, and economic effectiveness of population—often, in effect, to multiply anything that happens in China by eight hundred million, as if the six hundred million or so Chinese peasants (as opposed to the two hundred million or so urbanized Chinese) constitute an overwhelming physical, economic, moral, or political force in world affairs.

(2) A tendency to impute to the Chinese a nearly magical capability to galvanize immediate revolutions not only in adjacent or nearby regions but at great distances—a capability that clearly is not borne out by the record.

(3) A tendency to assume perfect discipline in China (eight hundred million "blue ants") and an inevitable and very successful industrial development in the next thirty-three years.

(4) A tendency to impute a degree of irrationality to the Chinese that makes it unlikely that they can be deterred by material or military threats—even if these threats are both credible and painful. (It seems a fair statement that on Mondays, Wednesdays, and Fridays the Chinese attempt to persuade us that they are crazy, and that seven days a week the Soviets try to confirm this impression.)

One source of these exaggerations may be that many people are attempting, consciously or unconsciously, to find a new enemy to play the psychological and political role in internal and/or international politics that Stalin and the Soviet Union formerly did. Yet almost all *expert* opinion in the United States seems agreed that China is today rather weak in its ability to use offensive force (though its defensive capability may be large) despite continued success in its development of nuclear weapons it is likely to remain so for the next decade or two; that its large population is as likely to be a weakness as a strength; that its economic prospects are at best uncertain and perhaps poor; and that its leadership, while likely to be inward-looking, chauvinistic, subject to biases, and perhaps as aggressive as practical, is, subject to such caveats and to its own values and goals, very likely to be as "reasonable and rational" as any other leadership in the world—particularly on issues that involve risking war with the United States or the Soviet Union.

In addition, the specter of Chinese mass armies fighting in India or Southeast Asia seems unrealistic; it ignores the logistic constraints on China. Even within China, the size of the population is no true gauge of the size of the armies that Peking could recruit and equip. Available Chinese surpluses—in money, food, and productive capacity—are small. Further, the Chinese Communists both have, and will continue to have, internal problems of morale, discipline, authority, and so on. What is true is that China is the enemy of both the United States and the Soviet Union and that much of what is taken for Chinese ideological excess—for example, its refusal to accept the Russian formulation of peaceful coexistence—is better understood as a form of nationalistic enmity to the United States and the Soviet Union and a desire to drive them both from Asia.

Some would also argue that, at least until the 1966 Red Guard riots, there was less savagery with respect to personal liberties in China than existed in the Soviet Union under Khrushchev, and that China has not yet approached the excesses of Stalin. Some further believe that, again at least until 1966, there has been more free enterprise, as well as scope for personal initiative in China, than there was in the Soviet Union. Whether or not one holds these views, the picture of the totalitarian, monolithic, "ant heap" completely responsive to the will of Mao Tse-tung is clearly wrong.

It is also important to note that the doctrinal statement on "rural" revolution of Marshal Lin Piao [3] has been widely misunderstood. One was, of course, impressed by the very angry tone. However, the actual assertion of policy was in fact very weak. The statement declared, in effect, that while China would help movements of national liberation, it would not do so very much. Others cannot depend on China but must carry out revolutions on their own; if they don't, revolution will not work; outside help cannot be decisive. Given that this was written in the context of the Vietnamese war, one could scarcely imagine a more restrained policy document coming from China.

It seems likely that this interpretation of China will become more widely understood and that as this happens and as other developments discussed earlier take place, the Chinese will lose something of their present international charisma. Thus suppose that they average an economic growth rate of 4 or 5 per cent a year and that their average growth in population is a little under 2 per cent. This would be quite an achievement, and they will have become substantially richer by the end of the century (GNP might increase by a factor of five or so to, say, four hundred billion dollars, and per capita income increase by a factor of three to, say three hundred dollars.

[3] See the *New York Times*, September 4, 1965, p. 2.

But this economic growth, although in many ways an extraordinary achievement, would not produce results that would be very impressive as compared to many surrounding countries or to the United States and the Soviet Union. Moreover, other Asian countries, such as Singapore, Hong Kong, Taiwan, South Korea, Thailand, the Philippines, and Malaysia, seem likely to grow much more rapidly. Most important of all, China would find itself technologically and economically much further behind Japan than ever. Thus whatever China's militant rhetoric, its influence is likely to be much reduced—in part because its extravagant claims and expectations will obviously be frustrated, and in part because Japan will begin to overshadow China as the dominant power in Asia. China's rhetoric may come to recall the traditional bombast of the Manchu Dynasty in the nineteenth century.

It seems reasonable in the Standard World to predict that, at least at the level of rhetoric, all of the existing characteristics of China will continue for some extended period of time and that this will be almost independent of specific developments as long as the general outlines of the Standard World are maintained. Neither the growth of Chinese missile forces nor admission into the United Nations would be likely to make very much difference. What is mostly at issue in the next thirty-three years is the extent of Chinese influence in Asia, Latin America, and Africa, and the degree of limited economic and military success it will actually have.

It also seems quite clear that a containment policy by the United States of some sort will be continued; but this leaves open the questions of what, when, and how. Thus few European nations would agree with the opinion held by some Americans that the world should condemn China as an extraordinary evil and lawless world force. Yet we would judge that the "world" would agree that the United States should contain China if this basically means military containment, that is, that the Chinese should not be allowed to cross important frontiers militarily. It seems clear that this containment policy, if adopted, would be the burden of the United States (and possibly the Soviets, British, Japanese, Indians, Australians, and New Zealanders), but that many Europeans (as opposed to many Asians) will not be very interested, or even mildly opposed, since they or their allies will not be directly menaced.

In the Standard World, at least, the Russians and the Americans, with whatever help they do manage to get from other powers, are assumed to be successful in this containment. (Any additional help that the Europeans could give is not really needed and not only would not change the situation very much but would involve the intervening country in difficulties. Thus even if Europeans felt that a containment, or "destruction," policy was important, they might not feel motivated to participate actively in the policy.)

We might also assume that, after Chiang Kai-shek dies, the Chinese

People's Republic is admitted to the United Nations on a "Two Chinas" basis, and that Taiwan is given a security guarantee by the United States. In return Taiwan gives up Quemoy and Matsu (or this problem simply loses intensity with the passage of time).

b. *The Soviet Union.* At the present time the Soviet Union is fifty years old. To some degree the system started by Lenin and developed by Stalin has evolved into an authoritarian rather than totalitarian society—one that is in many ways successful, but also in many ways disillusioned. (For example, to the great shock of traditional Marxists there is a good deal of continuous and intense discussion in both the Soviet Union and Eastern Europe of the problem of alienation between man and job and man and society. In the Soviet Union, as in the United States, such alienation may even be increased as affluence grows.) The secret police continue to be— with sporadic exceptions—increasingly curbed; not only do they rarely arrest people arbitrarily or at three o'clock in the morning, but there is a continuing growth of what is called "socialist legality." Although the party stays in control in the Soviet Union, it allows many kinds of dissent, partly to reward, to stimulate, and to satisfy people, partly as a safety valve and aid to flexibility and efficiency, and partly to reduce criticism from Western and Soviet intellectuals, both of whose views have increasingly significant impact upon Soviet publics and elites. Eventually this relaxation, if it continues, is likely to lead to other important political changes, including the legal toleration of some degree of organized political opposition. The Soviets still believe—but with lessened intensity, confidence, and enthusiasm—that they are makers of history; thus they still believe in world revolution and still actively support subversion in many places in the world. But they seem to do this with very little effectiveness or even hope of success.

While there is a continuing erosion of the police-state and an increasing embourgeoisement of the government, the managers, and the masses in the Soviet Union, the so-called "convergence phenomenon" is likely to stop well short of parliamentary democracy; thus the Soviet Union is unlikely to become as democratic and orderly a country as Salazar's Portugal or even Tito's Yugoslavia. However, even if Russia remains authoritarian, it is not likely to return to anything like the rampant and bloody totalitarianism of the Stalin period.

The Chinese are likely to continue to compete with the Soviets for leadership of the international Communist movement, emphasizing such current criticism as the Soviet Union is (1) capitulationist and revisionist (fearful of risking a confrontation with the United States and increasingly using capitalist techniques such as free-market mechanisms); (2) counterrevolutionary (rich and no longer in sympathy with the poor); and (3) not Afro-Asian (a multiracial nation thoroughly dominated by whites—indeed, a

European empire in Asia—and therefore not to be trusted by the nonwhite peoples of the world).

These charges sting—in part because they contain elements of truth. Yet the Soviets continue to build bridges to Western Europe and the United States and to avoid confrontations with the West, despite the fact that this will, to some degree, further validate these charges. However, it is unlikely that this bridgebuilding, despite surprisingly widespread expectations, will soon get to the stage of firm entente or alliance. Furthermore, communism (now to be written with a lower-case c) is likely to become even more fragmented and to lose even more of its traditional disciplined central direction and singleness of purpose, both inter- and intranationally. Although currently the major inter- and intranationalist deviations are mostly in culture and economic areas, political issues are increasingly likely to arise as well.

In addition, Soviet communism, at least, has become increasingly dated, and communism as an active ideology is shifting its center of gravity from Europe to Asia and Africa. Even here, while it will doubtless make some inroads, in most areas it is likely to be judged an increasingly irrelevant philosophy or to be modified almost out of recognition. This is particularly likely to be true if the Soviet Union and China continue to suffer diplomatic defeats.

c. Germany. Germany is likely to remain divided—with East Germany likely to become a more "legitimate" and viable country with the passage of every year. Eventually the Ulbricht regime will be replaced and the new regime may no longer need Soviet troop support. It might make judicious internal concessions and it might appeal to an increasing East German nationalism. If the new regime successfully opposed the Soviets on a series of minor issues, this could increase its prestige significantly.

There is also likely to be a withdrawal of troops from both Germanies, the United States reducing its force by at least one or two divisions and the Soviets reducing their twenty-two smaller divisions by, say, five or more. While the East Germans and the Soviets will doubtless continue to pressure the United States and West Germany over various aspects of the Berlin question, all four countries are likely to be careful not to probe so deeply as to unbalance the situation—to avoid incidents likely to escalate into a serious confrontation. (However, this care often shows up as small concessions by the West. These are often interpreted by many apprehensive or suspicious West Germans as weakness and irresolution on the part of their own government and a "qualified betrayal" by the United States of West German interests.) Some of the pressures in East Germany could be further relieved by allowing for the selective emigration of a small number of East Germans every year. Finally, the Hallstein doctrine is likely to be dropped or become so eroded as to become almost meaningless.

In the meantime, the postwar passivity of Bonn will gradually disappear. Germans who were young during World War II, say under fifteen in 1940 (by 1975 this is everyone under fifty), will increasingly refuse to accept for themselves (or for the German nation) any stigma. In East Germany the process of creating and using nationalism may go even further; indeed East German national assertions are now a familiar theme. Thus one can find in East Germany many articles and books that point out that while West Germany is rich, it has United States support, a capitalist system, and its riches are corrupting. They add that the East Germans have also been successful and without help—*and under Communism*. (They seem to take a wry satisfaction and considerable pride—as do many West Germans—in the ability of East Germans to do so well in spite of foreign subjugation and exploitation, the absence of foreign help, and the problems of a totalitarian society and bureaucratized economy.) This growing success combined with a Spartan, socialist culture may prove to have an unexpectedly great appeal to young people and to others in West Germany. In any case by the mid-1970's the East Germans may have an influential position as "true" Germans—austere, purposeful, and disciplined—thus restoring an important tradition, that of Prussian Socialism.[4]

In the rest of Europe there is probably a more lively fear of a revived West Germany than of Soviet aggression. Most Europeans feel that Soviet aggression is effectively and perhaps permanently deterred. In addition they tend to accept the "new" Soviet Union as a more or less responsible power. As a result the West Germans even today feel increasingly isolated and increasingly unwilling to believe that they can satisfy their aspirations within the NATO framework. This is likely to be even more true in the future because German "war guilt" problems are likely to play a much smaller role than they have in the past—certainly as far as German feelings are involved and very likely as far as those of other nations are concerned. The West Germans, partly as a result of their wartime experiences and partly because they are on the firing line, are more preoccupied with the Soviet threat than the other Europeans. As a result, United States and West European policies may remain in relatively close harmony: Washington and Bonn are are the two capitals of the Western alliance that take the Soviet military threat most seriously (but, nonetheless, not *very* seriously). On the other hand, it has become clear that the previous almost complete identity of interest between Washington and Bonn is now more illusory than real.

[4] This is not Marxian Socialism but as Spengler describes it, "Frederick William I's Prussian practice which long preceded Marx and will yet displace him—the socialism, inwardly akin to the system of Old Egypt, that comprehends and cares for permanent economic relations, trains the individual in his duty to the whole, and glorifies hard work as an affirmation of Time and Future." Quoted by Bruce Mazlish in *The Riddle of History* (New York: Harper and Row, 1966), p. 317.

Washington's interest in avoiding nuclear war with the Soviets and in arti-
culating the increasing number of issues—among them prevention of further
nuclear proliferation—on which Soviet and American interests coincide, is
moving West German aspirations to a low priority status. Thus West Germany is now being told that reunification will have to wait a settlement of
outstanding East-West issues. Previously it had been told that the settlement would have to await reunification. Many take this shift as a partial
betrayal of previous assurances. Bonn's major official interest, to regain
the "Soviet zone," conflicts with Washington's and Western Europe's willingness to accept a detente based on the status quo. Although Bonn will
doubtless go along with the detente and pursue bridgebuilding activities
of its own, and perhaps gain much commercially in doing so, it may also—
even if unreasonably—become increasingly resentful and restless. This is
clearly true of many German youth who increasingly ask their elders what
is being done about reunification. Ignoring the almost miraculous economic,
political, and military postwar recovery of West Germany, they repudiate
the postwar policies and leadership on the ground that they do not seem
to have facilitated reunification.[5]

Meanwhile, as Moscow's hold slackens in the "satellites," East Germany
is also likely to become more independent. It may, of course, remain almost
indefinitely as a kind of anomaly in the world—the last more or less abject
noncontiguous "colony" in the world. But we can expect that in five or ten
years we will be hearing in East Germany the slogan "twenty-five years (or
thirty years) are enough." This mutual restlessness argues that there is more
serious potential for trouble in both Germanies—through more or less popular revolt, through competition, and even through collaboration. But it is
also possible that the situation will evolve peacefully or stabilize itself on
the basis of a mutual but tolerable frustration.

Meanwhile, partly as a result of the reduction of United States and Soviet
troops in Germany and the lesser role these troops play in each Germany,
and partly as a result of natural evolution, Eastern Europe is likely to gain
full economic and political independence of the Soviet Union, even though,
except possibly for Yugoslavia, the area is likely to remain Communist and,
except for Albania, voluntarily to associate itself with the Soviet Union in
a sort of Soviet Commonwealth of Nations. While these states may be
somewhat contemptuous of Soviet economic performance, particularly in
the consumer goods area, they are likely to feel a bond with the Soviet
Union and defer to its leadership on many political issues. (So far as the
amenities of life are concerned, the Soviets are not likely to do as well as
most of the Eastern European countries, though their per capita income

---

[5] Polls indicate that, at least until recently, more than three-fourths of the young
West Germans thought of this as the major issue facing West Germany.

should be about the same, or higher. This could be one of many discouragements that may tend to turn the Soviets inward.) Thus, despite some continuing ideological and political ties to the Soviet Union, Eastern Europe is likely to become at least as close to Western Europe as to the Soviet Union—and closer in the cultural and economic areas.

d. *Japan*. Japan in 1967 was still the invisible nation of Asia—but beginning to appear. Like West Germany, Japan, the other major loser of World War II, was still characterized by great economic strength and relative political passivity, though with increasing signs that the passivity was beginning to end. It is, however, a bigger country than West Germany in population, has probably already surpassed Germany in industrial production, is growing much more rapidly, and most important of all is not held down by apprehensive allies and an overwhelming reunification problem. Thus Japan is likey to emerge in the 1970's as the true colossus of Asia—a further check, along with Soviet and American power, on Chinese ambitions. Yet there will no longer be either the temptation or easy opportunity for imperial expansion that existed in the half century preceding 1945, when Japan totally outclassed its neighbors in industrial development and political organization.

In part because of the intense Japanese desire for prestige and in part because Japan may have the most achievement-minded culture in history, as well as for other internal social, political, and economic reasons, Japanese growth rates are likely to continue to be high, say around 8 per cent, for the rest of the century. Yet if at any point there is a serious depression, it would be likely to affect Japanese internal politics in a very serious way, making much more likely a sharp swing to either the right or the left, or to some group outside these categories (such as the Soka Gakkai's *Komeito*). In the Standard World, of course, we assume that Japanese economic and political progress continues to go reasonably smoothly, and while there is likely to be an antiforeign and traditionalist reaction against the excessive "Americanization" of the two postwar decades, this is assumed, in the Standard World, to be limited in effect. Thus Japan is by and large likely to be an active as well as a passive force for stability in Asia—though in the early period its activity will be reluctant. And of course it will increasingly follow its own definitions and interpretations of "stability and progress."

e. *Afro-Asia*. The developing Afro-Asian areas manifest many of the disturbances that occur when unequal civilizations come into contact. Many different kinds of reactions are possible.[6] In the Afro-Asian areas, the most prominent current reaction is "quasi-talismanic": Afro-Asian "socialism,"

[6] See generally Edmund Stillman and William Pfaff, *The Politics of Hysteria* (New York: Harper and Row, 1964), for discussion of these.

which usually occurs in a nationalistic form. Both Marxism and nationalism have been learned from Europe, though often in garbled form. In addition the ideological content of political movements in Afro-Asia is frequently exaggerated. Although almost all Afro-Asian states describe themselves as "socialist," they are far from copies of the political or economic systems of Russia or even of China.

Much of the early force of the Afro-Asian "revolution" is already probably spent, and the future direction of this movement is now less clear than it has ever been. Beyond the basic desire for freedom and identity, the Afro-Asian revolution encompasses some elements that are extremely old— for example, xenophobia, racial hatred, and cultural exclusivism—and some elements that are new and even hypermodern—for example, certain perhaps romanticized qualities that attract many Westerners, especially hip or progressive adolescents, towards "social revolution," Asian religions, or African cultures.

New governments in Afro-Asian areas have claimed the slogans of "socialism" not only in succession and rivalry with the old colonial powers, but as a semitalismanic claim to postmodernity and as a rejection of an obsolete capitalist system. Of course, the fact that these movements call themselves socialist or Communist implies that they feel some identity either with the Soviet Union or China, or both, and that they expect and often get aid from these countries. It is even possible that if they are in any way successful with their Afro-Asian socialism, they will attempt to deepen this association. But the prediction in the Standard World would be that for most of the Afro-Asian countries socialism is *proforma* and largely rhetorical and that particularist and communal features overwhelm the somewhat remote Marxist origins of these movements and outweigh their relation with Chinese or Soviet Communism. Therefore we assume in the Standard World that only where nationalism or other communal issues have no other outlets and are driven to express themselves through Communist channels does Communism become a formidable Afro-Asian force —and even then it is likely to be a relatively rare and transitory phenomena—at least in the Standard World.

It appears that total rejection of the intruding culture is no longer either rational or practicable for most of the developing world. Purely talismanic syntheses whether violent or nonviolent also seem unlikely to permit solution of current problems. Most current syntheses are semitalismanic, although there are obvious pressures toward purely rational syntheses. Communism itself is mellowing in the Russian bloc as a consequence of pressures for economic rationality. Most close students of Chinese Communism expect the post-Mao leadership to exhibit increasingly rational or revisionist tendencies, although these same scholars must admit that they were surprised by the cultural revolution.

In any event, the developing countries cannot hope to solve their problems in any significant sense unless they employ their capital investments more rationally. Figures 1 and 2 show how Japan has increased its per acreage production of rice phenomenally while most other Asian nations have failed to keep pace. The sad fact is that the developing countries are now net grain importers; in part because their per capita consumption has increased, but this still does not augur well for their future. It is not clear that United States policy has been helpful in this respect.

An important and not atypical example is the food-for-India program. The United States currently supplies half the wheat consumed in India (this takes about one-fourth the United States production). While the Indians have increased their food production by 50 per cent in the last fifteen years, most experts believe that with relatively minor changes in programs and government attitudes—particularly toward such things as fertilizer—food production could have been increased even faster. Furthermore, if the government had been willing to initiate harsh and therefore very unpopular measures (such as raising the price of food), production would have gone up even faster and India could have had food surpluses. But for various reasons until recently even the mild and obvious measures

FIGURE 1

CURRENT RICE YIELDS IN SELECTED COUNTRIES RELATED TO JAPAN'S HISTORICAL TREND

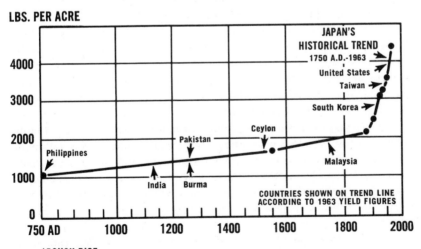

LBS. PER ACRE

JAPAN'S HISTORICAL TREND
1750 A.D.-1963
United States
Taiwan
South Korea
Ceylon
Pakistan
Philippines
Malaysia
India
Burma

COUNTRIES SHOWN ON TREND LINE ACCORDING TO 1963 YIELD FIGURES

4000   3000   2000   1000   0

750 AD   1000   1200   1400   1600   1800   2000

*ROUGH RICE
HISTORICAL ESTIMATES FROM JAPANESE MINISTRY OF AGRICULTURE

U.S. DEPARTMENT OF AGRICULTURE   NEG. ERS 3559-65(3) ECONOMIC RESEARCH SERVICE

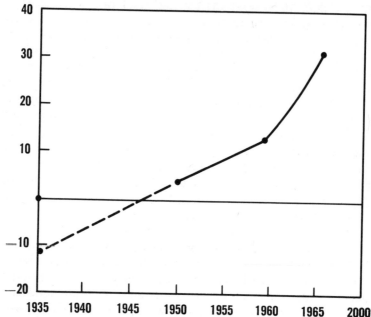

FIGURE 2

TONS OF GRAIN TRANSFERRED FROM THE DEVELOPED TO THE LESS DEVELOPED COUNTRIES

were politically unpopular, especially since many Indians had come to think of the stream of food from the United States as a vested right and therefore felt under no pressure to initiate such measures (and resented any direct pressure by the United States to have them do so).

f. *Latin America.* Since about the middle of the nineteenth century, Latin America has been chronically anti-Yankee. During the earliest period of revolution and independence it had tended to be pro-United States and, in fact, most Latin American revolutions were to some degree explicitly modeled on the American, but this changed. The subsequent antipathy to North America stemmed from both rational and irrational causes. Both of these causes were strengthened by the United States' proclivity for political and military intervention in Latin American affairs.

The "irrational" causes (and talismanic and semitalismanic manifestations) of this antipathy were many, but a crucial one that will presumably continue into the twenty-first century, is the simple necessity for Latins to distinguish themselves as a culture from the predominantly Protestant, commercial, aggressive North American civilization that might otherwise easily engulf them. In addition, there is no doubt a simple jealousy of a rich and powerful nation that has been, in Latin American terms, a *parvenu* on the world scene.

There are, however, some important changes now under way. Thus Brazilians, Mexicans, and Colombians, at least, seem now to have the kind of self-confidence that allows them, even if they wish to oppose the United States, not automatically to support an enemy of the United States (a practice that gave Hitler Latin American influence in the 1930's, Stalin and Khrushchev influence in the 1950's, and, for a while, Mao influence in the early 1960's). This confidence is mostly based on relative success in industrialization, but also on having developed respectively (1) a new kind of multiracial society, (2) a successful social revolution, and (3) an ability to handle the Americans. The Brazilians and Mexicans also take great pride in their artistic and cultural achievements and non-European heritage (while the Colombians tend to emphasize their continuity with Europe). Many Latin Americans no longer feel so overwhelmed by the colossus of the North, even though discrepancies of many kinds continue and even increase. Particularly in the large cities, in which there is a large and successful commercial, technical, and professional class, a feeling is developing of either equality or relative indifference to North Americans.

Further, the Christian Democrats (and other Democrats and Democratic-Leftists) are now leading a campaign for a new kind of relationship between the United States and Latin America involving more mutual respect and empathy. In addition, modernization has had its effects in Latin American attitudes. However, Latin attitudes toward family, commerce, wealth, administrative honesty, public obligation, and so on often remain surprisingly alien to those of the United States, but among the elites even this may be decreasing. In some important respects the urban sectors of Latin and North American society are growing more similar, though as with the United States and the Soviet Union, the convergence phenomena will hardly result in twin cultures.

As far as economic development in Latin America is concerned, unlike much of Afro-Asia where the problems seem overwhelming, most Latin American problems seem either soluble or tolerable. For one thing, the ratio of people to resources is far more favorable to development in Latin America than in most parts of Asia. In addition, particularly as compared to Africa and much of Asia, Latin America is now capitalistic and technological, an offspring of West European culture. Latin American elites do not suffer as much from the stress of having to adapt (and be adapted) to an alien tradition. There still, of course, are important cultural problems.

In spite of the relatively favorable conditions for economic development in much of Latin America, political conditions inhibiting parliamentary government are still evident. Relatively violent and "illegal" changes of government are likely to persist, and complex and subtle political systems resembling the current Mexican method of government may be more likely to succeed in maintaining a reasonable degree of order, liberty, and development than traditional multiparty parliamentary democracy.

Some believe that there is fertile soil for Communist development in Latin America, and that if Communist takeovers occur they will tend to be irreversible. It seems more likely that Latin American Communism, if it occurs at all, will be quite different from Soviet or Chinese Communism. For one thing, Latin American politicians claim to have learned that they can work with Communists and then drop them; the so-called Caudillo principle is supposed to hold, and the leader tends to dominate the situation, no matter what his organization does. And more important, the organization's total authority will not normally outlast the leader. The Castro phenomenon may still prove to be a case in point.

In any case, with some luck or skill most of Latin America ought to be able to achieve, by the end of the century, living standards comparable to or greater than Italy's today. It will also have, but in more extreme form, the Italian problem of great disparities in average income between sections of society. The problem is likely to be one of urban-rural discrepancies. (The newly arrived immigrants to the urban slums, having been impelled to leave the impoverished countryside, are the most obvious consequence of these discrepancies.) Eventually this problem too should be solved, and much can be done to alleviate the strains of the transition, but great strains will inevitably exist. In the Standard World this disparity gives rise to much turmoil, but not to overwhelming and violent movements. Our Standard World expectation is that many (or most) Latin American nations will achieve a workable synthesis of the old and the intruding civilization.

D. THE SURPRISE-FREE SPREAD OF NUCLEAR WEAPONS

In the first decade or so after World War II the five principal victors of that war either tested and procured nuclear weapons (the United States, the Soviet Union, and the United Kingdom), or initiated programs with the intention of carrying them through to the test and procurement stage (France and China—and for this purpose we will consider mainland China the inheritor of World War II victory). Since the initiation of the French and Chinese programs in the 1950's, no other nation has officially initiated a nuclear weapons program (though many countries have initiated "peaceful" nuclear energy programs which do or will provide them with an option for a military program). It is still possible that in the absence of immediate objective military pressures, precedents against obtaining nuclear weapons will become so strong as to prevent further proliferation. This possibility might be enhanced if the United Kingdom and/or France gave up its weapons to a European Nuclear Defense Community.

There are other possibilities. If there were widespread nuclear proliferation in the next thirty-three years, historians in the year 2000 would probably look upon the past decade (and perhaps part of the next one) as a gestation period during which the technological, political, and economic conditions were created for further proliferation. If one examines the candidates for becoming the sixth nuclear power, the obvious states are Israel, India, West Germany, and Japan. The first two have, in effect, created a basis or option for a nuclear weapons program. The last two are now doing so. However, it seems unlikely that Israel will get nuclear weapons, if only because the United States seems to have indicated to it that if it does so, United States support to Israel will either be withdrawn or sharply cut. Israel might then find itself alone against an Arab bloc supported by the Soviet Union.

India, of course, is now engaged in a great debate whether to acquire nuclear weapons. Although the outcome of the debate is uncertain, there is a good chance that India will abstain—in part because this has been the traditional Indian position and in part because the Indians may feel more secure facing China with implicit or explicit United States and Soviet guarantees and no nuclear weapons, than with nuclear weapons without such support. In fact one of the major motivations for India to acquire nuclear weapons is not China but Pakistan; but even here India is likely to find the disutilities larger than the utilities.

In the absence of major new developments West Germany, of course, is firmly precluded by political constraints arising out of the war (and some ambiguous treaty obligations) from going ahead on its own.

That leaves Japan. Most Japanese and observers of the Japanese do not seem to think that Japan is likely to become the sixth nuclear power. Informal polls taken at Japanese universities indicate that Japanese tend to expect to be number eight—that is to say that the Japanese expect Japan to go nuclear after India and West Germany. However, it may well become clear to the Japanese by the late 1960's that neither India nor West Germany will be nuclear power number six. At this point many Japanese may become concerned that this particular result of World War II will become increasingly hardened so as eventually to make a nuclear Japan politically impossible. In addition, the Japanese are likely to feel increasingly assertive and self-confident in their own economic strength, desirous of increased prestige and independence, and newly concerned for their long-run security. The easiest and most efficient route to increase Japanese prestige, independence, and security may seem to be nuclear weapons. (If China behaves dangerously the Japanese seem more likely to try to get closer to the United States than to strike out on their own. Only if, as with France, Japan is both confident of United States protection and judges its dangers low is it likely to strike out on a nuclear program.)

The internal Japanese and world attitudes toward nuclear weapons could be important. One can, however, easily overstress this constraint. As far as internal affairs are concerned, much of the expressed antinuclear sentiment in Japan probably is actually sentiment for independent international policies, against a return of militarism, of anti-Americanism, or of sheer domestic political partisanship, rather than of a genuine and simple expression of a deeply held nuclear pacifism. (It is not that these latter attitudes do not exist but that they may appear to be much more deeply and widely held than in fact is the case.) There are a number of internal political configurations in which these attitudes of independence, antimilitarism, anti-Americanism, and political partisanship would support the decision to procure nuclear weapons.

Furthermore it should be noticed that by the early or mid-1970's the Japanese will be in a good position to acquire a sophisticated nuclear establishment. For example, they will have developed a missile propulsion system by the late 1960's in many respects comparable to the United States Minuteman, as indicated in the following table of comparisons:

TABLE I
Japanese Missile Research

Item	Current Japanese MU-IV Test Vehicles	U.S. Minuteman A and B
Length	60-65 feet	53-60 feet
Diameter	5-6 feet	6 feet
Weight	about 80,000 lbs.	70,000 lbs.
Thrust	220,000 lbs.	270,000 lbs.
Speed	15,000 mph	15,000 mph-plus
Range	4,000-5,000 miles?	6,500 miles

In many of the aspects in which the Japanese are likely to be lagging behind the United States program (e.g., guidance and automation), they are likely to be advanced enough to be superior to any other country except *possibly* the Soviet Union and France. In terms of potential nuclear production, by the late 1970's they will have a peaceful nuclear power program from which, if all of the plutonium produced were available to weapons developments, they could produce between five hundred to one thousand small nuclear weapons a year.

It is also possible that the Japanese might ease their decision to buy nuclear weapons by first acquiring them as part of a ballistic missile defense system. It is an odd but reasonably reliable, conjecture, that Japan could make one of the best technical and political cases for deploying BMD that any country can. Their major opponent is China. It should be relatively easy for the Japanese to keep far enough ahead of the Chinese, both technologically and quantitatively, so that Japan could expect a BMD system to work against a relatively small and presumably unsophisticated Chinese attack. Furthermore the Japanese could probably stay that far ahead of the Chinese, at least for the predictable future. And it is not likely to appear to the Japanese people or the international community a completely unreasonable act for Japan to seek protection against Chinese missiles.

Thus, despite current appearances to the contrary, there are reasons for conjecturing that Japan might become nuclear power number six. If this does happen it will be a most significant event since it seems plausible that once Japan acquires nuclear weapons many in West Germany will wish to follow suit. (It is important to realize that once the "victors' monopoly" has been broken by one of the defeated powers of World War II, the other defeated powers will feel much less constrained.) Plausible military and political arguments can be made for Germany's acquiring nuclear weapons. In addition, there may be a decisive, if seldom expressed and possible erroneous, argument that only by refusing to accept any "unfair" nuclear disabilities can Germany assert her regained respectability and the end of expiation for the aggressions and crimes of the Hitler period.

Nor are the political constraints, in the situation suggested, likely to loom as large as they do today. Many in the West would be willing to tell the West Germans that they cannot revise the territorial results of World War II without going to war (a prospect they and most Germans would oppose); but few would be willing to say, "Until you win a war you are politically second-class." There are also many internal political situations in West Germany that could make acceptable to some of their allies, particularly the United States, their acquisition of nuclear weapons. For example, if an extreme nationalist party gained an important following, it could use the nuclear issue as an example of how Germany's allies still oppress Germany. If such a party and issue began to make themselves felt, almost any responsible, nonextremist German government might find a sympathetic hearing in the United States for obtaining nuclear weapons. (Such a government doubtless would point out that it was not until the Weimar Republic had been completely repudiated and Hitler came to power that the victors of World War I made important concessions to Germany, "and does the United States wish to repeat this mistake?") On the other hand, a sizable rightist trend in Germany could also reinforce foreign—including American —resistance to German nuclear status. Certainly Russia would oppose this most vigorously, at least by political means.

But assuming that the political situation is such that in four or five years Germany followed the example of Japan in acquiring nuclear weapons, the Italians might well follow very soon afterward. One can conjecture that such countries as Sweden and Switzerland would follow as well—no longer feeling that they were rocking the boat by achieving nuclear status. (Both countries have long traditions of procuring the most modern weapons possible for their own forces.) There is also a possibility that Australia and India would follow, sensing both national need and an international trend. If the above occurred in the 1970's, such countries as Argentina, Brazil, and Mexico in Latin America; Egypt and Israel in the Mediterranean; Pakistan, Indonesia, South Korea, and Taiwan in Asia; Yugoslavia, Rumania, Poland, Czechoslovakia, and perhaps East Germany in Eastern Europe, would be candidates for nuclear status in the 1980's. This in turn implies that by the 1990's as many as fifty countries might have access to such weapons.

It is important to realize that this scenario, while very pessimistic, does not necessarily increase the likelihood of a nuclear war between the United States and the Soviet Union. Nuclear war between two relatively undeveloped nations seems rather more likely. But even here, if proliferation continued, the attitudes about "first use," the risks of unsafe techniques, disproportionate response, and so on, which now inhibit the United States and the Soviet Union, might inhibit all or most of the other nuclear states as well. Thus all nations with large forces and most nations with small nuclear forces might acquire some capability for measured, controlled, and deliberate response. Just as President Johnson pointed out in his 1965 budget message that "our military and civilian leaders are unanimous in their conviction that our armed might is and always must be controlled so as to permit measured response in whatever crises may confront us," the leaders of other nations would be likely to discover a similar need for controlled capabilities and flexible strategies. An international system in which there had been widespread proliferation might thus be less accident-prone and aggression-prone than many people have estimated, although still other things being equal, an undesirable situation. Although proliferation increases many dangers, it alleviates some others; in any case political factors are likely to dominate in determining the risk of nuclear war.

The argument can even be made that nuclear weapons have the advantage of making possible a "fair" solution to the problem of national defense, since one country does not have to buy its security at the expense of its neighbors. In the past, even if a country had obtained security by only a moderate superiority, it could usually hope to use that moderate superiority to overwhelm its opponent without suffering catastrophic losses. Any country with a properly designed nuclear deterrent system can hope (so the argument goes) to be strong enough for deterrence and yet not strong enough to execute a disarming first strike against another nuclear power. Thus one country's strength need not necessarily mean its neighbor's weakness—deterrence, unlike superiority, can be both clear and symmetric. One might conclude with Pierre Gallois that "the further we advance in the ballistic-nuclear age, the more possible it becomes to outlaw violence, even if the aggressor nation is stronger and more richly supplied with combat means than the nation it threatens." Indeed many Europeans today seem to believe that with nuclear proliferation the "zone of peace" which we have suggested for the "older nations" might spread to the "new nations" as well. (By contrast, we suggested earlier that this zone of peace among the older nations is due more to an absence of aggressive pressure than to nuclear deterrence.) In any case it is not certain that proliferation would increase the probability of a serious catastrophe for the United States or for mankind.

Yet despite these arguments, one cannot be confident that the effects of proliferation would not be seriously harmful. There is a consensus—the extent of which would be rare on any issue—among analysts, scholars, policymakers, and men in the street against proliferation. According to this consensus, in order to decrease the likelihood of nuclear use by those who possess nuclear weapons, it is crucial to stop the spread of those weapons to additional countries. Although all of these people may be wrong, they at least are prudent. We would support their consensus.[7]

[7] For recommendations for security arrangements addressed to these problems, see Herman Kahn, "Nuclear Proliferation and Rules of Retaliation," 76 *Yale Law Journal* 79 (1966), and Herman Kahn and Carl Dibble, "Criteria for Long-Range Nuclear Control Policies," 55 *California Law Review* 473 (1967).

CHAPTER VI

Some Canonical Variations from the Standard World

In the Standard World discussed in the previous chapters such questions as access to markets, frontier defense, and many other national security or economic issues are no longer crucial for most of the older nations of the world. Furthermore, even most of the newer ones will not be inclined toward territorial expansion nor feel it is urgent to prevent the aggrandizement of other nations. But within this basically stable framework of boundaries and markets many important problems could still arise and could even have major and "surprising" long-run consequences, far into the twenty-first century.

In addition to the many possible long-run problems we have already pointed to explicitly and implicitly, there will very likely be some surprises even in the short run—some trends or intense crises that will arise well before the end of the twentieth century and upset the delicate balance of forces required to maintain the smooth trends of our Standard World. The Standard World may seem implausibly evolutionary and crisis-free to those who expect serious crises, and their expectations may indeed prove correct.

There are, of course, many plausible scenarios for more serious world troubles—too many to discuss. One must concede in addition that any lengthy period without serious challenge does indeed tend to create its own particular tensions that can degenerate into or create disruptive forces. The question is how likely and disruptive will such forces actually be? While we have been somewhat skeptical of the overall credibility of our Standard World, we should not completely dismiss the possibility that these disruptive forces may well be containable and the general trends of this Standard World—both good and bad—may thus continue and dominate other developments. While we went on record, in Chapter I, as being willing to wager that the old nations will change less (aside from possible spectacular economic and technological progress and the direct internal consequences of such progress) in the final third of the twentieth century than they did in the first two-thirds, it is less a gamble to assert that the old nations will probably enjoy a lengthy period of relative stability and evolutionary change. But plausible or not, our Standard World does present a useful subject for discussion and comparison, and, of course, many different specific scenarios can be fitted into its general perspective. Some such "possible" or plausible scenarios are considered next.

We will now consider some of the likely characteristics of three variant worlds, constructing two or three versions of each. We have called all of these worlds "Canonical" because we have deliberately chosen their characteristics for methodological convenience rather than on the basis of realistic criteria, and because we have put them in more or less comparable form. Table I summarizes the eight worlds.

In the next section of this chapter, we describe each Canonical Variation in greater detail. (We use the outline form of Table I, rather than the more usual numbering, in order to facilitate later references.)

TABLE I
Canonical Variations

A. More integrated:

Relatively peaceful, relatively prosperous, relatively arms-controlled worlds with a relatively high degree of consultation among nations, and the existence of political coordination or even integration among all, or almost all, the "major" and/or minor powers

1. Stability or Status Quo-Oriented
2. Development or Aid-Oriented

B. More Inward-Looking:

Worlds that are almost as peaceful and prosperous, but with little arms control or general coordination

3. With an eroded Communist movement
4. With an eroded democratic morale and
      some Communist dynamism
5. With a dynamic Europe and/or Japan

C. Greater Disarray:

Relatively troubled and violent worlds, but in which no large central wars have occurred

6. With an eroded Communist movement
7. With a dynamic Communist movement and
      some erosion of democratic morale
8. With a dynamic Europe and/or Japan

A. MORE INTEGRATED WORLDS

The characteristics of the "integrated worlds" are a high level of coordination or integration among the major powers, including arms control and
international aid programs, and in the world generally a low level of conflict
and of perceived, potential conflict. This stability will be a major objective
(and product) of international cooperation.

1. Integrated World—Stability or Status Quo-Oriented

The essential characteristic of this world is that political and economic
coordination exists mostly among the advanced powers and is designed
mainly to secure and improve their position. While there is some interest
in improving the condition of the third world, there is effective exclusion
of this third world from major influence as well as mixed prospects for its
development.

The advanced industrial powers, including a fourth generation and ideologically revisionist Soviet Union, have close relations and a sense of common interest. While there is a political federation composed of the EEC, the
United Kingdom, Denmark, and Norway, organized more or less on the
lines of the original Fouchet plan and governed by a commission in which
most issues require a nearly unanimous vote, there is no Iron Curtain. Eastern Europe has close relations with both the Soviet Union and the federation. The federation has a seaborne strategic defense community (SDC)
deterrent and no longer feels critically dependent on the United States for
its defenses. Except for the forces in the SDC, European military forces are
independent, though allied. Europe and the United States, Canada, the
Union of Soviet Socialist Republics, Australia, New Zealand, Japan, Argentina, Brazil, and Mexico, in their own estimation, and in many objective
ways, run everything of importance in the world. Chinese failures and the
rise of Japan have deflated the West's obsession with Asian revolution.
Afro-Asian politics are largely disregarded. There are development aid programs funded at a fairly high level but they are trivial in terms of Western
wealth and are carried out in part as a charitable obligation and in part as
payment of a kind of moral blackmail. Except for small, strictly defensive
nuclear deterrent forces in Japan, China, and possibly India, Afro-Asia is
largely powerless. There is much turbulence, some of which is policed by
the advanced nations when it spills over borders, but most of which is allowed to work itself out. There are many "neo-colonialist" relationships but
the advanced nations, at least, regard each other's "neocolonialism" as more
benevolent than exploitive, though the programs may be administered in a
patronizing or even contemptuous fashion.[1]

[1] There might also be a growing interest among some of the developed nations in
a neoimperial division of spheres of influence and responsibility over Afro-Asia as it

National ambitions in this kind of world could be quite selfish, the rich working to keep things as they are, supporting international organizations and aid programs mainly to preserve order, assuage discontent, and sweep aside awkward or unpleasant questions. Within the advanced states there might be significant tension, probably less between states than among groups —important minorities being in a state of alienation from or possibly revolutionary opposition to the complacent majority that dominates policy. The third world in such a situation might be expected to be a mixture of conservative regimes, revolutionary but (still) ineffectual ferment, and some degree of political-moral collapse. There might be a crisis in the works, but in the 1970's and perhaps by the year 2000 it probably would still seem some decades away.

Even those nations of Afro-Asia that have worked hard for internal development with competent regimes are, in this projection, assumed to be largely—or partially—disappointed, but much less so than the other Afro-Asians.[2] Population problems, a scarcity of skill and resources, inappropriate economic and aid doctrine, and political diversions will have hampered them to varying degrees. Latin America and African free trade or common market programs and cooperative Asian groupings might have hopes for future successes even if only modest accomplishments thus far. It is assumed that the European and North American powers contribute to these international efforts but largely concentrate on domestic programs and Europe's Mediterranean area, eliminating poverty in Greece, Southern Italy, Spain, and Portugal. The American poverty program is assumed to have succeeded by the early 1970's (at least in that there is—in effect—a minimum guaranteed income). Thus in the West, including European Russia, there is almost no extreme poverty—though the lower income groups may feel severely deprived and even bitter in relation to the rest of society. But dramatic poverty—a lack of elementary necessities—is almost completely a "nonwhite" problem—and Japanese, American Negroes and Indians, and so on, for this purpose are in effect "whites." The distinguishing marks of this Integrated-Status Quo World, then, are that while the rich and the poor both grow richer, the rich (as described in 1985 and year 2000 projections) are beginning to achieve a basis for a "postindustrial" standard of living. The third world experiences varying degrees of economic frustration and is politically and militarily largely powerless, while the institutions of international cooperation are employed largely to preserve a status quo congenial

becomes clear that much of Afro-Asia will not be developed (say six hundred dollars per capita) until after the end of the century. This interest could be prompted less by a desire for exploitation than by a mixture of other motives, including desires for prestige and power, social engineering impulses, and feelings of responsibility and humanity.

[2] Of course if they compare themselves with the ones doing badly—or to the long run—their probable 3 to 7 per cent a year of growth is likely to appear quite satisfactory (a doubling of the economy every ten to twenty years).

to the established industrial powers. This status quo may also provide a valid environment for third-world growth, but nevertheless this may seem more or less accidental; at the least few compromises will seem to have been made by the governing powers to this end.

2. *Integrated World—Development or Aid-Oriented*

The essential characteristic is extensive and successful world organization for progressive and welfare purposes, with a subordination of politics and ideology to pragmatism.

This Integrated World unites rather than separates the rich and poor nations. In addition to having a growing number of functional international organizations dealing with international finance, foreign aid, trade, and national defense, there has been a relatively concerted, serious, and successful international attempt to develop the third world (now known as the second world?). And whether success is due primarily to aid or to the energy and discipline of the developing states, this "second world" is doing very well, and enjoys a relatively healthy and constructive relationship with the developed world. (A variant of this world might be one in which extensive aid had been given and had failed, the failure resulting in large-scale disruption, corruption, and disillusionment, especially but not only in the third world.)

In our projection, the economic pace of this world has then largely overshadowed most political discontents, and the ambitions of the third world states have not only received some gratification but there is a widespread sense that change is possible and even probable, and moreover that the nations as a whole are working intelligently together to this end. Communism in this world is more and more regarded as a vehicle of economic modernization rather than a political creed, and by this standard is an indifferent competitor to the varieties of "mixed" economies that most of the world employs. There are a few self-consciously revolutionary third-world states, mostly professing deviant communisms ("infantile leftism" in the formulation of a conservative and "satisfied" Soviet government and party), but they are mostly the most impoverished states with the fewest resources for change. China could still be in a troubled state but even it is assumed to have moved out of its aggressively revolutionary stage, to be reconciled with the world community and, for practical—but not necessarily all rhetorical—purposes, with the United States and the Union of Soviet Socialist Republics.

As in the preceding projection, there is a West European political federation with East European associates. A general political settlement in Europe has brought the withdrawal of Soviet and American troops and a provisional settlement of the German problem. The Soviet Union more and more regards itself as a European power with interests in common with those of the other advanced states; its ideological commitments by now make up hardly more than an alternative definition of a planned economy, although in government the Soviet state remains an oligarchy under a Communist party whose policies are increasingly consultative.

The ambitious development programs that are practiced by the international community in this projection are probably carried out through successful Latin American, African, and Asian free trade or common market groups. Japan is very active as leader and banker of Asia development. As in the previous world, poverty has been eliminated in the advanced states, European Russia, and the northern Mediterranean.

The distinguishing marks of this world are ambitious and successful economic cooperation, a general sense of progress, and a successful subordination of politics and ideology to economics and to values of rationality and humanity. There is at the same time a willingness on the part of the underdeveloped world to work for (and be satisfied with) "reasonable" and moderate short-term gains that carry excellent long-term prospects.

Note on Cumulative Growth Through Foreign Aid:

The following note is appended to our discussion of the Aid-Oriented World in order to point out that it is a priori possible to achieve a surprising amount of development over a ten to thirty-five-year span if modest amounts of capital are made available by the developed countries (say 1 to 3 per cent of GNP's) and if this capital is efficiently absorbed by the underdeveloped countries. Of course it has become increasingly clear that for most of the underdeveloped nations the limitations have as much to do with inabilities to absorb capital productively as with unavailability of capital. Nevertheless the following calculation may be relevant, since those who would argue for an aid-oriented world in which very large amounts of capital would be made available to the Underdeveloped World would presumably also argue that programs could be designed to make the absorption of such capital efficient.

Assume that in the first year there is a gross product of P in that part of the developed world that is giving large-scale aid and that this product grows annually by a factor $(1 + a)$ so that the gross product after the nth year is given by the formula $P(1 + a)^n$. Assume also that a portion f_n of this product is put into foreign aid in the nth year and that in N-n more years this investment grows by a factor of $(1 + \beta)^{N-n}$ as a result of savings and reinvestment in the economies of the underdeveloped nations. Then the net capital invested in the underdeveloped areas by the Nth year as a result of foreign aid given in the nth year is

$$P(1 + a)^n f_n (1 + \beta)^{N-n},$$

and the total capital due to foreign aid and reinvested savings is

$$P(1 + \beta)^N \sum_{n=1}^{N} f_n \frac{(1 + a)^n}{(1 + \beta)^n}$$

Let $\gamma = \dfrac{I}{N} \displaystyle\sum_{n=I}^{N} f_n \dfrac{(I+a)^n}{(I+\beta)^n}$.[3] Then the total invested capital available in the Nth year as a result of N years of foreign aid is $N\gamma P(I+\beta)^N$. Let us assume P is \$1.5 trillion and $N=35$. Then for typical values of γ and β we get:

$$\text{Capital} = (1.5)(35)(I+\beta)^{35}\gamma$$
$$= .525\gamma(I+\beta)^{35}$$

In Thirty-Five Years			In Ten Years		
γ	β	Accumulated Capital (trillions)	γ	β	Accumulated Capital (trillions)
.005	.03	.74	.005	.03	.10
.010	.03	1.48	.010	.03	.20
.020	.03	2.96	.020	.03	.40
.030	.03	4.44	.030	.03	.60
.050	.03	7.40	.050	.03	1.01
.005	.05	1.45	.005	.05	.12
.010	.05	2.90	.010	.05	.24
.020	.05	5.80	.020	.05	.49
.030	.05	8.69	.030	.05	.73
.050	.05	14.49	.050	.05	1.22

A β of .03 to .05 assumes that there is a significant rate of net saving, that the added savings are wisely invested, and that the capital output ratio in the underdeveloped nations—even if large amounts of capital are invested—is constant. Thus if the marginal (on the income from the development projects only) savings-investment rate is 20 per cent, and the capital output ratio on these savings when invested is 4, $\beta = .05$. A savings rate of 15 per cent and a capital output ratio of 5 would give a β of .03. While these are reasonable levels for current conditions, it may not be possible to maintain them if marginal investment opportunities become less favorable.

The conclusion, then, is that large amounts of capital can be accumulated within the underdeveloped nations by the year 2000. If we assume that it takes about \$4 of capital to generate an income of \$1 per capita, then \$1 trillion of additional capital is sufficient to increase the income of one billion people by an additional \$250 per capita (over the \$100-\$300 otherwise to be expected). Thus by the year 2000 there could be enough capital available to put most of the underdeveloped nations over \$500 per capita and all of them over \$300 to \$500 per capita.[4]

Of course, much less can be done on a more short-run basis—by say the middle and late 1970's.

[3] Note that if $a = \beta$ and all f_n are equal, then γ is equal to f_n. This gives an "intuitive interpretation" of γ.

[4] Of course, our "surprise-free" projections in Chapter III did not assume such impressive progress.

Thus even a decade after after the program started we would have around a tenth as much as in thirty-five years (the wonders of compound interest). Still the sums conceivable are impressive—running between a hundred and a thousand billion dollars—enough to get things started by the late 1970's and to make clear that development can occur.

B. MORE INWARD-LOOKING WORLDS

These worlds are characterized by pluralism of power and political influence, a general preoccupation with national interests, and a low level of conflict—though not necessarily of potentialities for conflict in the future. They are stable worlds, with stability the result of domestic preoccupations, political disappointment, political diffidence, prudence, or ideological decline.

3. More Inward-Looking—Communism Eroded

The essential characteristics are a relative withdrawal of the United States and the Soviet Union from world affairs, sharply increased European and Japanese influence, and Communist ideological decline.

Here there is a relatively stable multipolar system with the United States and Union of Soviet Socialist Republics much reduced in influence, probably emerging from periods of "neoisolationist" consolidation and reappraisal following a series of disappointments and frustrations in the 1960's. The West Germans have either accepted some sort of plan for a provisional settlement on the basis of two Germanies or there is a gradual erosion of the cold war between the GFR and GDR. In any case there are two Germanies, and there is a clear if unstated opinion in most of Europe that this is just as well. Europe enjoys extensive East-West economic and political relations, but there is no new European political authority. European world influence is large but chiefly economic; the Continent is politically diffident. In part this is because the European Common Market works and the political community does not, and as a result there is a desire not to undertake "political adventures" that might jeopardize the Common Market. The French are an important influence in Western Europe, but do not succeed in mobilizing and focusing major positive efforts by the other Europeans.

China is nearing its third revolutionary generation, with considerable economic gains, a direct collision with the United States having been avoided in the 1960's, now a member of the United Nations and with diplomatic relations with most of the world, including the United States. While a more stable and powerful social base exists for assertive foreign policies within the context of a revolutionary doctrine, China tends to be more prudent and less shrill than today, possibly because of the ascendency of technocrats within the Chinese power structure.

The great issues of the early cold war have a vestigial survival in the affairs of the United States, Russia, and China. The Russians and Chinese still assert a claim to lead international revolutionary movements (the Chinese may have established a new Communist international in the late 1960's), but in fact the revolutionary parties of the third world tend to be post-Communist and Jacobin and to make only tactical alignments with the Soviets and Chinese. While the United States has largely cut its foreign involvements and avoids military interventions in Latin America, it is still in a period of difficult and sometimes hostile economic and diplomatic relations with various Latin American states—often as a result of trying to influence them to be more "orderly."

Japan is self-consciously autonomous, still somewhat diffident in its international posture but rapidly changing; however, its primary foreign concerns are still with worldwide trade and economic relations. The third world is troubled, largely unchanged overall with much minor or regional instability, many new revolutionary movements, but with many of its authoritarian or technocratic governments chiefly interested in internal stability and growth rather than in making a mark on the international scene.[5]

In this kind of world European and Japanese ambitions would be largely economic but possibly tending toward future assertiveness; thus we might expect both to have gone seriously into the third world with foreign aid but probably a kind of aid designed chiefly to develop and enlarge specific markets for trade and to build up the sectors in the less developed nations (presumably mostly raw materials and simple industry) that help to support the trading system. Such an exercise in "enlightened capitalism" might be tolerable to the pride of the third world chiefly because it is uninterested politically.

Any assessment of the longer-range ambitions of Europe and Japan would have to include the probability of new political assertions. But these are assumed here as not likely to be disturbing or dangerous in the 1970-1980 period. Russia and the United States, however, might seem potential disturbers of balance in this world because both might be emerging from their "neoisolationist" stages in a mood to regain the kind of place and prestige held a decade earlier, at the expense of those who had been the interim inheritors of such international authority as existed in a world chiefly distinguished by pluralism, Communist decline, European and Japanese influence, and general if unsecured stability.

[5] This could also be true in World No. 1, the More Integrated, Stability or Status Quo-Oriented. In both cases it would be facilitated by a decline in "revolutionary" and "idealistic" rhetoric, and a less intense interest in the third world on the part of the big powers, encouraging a more moderate and "businesslike" atmosphere.

4. More Inward-Looking World—Eroded Democratic Morale and Some Communist Dynamism

This world is characterized by the power pluralism, United States and Soviet withdrawal, and the European and Japanese political diffidence of the preceding, but assumes that Communism remains the rationale of third-world revolution and that the Soviets, who remain hostile to the United States, have a real influence within this world movement.

This world is much like variation number three except that Communism as an ideology and revolutionary force is far from spent. Western Europe, in part because of its close relations with Eastern Europe, no longer regards Communism as a meaningful political threat but rather as a "legitimate" mode of revolution in backward countries. The Europeans oppose any intervention by the West in such situations. To some degree the United States accepts this, in part because there is some validity in the interpretation of these revolutions as essentially indigenous and nationalistic, and in part because of European influence—both diplomatic and intellectual. The result, however, is that much of the third world espouses some variant of Marxism and, more significant, considers itself generally aligned with Russian and China. In this projection there is a great deal of controversy among various Communist nations, with little or no centralized discipline, but this major part of the world considers itself essentially hostile to the United States. Thus the Soviet Union, while it may have gone through a period of retreat coming to terms with this new and intensely fractionalized Communism, may emerge as at best a leader and at worst an "elder statesman" of a revolutionary world movement of great importance. The United States, on the other hand, finds itself largely alone as an anti-Communist power, possibly having been involved in an inconclusive series of interventions in Asia or Latin America. By the time of the projection it is a powerful but beleaguered force.

This projection, then, foresees an essentially bipolar division of world politics in the context of a multipolar division of material power. Japan and Europe are largely withdrawn from the struggle. There is a sharp hostility between Communism and the United States, though Communism itself is a phenomenon taking many forms. The Communist movements experience internal conflicts that may occasionally be exploited by their opponents, but, by and large, the Communists side with one another against the non-Communist world, while the reverse tends not to be true. The Communist non-Communist rivalry is essentially political, moral, and material, but not military. The points of United States-Soviet and United States-Chinese military confrontation (Germany, Korea, Indochina) have been withdrawn.

5. More Inward-Looking—Dynamic Europe or Japan

The distinguishing mark of this projection within the context of this general class of worlds is that the Soviet Union and the United States are outpaced in political initiative (and ambition) by Europe and/or Japan.

Again this world is plural, prosperous, and for the present stable, much as in the first Inward-Looking World, but now an assertive Europe or Japan emerges. This European community may be politically united, perhaps along the lines of the Fouchet plan—perhaps even more closely, and perhaps including an integrated or associated Eastern Europe. We may assume that the dynamism of this Europe is chiefly expressed by 1975 in terms of rivalry for influence in the third world and in maintaining an aggressive independence—political, economic, and military—of both America and the Soviet Union. In the case of Japan, we can assume much economic penetration of Africa and Latin America but a political role in the 1975 time-period mainly confined to Asia, particularly South and Southeast Asia. Again there would be a strong desire for independence from the Americans, but in this case this desire might be combined with important areas of co-operation. The Communist bloc might be expected to be in a condition of advanced ideological disintegration although the individual Communist states might be prosperous and assertive. The distinguishing feature of this world is pluralism even greater than in any earlier projection—Japan and/or Europe competing much more directly with the superpowers.

C. GREATER DISARRAY WORLDS

These are unstable worlds, variously of multipolar power distribution or renewed world bipolarity. The sources of the instability may be conflicting national interest and ambition, or renewed ideological influence in world affairs.

6. Disarray World—Communism Eroded

This world is marked by the aggressive policies of one international actor in a situation of multipolar power distribution. Communism is not an important world force.

One major world power in this projection presses interventionist programs seeking a fairly well-disciplined bloc of allies, clients, or conquests. For the 1975 period the obvious candidates are Russia and the United States. If the projection were for the late 1970's or early 1980's, some European union or even Japan could assume the role of protagonist, and thus this projection could represent a development of the preceding one.

Russia, we assume, would be acting out of motives of national aggrandizement, with Communist ideology a moderately useful vehicle for advancing her international influence. The revolutionary mantle, though, would probably have been seized by a China which, while it does not yet have the power, would try to play a major role in world affairs. Despite its rhetoric the Soviet Union would perhaps be regarded as conservative, if not counter-revolutionary, by China and much of the third world. The other major powers may (1) have responded in kind by regrouping defensively, or competitively, in which case tension might be high and war, or at least limited wars, not unthinkable; or (2) they might lack dynamism and orientation —reacting in defensive ways, seeking isolation, being seriously vulnerable to the aggressive power. Tension would then also be high, with perhaps even greater opportunities for an explosion.

Another version of this world is conceivable if Chinese-Soviet tensions were to produce a war between now and 1975. The Communist movement might be expected to receive a fatal blow—in its contemporary formulation, at least; various deviant communisms might survive as the doctrines of individual revolutionary third world states. Moreover, the Europeans and the United States might be expected to attempt to isolate China and Russia in their crisis. Or the kind of disarray we are projecting could come about as a result of a war between the United States and China in which Russia refused to support China—ending its own ability to claim leadership of the Communist world—and the Europeans refused to support the United States. The result in any of these cases could be a multipolar international system with Communism, as a meaningful international movement, eroded, yet a high degree of tension prevailing among the powers—and these make up the special characteristics of this projection.

Ambitions in this kind of world presumably would be framed in crisis terms, the antagonists obsessed with defense against or evasion of their challenge and perhaps formulating their positions in messianic or other "high" articulations. The third world might again be disrupted by external pressures and interventions, quite possibly with fewer resources with which to cope—that is, with a good many nationalist and developmental ambitions discredited. Or there might be a collapse of new nations in some areas, especially Africa, with "neoimperialist" interventions to restore order by major powers or by secondary actors playing the jackal (or restorer of order) as the bigger powers confront one another.

7. Disarray World—Dynamic Communism

The distinguishing mark here is of renewed Communist ideological power and ambition, but without necessarily reestablishing a world of bipolar conflict—the Communist world could still be divided and the non-Communist world in disarray.

In this world the Communist movement might be seen as divided into sects yet still essentially united on basic issues. Or a substantially unified Communist movement might have been achieved again by a new "left" leadership in the Soviet Union. Presumably this leadership would not be what we know as Stalinist but would arise from a romantic resurgence among younger elements in the Soviet Communist party, confidently managing a strong Soviet society in a revolutionary and risk-taking foreign policy. We might assume that this new spirit could arise in reaction to the defection of some of the East European states from the Bloc in the late 1960's or 1970's, so that the new Communist alliance could be smaller than today but much more coherent and dynamic, again commanding disciplined foreign parties. Non-Communist Europe—to add another element contributing to this new Communist dynamism—might have experienced some unexpected social or economic failures or stagnation. In one projection the Soviet conflict with China could be overcome, for a time at least, by the new "leftism" of the Russian party and—possibly—by Chinese internal failures or foreign crises in which the Chinese had to seek Soviet aid or protection (that is, an intense crisis with the United States in which the Soviet Union successfully extended to China a nuclear guarantee).

If we postulate, then, a new kind of Soviet leadership, some unfavorable social and political trends within Europe, and possibly a United States that suffers some such setback in a confrontation with China or Russia as Russia's "Cuban missile" defeat of 1962, or perhaps a severe frustration in Vietnam in the 1960's, we could have a world in disarray in which Communism, by exploiting this disarray, is again on the march.

It should be noted that as in variation number four (Inward-Looking, Democracy-Eroded) discussed earlier, this world could come about even if Communism, as an ideology and revolutionary force, is largely spent at the center but remains vigorous at the "edges." Europe, in part because of its close relations with a still ideologically oriented Eastern Europe, could consistently interpret movements espousing Marxism as legitimate or tolerable, and oppose efforts to boycott, suppress, or intervene against them. Indeed, insofar as foreign Communist movements are concerned, Europeans might be more likely to take a "neutral" broker's position than one of any hostility. To some degree the United States might follow this interpretation. As a result, in many cases it might take relatively little to launch and sustain movements of radical insurrection or *coups d'etat* in backward countries. The West might console itself by emphasizing such criteria as gross national product, arguing that the revolutionary "rural" (underdeveloped) areas cannot expect to overwhelm the "urbanized" (Western) areas. Yet the result might be the creation of a "fortress North Atlantica" of industrialized Western states within a hostile and uncongenial world.

The basic argument here is that much the same world projection can be arrived at by assuming dynamism, unity and aggressiveness in the Communist movement, or by assuming relative disunity and fragmentation among the Communist states but an even more disunited opposition. In the second case a growing pessimism in Western Europe and the United States might produce a fairly passive foreign policy where only stark, aggressive provocations or challenges could evoke resistance. In such a situation, despite their disunity, the morale of the Communist states might be high; as a worldwide, even if discordant, Communist commonwealth became a reality it might indeed seem the wave of the future.

8. *Disarray World with a Dynamic Europe or Japan*

The essential note of this world is the assertion of European or Japanese power and ambition in conditions of tension and potential conflict. The projection also assumes, as plausible but not essential, defensiveness or withdrawal on the part of the United States and Russia.

This projection might assume that the settlement of Europe's divisions came about through an eventual assertion of European power against American and Soviet inertia or resistance. One such scenario might see NATO repudiated by Western Europe and the United States withdrawing forces in an atmosphere of acrimony and threats. Western Europe then demands a parallel withdrawal of Soviet forces from Eastern Europe with considerable East European diplomatic support and in circumstances in which the two Germanies propose terms of reunion that include a voluntary renunciation of nuclear forces. The Soviet withdrawal is also carried out in a crisis atmosphere with a Soviet denunciation of the East Europeans, and specifically the East Germans, for treachery. An Iron Curtain is reestablished with heavy fortifications along Soviet borders. An integrated European military organization, conceived as a defense group and to guarantee (and contain) Germany, subsequently shows signs of developing into an effective military machine with a unified general staff dominated by France and Germany— perhaps a France and Germany that have neoconservative governments. This Europe might develop ambitions to extend its African influence, or might raise Europe's claim to the former Polish, German, and Rumanian territories now within Russia. The United States could be building "fortress America." Japan could be isolated and rearming; Asia perhaps experiencing indifferent development success and increased European economic and political penetration.

If Japan were the assertive power in this world we might expect a renewed effort to mobilize Asia, this time perhaps initially justified on anti-Communist and anti-Chinese grounds, but possibly taking on an anti-

Western character as well. There could be Japanese sponsorship of anti-Communist alliances or federations in South and Southeast Asia, perhaps (in this period) the first steps in creation of an Asian nuclear deterrent community dominated by Japan and initially in cooperation with the United States but also providing a rationalization for Japanese nuclear armament. China might in this situation be driven toward a reconciliation with Russia —or Europe—as Japanese policies came more and more to have a tone of menace to them. This would be a powerful Japan, with a 1975 per capita GNP between one thousand five hundred and two thousand dollars and a total GNP between one hundred seventy-five and two hundred billion dollars. By the year 2000 this Japan might have a GNP of over a trillion dollars and a GNP per capita of close to ten thousand 1965 dollars. (See Chapter III.)

Whatever the scenario, the distinguishing marks of this world are of a multipolar distribution of military, political, and economic power, and with the world's major dynamic political protagonist being a renewed Europe or Japan.

D. THE USE OF SCENARIOS

In this section we shall elaborate some of the Canonical Variations outlined above through "transition scenarios." These are attempts to describe in some detail a hypothetical sequence of events that could lead plausibly to the situation envisaged. Some scenarios may explore and emphasize an element of a larger problem, such as a crisis or other event that could lead to war, the process of "escalation" of a small war or local violence into a larger war, the spread or contraction of a limited war, the fighting of a war, the termination of the war, or the subsequent peace. The focus of such a scenario can be military events and activities, the internal dynamics of various countries, bargaining among enemies or inter-ally relations, and so on. Other scenarios can be used to produce, perhaps in impressionistic tones, the future development of the world as a whole, a culture, a nation, or some group or class. The scenario is particularly suited to dealing with events taken together—integrating several aspects of a situation more or less simultaneously. By the use of a relatively extensive scenario, the analyst may be able to get a feeling for events and the branching points dependent upon critical choices. These branches can then be explored more or less systematically or the scenario itself can be used as a context for discussion or as a "named" possibility that can be referred to for various purposes.

Some of the advantages of the scenario as an aid to thinking are:

(1) They serve to call attention, sometimes dramatically and persuasively, to the larger range of possibilities that must be considered in the analysis of the future. They are one of the most effective tools in lessening the "carry-over" thinking that is likely even when it is clear to all that 2000 cannot be the same as 1965 or even 1985. Scenarios are one way to force oneself and others to plunge into the unfamiliar and rapidly changing world of the present and the future: They dramatize and illustrate the possibilities they focus on in a very useful way. (They may do little or nothing for the possibilities they do not focus on.)

(2) They force the analyst to deal with details and dynamics that he might easily avoid treating if he restricted himself to abstract considerations. Typically no particular set of the many possible sets of details and dynamics seems specially worth treating, so none are treated, even though a detailed investigation of even a few arbitrarily chosen cases can be most helpful.

(3) They help to illuminate the interaction of psychological, social, economic, cultural, political, and military factors, including the influence of individual political personalities upon what otherwise might be abstract considerations, and they do so in a form that permits the comprehension of many such interacting elements at once.

(4) They can illustrate forcefully, sometime in oversimplified fashion, certain principles, issues or questions that might be ignored or lost if one insisted on taking examples only from the complex and controversial real world.

(5) They may also be used to consider alternative possible outcomes of certain real past and present events, such as Suez, Lebanon, Laos, or Berlin.

(6) They can be used as artificial "case histories" and "historical anecdotes" to make up to some degree for the paucity of actual examples.

While the conscious use of scenarios has become widespread, it has also been criticized. One criticism is that only a "paranoid" personality, unjustifiably distrustful, suspicious, and preoccupied with hostility, could conceive of the kind of crises, provocations, aggressions, and plots that characterize many politico-military scenarios. Unfortunately this characterization seems to have more to do with the kinds of politico-military events the real world provides and planners must prepare for than with the psychodynamics of the planner. His responsibilities require him to be most interested in the many unpleasant ways in which things can go wrong; he should also be interested in what can go right, but the latter tends to be both more difficult and usually less useful to explore by means of scenarios. Of course, any particular scenario may in fact contain paranoid ideas, but this must be judged on the basis of the plausibility of the particular scenario—often a difficult judgment in a world of many surprises—and care must be taken to allow for a possibly realistic inclusion of a not-implausible degree of paranoia in one or more decision-makers who have roles in the scenario.

A second criticism is that scenarios may be so divorced from reality as not only to be useless but also misleading, and therefore dangerous. However, one must remember that the scenario is not used as a predictive device. The analyst is dealing with the unknown and to some degree unknowable future. In many specific cases it is hard to see how critics can be so certain there is a sure divorce from a reality that is not yet known and may present surprises. Imagination has always been one of the principal means for dealing in various ways with the future, and the scenario is simply one of many devices useful in stimulating and disciplining the imagination. To the extent that particular scenarios may be divorced from reality, the proper criticism would seem to be of particular scenarios rather than of the method. And of course unrealistic scenarios are often useful aids to discussion, if only to point out that the particular possibilities are unrealistic.

It is also worth noting that for some purposes mistakes in particulars may be of secondary importance. For example, many today are concerned about France as an increasingly important nuclear power with vague and uncertain motivations and a dynamism unsuspected fifteen years ago. By 1980 France may be weak and disunited. But similar problems may then be posed by Italy or Japan. Many of these specific problems as viewed by the United States would be much the same as though the new power were France. This does not mean all problems would be the same, only that those problems of the real Japan of 1980, which perhaps could have been predicted by a supremely competent planner of 1967, might not look very different—in the abstract—from those problems actually predicted for the hypothetical France of 1980. However, if a scenario is to seem plausible to analysts and/or policy-makers it must, of course, relate at the outset to some reasonable version of the present, and must correspond throughout to the way analysts and/or policy-makers are likely to believe decision-makers and others are likely to behave. Since plausibility is a great virtue in a scenario, one should, subject to other considerations, try to achieve it. But it is important not to limit oneself to the *most* plausible, conventional, or probable situations and behavior. History is likely to write scenarios that most observers would find implausible not only prospectively but sometimes, even, in retrospect. Many sequences of events seem plausible now only because they have actually occurred; a man who knew no history might not believe any. Future events may not be drawn from the restricted list of those we have learned are possible; we should expect to go on being surprised.

E. FRAGMENTARY SCENARIOS FOR THE MORE INTEGRATED WORLDS

We indicated in Chapter I that there are likely to be ten major powers dominating international affairs during the last third of the twentieth century: two of them "super" (United States and Soviet Union), five of them "large" (Japan, West Germany, France, China, and the United Kingdom), and three of them "intermediate" (India, Italy, and Canada). Most of these powers clearly will be conservative, disposed to avoid violence and crises, and anxious to preserve the momentum of their economic progress or eager to increase it. One can easily imagine these larger nations (with the possible exception of China), collaborating fairly closely (if informally) to set rules in international relations that seem likely to prevent turmoil— they might attempt, in effect, to "police" the world.

This cooperation might take place in an enlarged OECD context, the Soviet Union and part or all of Eastern Europe first becoming associated with OECD for one purpose and then others. One ostensible or real purpose of their cooperation might be to facilitate trade and economic development among both the wealthy and poor nations. But in practice they could act much as did the Concert of Europe between 1814 and 1914. Cooperation could become especially close if there were events that tested or molded it. One could imagine serious crises in Africa or some issues revolving around the containment of China that dramatized the mutual interest of this new Concert of Nations in cooperative political action. Or their dominant motive might be to make a serious and concerted attempt to facilitate development in parts of the third world.

Another way in which an Integrated World could come about, if a less likely one, would be if the nonnuclear powers of the world made a joint effort to exclude the influence and contain the power of the large powers. Some of the large or intermediate nations, such as Japan, West Germany, India, Italy, or Canada, might assume important roles among the non-nuclear powers, or might even choose to become nuclear powers themselves (or might end in some intermediate or ambivalent role). Particularly if China stayed outside the arrangement, the new division might easily override Communist and non-Communist, white and nonwhite, or developed and undeveloped distinctions. In any case it is possible to imagine a combination of the underdeveloped and/or nonnuclear nations of the world that by coordinated effort forced or induced the developed nations to a new level of cooperative effort or policy. Or one or more of the large and/or nuclear nations might take the interesting and important initiative of declaring itself protector of the nonnuclear bloc—insisting on a "hands off" attitude toward their "internal" affairs. Or a group of almost all of the large nations might accept this role, feeling that the best way to reduce turmoil would be to have the smaller nations police themselves and act as a pressure group versus the larger nations. And also less likely is the possibility that Marshal Lin Piao might turn out to be a prophet and the third ("rural") areas of the world might unite against the First or the First and Second Worlds. This would, of course, cause a counterunity, but now the description would seem to be one of the "Greater Disarray" or even more violent worlds.

A United States-Soviet entente or even alliance seems quite plausible to many people as a new international configuration. It is no novelty for senior Soviet figures to suggest privately that at some point the Soviet Union and the United States will get together against China. Informal polling suggests that this position is also commonly found among United States businessmen and even among United States government officials. Similar attitudes are held by many Europeans (who in fact sometimes fear that such an alliance would ignore their interests or even be directed against them). On the other hand, some Europeans, mostly in Germany or France, hope for a Soviet-West European alliance, perhaps caused by Chinese pressure on the Soviets. The authors tend to regard these forms of Integrated Worlds as unlikely. The usual justifications for predicting United States-Soviet (West European-Soviet) alliance are that there will be an almost complete "convergence" of social and economic systems, a common interest in containing a common enemy, China, or a mutual fear of and interest in containing the arms race. The first basis seems to us most unlikely; the second as unlikely to provide enough or the right kind of pressures; and the third, which in the conditions of the late 1950's we took very seriously, now seems likely to raise extreme counterpressures if it should take the form of bilateral United States-Soviet decisions rather than action by consensus of the major powers.

F. A GENERAL RATIONALE FOR INWARD-LOOKING AND GREATER DISARRAY WORLDS

For the most part, analyses directed to problems of the political future envisage logical or traditional sequences of events. Even in scenarios that are invented to explore little-thought-of possibilities we usually assume that states will not behave wildly irrationally or in newly irrational ways in advancing reasonably defined interests or gaining reasonable objectives—even if these interests or objectives may themselves be selfish or self-aggrandizing, or dangerous to the stability of the international community. But the possibility of newly irrational or wildly irrational behavior must be explicitly taken into account. For example, by any narrow definition of self-interest, the history of both Nazism and Stalinist Communism shows a series of decisions that in fact hurt those movements and the states that they ruled, yet were persisted in for "higher" reasons of ideology, or at least out of motives that were given an ideological rationalization. The most obvious examples are Nazism's slaughter of Jews and Poles, a "senseless" destruction of potentially useful manpower and a diversion of large numbers of military and paramilitary personnel, and Stalin's prewar purge of the Red Army that seriously weakened it at a crucial point. In foreign policy Nazi Germany's fatal commitment to a two-front war had a reasonable strategic gloss but was ultimately inspired by Nazism's ideological hostility to Communism and a racist view of Slavic Europe.

To see unreasonableness in politics retrospectively is, of course, a good deal easier than to estimate its force in future events, but the problem is worth some attention in order to emphasize the importance of trying to imagine ways in which the irrational or nonrational may seem as factors in human affairs.

An example can be given in the form of a general predictive statement about the future. It can be argued that the period between 1966 and 2000 will generally be one in which "objective" and traditional terms of political conflict—over territory, resources, class and economic interests, governmental succession, forms of government—will be increasingly supplanted by conflicts of sociocultural origin (in Asia), and possibly by irrational political movements and ideologies elsewhere in the world. Cultural "deracination," individual alienation within transitional (or failed transitional) societies as well as in the advanced urban-industrial states, to say nothing of racial stresses, the nuclear threat, and economic crises, will produce anxieties that may find public outlet in romantic, implicitly Messianist, "total" political movements. The parliamentary system worldwide is likely to find itself in increasing difficulties because of practical inadequacies in dealing with mass government and mass society. The result may be a trend toward elitist or oligarchic power, possibly technocratic in character; possibly totalitarian (as above); possibly revolving around romantic personalities.

This argument can be developed in the form of three propositions. The first is that the totalitarian experiences of the 1930's and 1940's, and fascism in particular, provided the first examples of a new kind of "revolution" that we may expect to see more of in the future. The second general proposition is that violent reactions against the West—against the advanced industrial societies of North America and Europe—may be expected during the next thirty-three years from among the economically and technologically *advanced* Asian countries—the "successful" examples of development. The third is that the chiliastic or revolutionary Messianist impulse will be extremely important in Asia and Africa during this period.

Fascism and communism in Western Europe (communism in the Soviet Union has, it may be, too many particularist characteristics to be included here), like the anti-Western imperialism of Japan in the 1920's and 1930's, may be seen as responses to kinds of social and political conditions which—in their major elements—may be expected to recur. It would obviously be unreasonable to expect the future responses to be identical to those of the past, but the new responses, like the new conditions, may be expected to bear a family resemblance to things past.

While the subject of European totalitarianism admittedly is one of great complexity and controversy, we propose that fascism, and communism in Western Europe, constituted "new" responses to a European crisis. This crisis was manifest when the formal structure of liberal society could objectively be judged as failing or in crucial respects discredited (having produced the Great War, seemingly helpless before the postwar economic collapse and inflation), but also when the established social structure was subjectively rejected by large groups within West European society. The early leaders of fascism and communism in Western Europe were representatives of the romantic antibourgeois, anticapitalist, antiplutocrat political and intellectual tradition that had been in more or less permanent rebellion against European liberalism since before 1848. By 1918 it had come to include almost all of Europe's intellectuals and artists.[6] (The early Nazi leaders were something else, mostly representative of the adventurist and "outlaw" fringes of society, but their pretensions were to a Nietzschean intellectual position, to "volkish" ideologies very much in the mainstream of the romantic antibourgeois movement.)

The crises of the First World War and its aftermath provided a mass following for this romantic leadership. While the factors in this mass response are complex, one thing stands out clearly. Popular support for fascism and the communist parties was not fringe support, not confined to the "Lumpenproletariat," or to groups excluded from self-confident national communities. Typically, fascism and communism both found their support among workers and the middle classes, and while the workers suffered economic exploitation and were victimized by economic crisis, they were, in both Italy and Germany, organized and with parliamentary representation in workers' parties, and enjoying established channels for affecting the policies of the government. But in the crisis of Europe's 1920's and 1930's significant numbers of them abandoned "practical" trade unionism and democratic socialism for visionary fascism, Nazism, and communism.

They were part of a general retreat from established liberal politics, from the established structure of Europe's government and society. The older conservative, liberal, socialist, and agrarian parties, representing class interests, and the regional and sectarian parties, were overwhelmed or

---

[6] "Mussolini's call to a stoical, austere and energetic life . . . is almost exactly Bernard Shaw's attitude; a sovereign contempt for a civilization whose supreme achievement is the production of chocolate creams." Herman Finer, *Mussolini's Italy* (London: Gollancz, 1936), p. 183.

broken by fascist movements that addressed no specific class interest and found support among all classes.[7] The communists, by definition a class party, none the less in the same period found most of their leaders and their most influential converts from outside the working class.

The new movements not only transcended the established structuring of European politics but did so by setting forth visionary and historicist goals and irrational justifications for action (including, notably in Germany, Romania, and Hungary, and to a limited extent elsewhere, the invention or assimilation of "volkish" nationalistic religions, essentially revivals of paganism that had been the freakish outgrowth of the folk-revivals of the prewar European romantic movement).

The rebellion, then, was not only against the established liberal-bourgeois standards of Europe but against reason. The individual inspirations of the rebellion lay in the antibourgeois intellectual tradition of modern Europe—although these individual sources do not adequately explain or necessarily culminate in totalitarianism. Membership in this rebellion cut across (nearly) all classes. Part of the explanation of this must, of course, be seen in the failures of liberal society, the comprehensible lack of confidence that Europeans felt in the competence of the established system to deal with the crisis of the period. Part of the answer must also be sought in the problem ordinarily described in such terms as *anomie*, or individual isolation or alienation within industrial-urban (or transitional) societies.[8] The First World War had created the "totalitarian" state in that it had provided an unplanned and unprecedented demonstration of the resources of mass organization, industrial production, national mobilization, and militarization

---

[7] "National Socialism was an aggregate combining all the features of the Right and almost all those of the Left in German political history." Ernst Nolte, *The European Right*, edited by Rogger and Weber (Berkeley and Los Angeles: University of California Press, 1965, p. 303. The composition of the Italian Fascist party in 1921 showed (according to party figures) among 152,000 members, 62,000 who were proletarians (incuding landless agricultural workers) and 90,000 members of the middle classes. (Finer, *Mussolini's Italy*, p. 143.) The Hungarian (Arrow Cross) fascist party in 1937 had a membership which was 51 per cent industrial workers, 29 per cent professionals (including army officers), and only 8 per cent peasant (in a population which as a whole was 52 per cent peasant, 23 per cent industrial and mining). Istvan Deak, *The European Right*, pp. 396-397. A slogan of the Belgian fascists (Rexists) was "Workers of all classes, unite!" Typically, peasant or farmer rebellions or "revolutions" are antiurban, antilandlord, and reactionary. Peasant membership in European fascism was disproportionately low.

[8] "All fascisms attempted to capture and direct bourgeois dissatisfaction with existing industrial and political reality, a dissatisfaction which began to take concrete revolutionary form in the late 19th century. . . . Fascism was against conventions, but on another level it attempted to find a new sense of 'belonging' that might be combined with the revolt. . . ." George L. Mosse, *The Crisis of German Ideology* (New York: Universal Library, 1965), p. 312. Hannah Arendt also deals at length with this aspect of fascism in *The Origins of Totalitarianism* (New York: Harcourt Brace and World, 1966).

available to the modern state; it drastically accelerated the social transformation of Europe begun a century earlier by the technological revolution. The uprooting (both physical and social) experienced during the war by millions of individual Europeans melded with the antiliberal intellectual and revolutionary traditions (or their vulgarizations) to result in the general phenomenon in Europe of romantic and violent movements preaching irrational doctrines and visionary goals. At the crux of the totalitarian problem is the fact that these essentially irrational and visionary movements appealed to precisely the social groups who, by the standards of a reasonable politics, should have been among the least vulnerable to this kind of action and argument.

In Italy this trend took a militarist, imperialist, and socialist form—promising national renewal and glory, and radical social and economic reform. In Germany it was militarist, socialist, racist, and revisionist—later millenarian—in foreign policy. (Nazism, unlike fascism, was not content to seek a new national empire. It proposed a radical reorganization and purge of Europe, doing away with nation-states, unifying the Continent, making Poland and the Ukraine "rationalized" agricultural appendages to the integrated West European economic complex—all ruled by Germans in alliance with native fascist allies.) In European communism the attempt was socialist, militarist (militarizing society for its historical struggle, while condemning traditional militarism), and internationalist—with the objective of doing away with nations. All had scapegoats, racial in Germany and the Balkans, primarily class scapegoats in communism and in Italian fascism (the most "socialist" of the National Socialisms). In these attempts Left and Right came together in their rival—or simultaneous—attempts to find radical solutions to the blatant dysfunctions of the bourgeois economy and class structure.

Now a notable achievement in society and economics since the Second War has been the assimilation of large elements of the American and European working classes to bourgeois values and standards. Many of the grosser forms of economic exploitation and discrimination have been ended. This is perhaps most marked in the United States, but even though class consciousness is still an important factor in European society the invidious differences between workers and bourgeoisie have been much reduced. We are obviously much closer to the classless society than ever before—and closer, in some ways, than the Communist countries—though not soon likely to achieve it.

Social integration does not, however, necessarily follow economic assimilation to bourgeois society. It may indeed be lessened among some working groups (notably in Europe) to the degree that a sense of proletarian solidarity is diminished. The continued urbanization of the industrial nations may, as it certainly has in the United States, increase the overall incidence of isolation and social alienation as rural and small town or village society is further undermined by migration to cities, typically migration to ghettos—including the lower middle-class ghettos. We need only consult the current literature of America's "urban problem" for evidence of this. In Europe the new migrants to cities are in large part foreigners, except in Italy, Spain, the Balkans, and Greece. It may thus be that where Europe before World War II included the largest groups of economically alienated and socially isolated workers, it includes the fewest today—among the nationals of each given country. America today may have one of the largest groups (and with race added to the urban problem, ours may have the least encouraging prospects for integration).[9] The industrializing states of Asia have a large number.

Europe, since 1945, has also largely been "depoliticized" under an American protectorate, now nearing its end. Several of the European states are governed by permanent coalitions of parties on the basis of a national consensus that is essentially economic and only minimally political. Several others have experienced a significant separation of national administration—conducted by a bureaucratic or technocratic class on the basis, again, of a general consensus on national economic and social objectives— from the parliamentary and political mechanisms that ostensibly establish national policy but in fact have been unable or incompetent to do so. Thus there are "postparliamentary" elements in a number of the European governments and a postparliamentary regime in France.[10]

Yet just beyond this era of depoliticization and drastic social change within Western society lie new problems and crises possibly too grave to be dealt with within existing political structures and practices. Nuclear war or the serious threat of nuclear war might be one such. An economic crisis that existing techniques of economic and financial management could not resolve is another. The much discussed "black-white" or "north-south" or "Asian-Western" crisis is still another. Still others, unforeseeable now, must be expected within any thirty-three-year period. One of these, or several in conjunction, could prove to be for the Europe (or conceivably the America?) of the future what the First World War and inflation and depres-

[9] Since the 1940's we certainly have been in a new stage of national urbanization, of vast movements of population, of physical movement but also social movement, of transiency of place, status and association, quite unknown before the war. There are also sizable groups alienated not only from the current policies of the government but also from the possibility of changing those policies—or that government— by conventional methods. (It is not clear whether these groups are of any more significant size than during the Harding and Depression years.) One saving quality may be that America, unlike European nations, has no tradition at all of distinguishing between survival of the nation—the *patrie*—and survival of the form of government.

[10] See Ernst Haas in *A New Europe?*, edited by Stephen R. Graubard (Boston: Houghton Mifflin and Co., 1964), pp. 70 ff.

sion proved for the Europe of the recent past—a test of the established system that that system could not deal with. There is no reason to think that we are immune to new crises and problems even larger in scale and impact, more devastating in their possible consequences, than those that disrupted the European society of a generation ago. We may be spared facing such eventualities before the year 2000—we are certainly in a phase of historical lull, even of reaction today—but there is no guarantee that this will be so.

If such a crisis should prove beyond the competence of existing political structures, we must expect people to go beyond politics to find a remedy. A romantic response to problems that reason does not solve, a metapolitical response to a crisis that established politics fails—these are not extraordinary presuppositions. Obviously the new movements—the new responses—will not be "fascist" or "communist"; fascism and communism are somewhat discredited today, or out of fashion. But they were "modern" movements in that they made use of mass communications, new techniques of mass organization and administration, the industrial and economic techniques of modern society, to obtain a scale and intensity of impact and action denied earlier parties and movements. More important, they were "modern" in their ability to appeal to, to enlist and mobilize the most modern of social elements, the urbanized middle classes and workers of industrial society, the socially mobile (or, in another context, "rootless") classes, the alienated intellectual and artist. The essential elements of the totalitarian movements —their providing of a new moral as well as political rationale for insecure national societies and alienated elements within those societies—must be distinguished from the right-wing, or left-wing, character of historical totalitarianism. The response that these movements made to the crises of their day was visionary and moral: faced with seemingly insurmountable problems, they set forth to make a "new" society in which the crises would be transcended. With the resources of pragmatic action seemingly exhausted, and with the moral warrant that historicism can provide, they sought their ends through violence. Today there seems little evidence that men have lost their willingness to use violence in great causes or their willingness to listen to romantic interpretations of history and political possibility.

The argument is frequently made that Asian-Western or "north-south" conflict or tension in the future will be provoked by the economic disparties between the advanced industrial nations and the societies of Africa and Asia. Without discounting this possibility we would suggest the possibility of tension or conflict between the most successful "developing" or developed non-European states and the established industrial powers. This seems more probable than a conflict between the poorest and the richest, and more serious in its potentialities.

Where economic and political development within the West has been a matter of progressive development in ideas and institutions within a society, in Africa and Asia "modernization" can only come about by importing ideas and institutions that are of foreign origin. The "modern" world is Western. This is a result of Western industrial superiority, but it is also a result of the West's having used its superior techniques of power to subdue and undermine Asian civilizations that in the sixteenth century were in respects other than physical power the equal or superiors of the Europe of that period. But the fact with which we must deal today is that China, Japan, India, Islam—to take the more important Asian civilizations—have since the sixteenth century been discredited as cultures able to deal with the contemporary world on *native* terms. To possess science, technology, modern means of political organization, modern forms of social organization, and military power, they must assimilate ideas and institutions of Western origin and development.

These required changes are immense ones. We readily acknowledge this but without, perhaps, appreciating just how immense they really are. The sociocultural change demanded by "development" of Indians or Chinese today is hardly smaller than would be required for the contemporary United States—in order to achieve still higher levels of prosperity and international status—to adopt the traditional government structure of China, establishing a monarchy, adopting China's educational syllabus, and making rice cultivation the principal economic activity. The changes in personal lives, social values, political assumptions, in the education of the young and the revaluation of culture, surely would be no greater than are presupposed in the contemporary "development" of Asia's great cultures. They are greater than those changes that took place in Japan between 1868 and 1914 (even though Japan had a complex and active commercial and entrepreneural society that was less distant, in these respects, from the contemporary West than the China of 1868).

The Japanese case is fundamental to this argument. There were two stages in Japan's development. The first was one in which Japan, faced with the manifest superiorities in power, economics, and social organization of nineteenth-century Europe, tried to adopt the institutions of liberal Europe wholesale. It is not too much to say that—in the language of contemporary race relations—Japan tried to "pass" into European society. The evidence of this lies not only in the reform of public institutions in Japan but more important in the private changes—the adoption of European clothes, the cultivation of foreign literary models, many of the conversions to Christianity. The political evidence lies in Japan's frank attempt to obtain "European"—which meant imperialist—status *vis-à-vis* China and Korea. It was implicit in the alliance with Great Britain, which enjoyed a public value in Japan wholly disproportionate to its real importance.

The liberal accommodation to the West for Japan ended in the 1920's. The attempt to "pass" had failed. Japan's effort to gain colonial rights over China equivalent to those that Britain held in India or Holland in Indonesia was blocked by the Western powers. Japan's attempt to insert a declaration of racial equality into the League of Nations Charter was rebuffed by the European powers and by the United States. The United States passed oriental exclusion measures in its immigration legislation of the 1920's— which became a major public issue in Japan and the subject of diplomatic protests.

But more important than the rebuffs that Japan received from the liberal states that it had emulated was the sense of deracination or deculturation within Japan—again a matter that is clear enough in the Japanese literature of the period. There was a sense that things had gone too far in this accommodation to the West. A violent "correction" ensued—a new xenophobia and nationalism in both policy and theory, a revival of Shintoism (which was a medieval religion, not one with a dominant place in pre-Meiji Japan), the formulation of a new foreign policy that was pan-Asian and frankly anti-Western. Japan went to war in 1941 with a nationalism, a self-conscious cult of divine empire, a xenophobia, hardly precedented in Japan's past.

Japan is a dramatic example. Less imposing instances of anti-Western "correction" and reaction could be adduced in India (in aspects of Gandhiism and Subandra Bose's wartime movement), in Indochina's bizarre syncretist religions of the late nineteenth and twentieth centuries, in the anti-Soviet and implicitly racialist twist that Maoism has taken in China, and, of course, in the rhetoric of "New Emerging Forces" in Indonesia and certain other of the new Afro-Asian nationalist ideologies that are so close in spirit to Mussolini's movement of the 1920's.[11]

Since 1945 Japan has undergone a new accommodation to the West, and specifically to the values of the liberal American version of contemporary Western culture, nearly as vast in scale and social effects as the Meiji restoration itself (which however had been self-motivated and carried out wholly on Japanese initiatives). Recently Japan has been uneasily passive in politics, pacifist in a violent world. Japan obviously will resume an active role in policy in the near future; a state of this power and of Japan's geopolitical position cannot avoid an active foreign policy. Is it extraordinary to expect that this resumption of political activism in succession to American tutelage will—in much less than the next thirty-three years—be accompanied by a "correction" in Japanese cultural and social orientation?

But Japan again is a dramatic example of current accommodation to the

---

[11] This subject, and the problem of anti-Western reactions in postcolonial Asia and Africa, is discussed at length in Edmund Stillman and William Pfaff, *The Politics of Hysteria* (New York: Harper and Row, 1964).

West, and accommodation enforced by defeat in war and a long occupation. China's turn against not only the United States—which had for more than a century, and with general disinterest and lack of selfishness, championed China's independence and development—but also against Russia, surely includes elements of such a nationalist reaction against the alien accommodations forced upon modern China. (The identification of the United States with all the world's imperialism and exploitation is comprehensible but, one would think, excessive; not even Stalinist Russia had to find so specific a devil-figure in international politics. And the turn against Russia, while it is explicable in practical terms, is not wholly explicable in such terms. China surely is reacting against more than "modern revisionism," or even Russia's occupation of trans-Siberian territories.)

Such national and nationalistic reactions may well be a pattern for future events. And if this kind of sociocultural reaction is allied to the factors of urbanization and the social dislocation caused in traditional Asian societies by the industrial revolution, one may even foresee "modern" Messianist and visionary movements that make use of modern methods of mass politics and mass violence, erected upon a substructure akin to that that produced the Boxer upheaval or the imperial explosion of Japan in the 1930's and 1940's.

This is a third factor in the situation. Disturbed or frustrated societies in both the West and in Afro-Asia have a record of resort to chiliastic or messianist behavior. Medieval revolutionary chiliasm in the West—the "tense expectation of a final, decisive struggle in which a world tyranny will be overthrown by a 'chosen people' and through which the world will be renewed and history brought to its consummation" [12]—took its most notable active political forms in the peasant crusades, various peasant or anarcho-communist rebellions in Flanders, France, and England in the twelfth and thirteenth centuries, in the lowlands and Germany in the three hundred years that followed (mostly centered on the "future Frederick"—a resurrected Frederick Barbarossa who would prepare the second coming of Christ), and in the Anabaptist movement of the sixteenth century. It was alive at the time of the French Revolution, and Norman Cohn convincingly argues that not only the apocalyptic spirit but some of the historical ingredients of these early movements were evident in modern Nazism and Bolshevism. Even the leadership is drawn almost without exception from the same stratum, the lower clergy and the declassé or neointelligentsia.

The nonpolitical components of European communism and fascism may be a matter of controversial discussion, but the existence of explicitly eschatological factors in many of the important Asian and African political

[12] Norman Cohn, *The Pursuit of the Millennium*, 2d ed. (New York: Harper Torchbooks, 1961), p. 309.

movements, or movements of political-social effect, in the present and recent past, is indisputable. The Tai Ping and Boxer movements in China, the Cao Dai and Hoa Hao in Vietnam, the messianic Buddhist sects of modern Japan, and notably the Komeito, have all been of considerable importance in the development of modern Asian politics and the contemporary Asian scene. All are nativist in character, which is to say they are concerned to revive or vindicate national traditions as against foreign influences, most are in some degree syncretic, adopting elements of foreign religion or culture, and all are or have been influential in the development or expression of revolutionary political nationalism in their societies. Their common features with the multitude of naïve messianic sects of modern Africa, which synthesize Christian symbols or "magic" with African nationalist and racialist assertions, are generally recognized. The important differences, aside from those that are of anthropological interest, are that the Asian movements have often been quite sophisticated in doctrine, organization, and political objectives, and that they have been effective to a degree that their African counterparts have not.

It is also worth noting that while the Vietnamese, Chinese, and African movements were syncretist, bearing evidence of the influence of Christian missions and Western eschatology, this seems less true of the neo-Buddhist movements in Japan. And in Indonesia there has been an important messianist tradition that is of Islamic origin. In Sumatra and Java the Mahdist influence on Islam has been great. (A Shiite sect, Mahdism holds that the judgment will be preceded by a period of confusion and oppression ended by the advent of a Mahdi, an enlightened one, who in turn will be overthrown by evil with Mohammed then returning to the earth to destroy evil and bring justice). Mahdist religious expectations were easily linked to the social confusion and disorder of the twentieth century in Indonesia, and took explicit political form during the anti-Dutch war of 1945-1949. Mahdist groups took part in the Republican Revolution, waging holy war on Europeans and Chinese. The postrevolutionary Darul Islam, a Mahdist movement, sought a theocracy and was in persistent conflict with the Sukarno government.

Vittorio Lanternari also traces Hindu and Buddhist (and Paleo-Malaysian pagan) elements as well as Mahdist in some other Indonesian messianist cults of recent years.[13] While the chiliastic movements of the West undoubtedly were formed by the influence of Judeo-Christian eschatology on the Western consciousness, it would seem that what we have here is a phenomenon of mass behavior in situations of stress that is not limited to

[13] Lanternari, *The Religions of the Oppressed: A Study of Modern Messianic Cults* (New York: New American Library, 1963).

any single cultural tradition. It has appeared in a number of places in conditions of sociocultural upheaval and the discrediting of established values (as in the population growth and rise of industry and commerce that undermined medieval European peasant society, the Protestant reformation, the collision of Western with Asian or African cultures in modern times).

Is it possible to generalize from this about new chiliastic movements in the 1967-2000 period? Certainly it would seem that the political content of some contemporary events—in China, in Vietnam, in the "anti-Communist" and anti-Chinese Indonesian upheaval of recent months—can easily be overestimated.

The mass movement that is inspired (or largely inspired) by nonrational motives and aims at a redemptive alteration in the condition of its members probably should be seen as subject to the following distinction: some such movements purport to bring about redemptive changes through a specific and attainable series of political measures—altering the economic base of the nation, changing the structure of agriculture, deposing a ruling class and replacing it with the agents of another class, eliminating disruptive or obsolete social or racial elements in the society, educating or reeducating the masses. For some others, methods and ends are for practical purposes indistinguishable. In the latter case revolutionary action is of imminent value. So far as there is a doctrinal belief among the leadership, the redemptive transformation of society is held to be a matter of changing the consciousness of men themselves. The revolution is "spiritual" rather than political. And for the masses themselves, the objectives of the revolution are often hardly definable, or they amount to an elimination of toil, humiliation, and frustration from life itself, the advent of a supernatural salvation. "Give yourselves to the fire of revolution like dry logs" was a characteristic injunction of Indonesia's President Sukarno to his people. But how, by what actions, to accomplish what practical changes? Those questions had no clear answers.

Among primitive societies placed in situations of great stress, the phenomenon of redemptive mass movements has been most nakedly magical and naïve. The totalitarian movements of modern Europe have (or had) highly sophisticated rationales, although their ultimate objectives defied reason. But it could be argued that there is a common impulse in all of these, that the kind of social crisis that produced them will deepen in Asia during the next thirty years, not be reduced, and that to expect that we have seen the end of such movements even in the advanced societies of the West must constitute an act of faith in human reason and progress rather than an argument from evidence.

G. FRAGMENTARY SCENARIOS FOR INWARD-LOOKING WORLDS

One may assume a continuing general prosperity, but with trade tending to be bloc-oriented or a matter of balanced bilateral arrangements. A tendency toward political withdrawal, a semi-isolationism, could also be influential in the West. The threat of large central war might be minimal, and there could be little or no real "arms race." (For example, Ballistic Missile Defense systems might be renounced, or kept so simple or limited as to provide protection only against the less advanced Nth countries; Red China might experience serious difficulties in bringing its advanced weapons systems out of development so that it continued to lag decisively behind the West and the Soviet Union; and a general sense of "free security" combined with antinuclear attitudes and judicious pressures employed by the big powers might restrain the arms race.) Thus disinterest and constraints together might effectively limit modern nuclear weapons systems or at least make their acquisition a matter of prestige for some nations rather than of serious capability.

The West (and perhaps the Soviet Union as well) might adopt an increasingly skeptical or indifferent attitude toward the less-developed world. This could occur from some combination of a reevaluation of national interests and disillusionment with the results of both aid programs and political and military intervention in the Third World. Thus even with aid, Indonesia, Ceylon, Burma, Black Africa, and the Arab world might not have made much progress in increasing per capita income. The classic problems—intractable cultural traits, lack of real savings, the pressure of population on new real growth, a shortage of skills, and a waning of desire to "achieve" in the face of solution-resistant economic problems—might have proved insurmountable. Yet these states might nonetheless be largely impervious to Communist (or democratic) blandishments or subversion. A mutual "hands off" attitude might easily develop.

The pessimism or indifference to the problems of the Third World could be reinforced by adverse experiences. Thus if India is taken as the major test case of the efficacy of large-scale United States foreign aid, failure there is likely to have important consequences on United States policy and public attitudes generally. If the United States were to make a large effort in the Mekong Delta (after the Vietnam war) which, even if it proved to be of substantial benefit to Southeast Asia, had inconclusive (and expensive) effects for the United States or even coincided with political losses to the United States position, then the United States appetite for grandiose projects might be sharply reduced.

Similarly the Soviet Union could find that its aid to Cuba, Egypt, Indonesia, and India produced little benefit for Russia, and its subversive activities elsewhere might also be unrewarding; given the detente and lagging internal development, the Soviet Union too could lose much of its interest in revolutionizing the Third World.

France might continue an energetic program toward the poorer nations in the French (or Latin American) culture areas, but this too could flag if there were major inflationary, balance of payments, or other economic problems, or if there were a change in the attitudes of the French government or the French people, perhaps also as a result of disillusioning experiences or even because of the example of the two superpowers.

In these conditions some of the less-developed nations might nevertheless achieve self-sustaining economic growth. These could include the relatively wealthy nations of Latin America (i.e., Venezuela, Chile, and Argentina); Colombia and Mexico from the middle group might also do very well; and even among the poorer states, a nation like Brazil might succeed. South Korea, Taiwan, Singapore, and Hong Kong, possibly Egypt or Algeria, possibly Pakistan, might develop significantly, but this differential development could be interpreted as follows: experience indicates that the burden of economic growth (or resistance to subversion) cannot be shouldered by external sources. True, military aid or external investment can be "strategically" important in special situations, but the main impetus for internal security and economic development must come through painful processes of internally motivated discipline, energy, and sacrifice. Foreign aid not only has limited effect, it is often contraproductive because it may weaken or dilute these internal motivations.

The Third World, of course (and with some justification), could see this as a rationalization of indifference, and it could then see itself compelled to pursue its own fate, depending wholly on itself, probably adopting narrow nationally, or at most regionally, oriented policies. The self-reliance fostered might be advantageous in some cases; in others the problems are likely to seem (and be) awesome, and even virtually hopeless.

Among those countries that are likely to do well are those that face serious but manageable external threats and use these as a spur. If enemies do not exist they might in some cases be invented. Thus the use of real or contrived crises is likely to be a recurring theme in the programs of the more ambitious (and capable?) Third World governments. They might also adopt the view that they have every justification for hostility toward the developed nations and for independent action—including, of course, procuring nuclear weapons.

On the other hand, the very weakness of the underdeveloped nations might make them accept a lower status in nuclear matters and the indifference of the developed nations might convince them they have little to bargain with as a condition of nuclear abstinence. In this case the Inward-Looking Worlds might be surprisingly stable.

H. A SKETCHY SCENARIO FOR AN INWARD-LOOKING WORLD WITH BOTH UNITED STATES AND SOVIET EROSION

The easiest way to develop a scenario for eroded United States morale and prestige and reduced influence would begin with an expanded Vietnamese war in which the United States does very badly. One such scenario could go as follows:

The war in Vietnam continues inconclusively into 1968. The United States then decides—without a formal declaration of war—to invade North Vietnam, destroy the Hanoi government, and reunite the country under a friendly government. A major amphibious assault meets an unexpectedly effective defense. Resistance is tenacious. American and North Vietnamese casualties are high, the latter including a large number of civilian deaths. Hanoi is finally taken after months of bitter and costly fighting, but the government continues resistance—falling back toward the Chinese border and in the countryside. There is effective guerrilla harassment of United States forces even within the area of United States occupation. Because the agony of the siege of Hanoi is prolonged over months, there is time to dramatize the horror of the attack and the heroism of the defenders. As a result there is—both domestically and abroad—an avalanche of hostility to the United States "aggression."

When Hanoi finally falls there is a crescendo of indignation in the world press and a new outburst of demonstrations. Many periodicals come out in black bands and signs of mourning can be seen everywhere. These sympathizers for the Hanoi regime are joined by many "middle of the road" as well as left- and right-wing critics of the United States administration who argue that the attack was politically motivated to gain an election success in November 1968. The fear of escalation and sympathy for the victim of "white imperialism" is increased by what appears to be a combination of United States military ineptness and brutality with partisan self-seeking by the administration.

As American forces approach the northern border of Vietnam, Chinese regular forces cross and engage them. It is not clear whether they are doing this to cover retreating North Vietnamese divisions or whether they intend to enter the war as a full-scale combatant. There is a worldwide fear that there will be further escalation—at least into a United States-Chinese war, perhaps more.

Russia, France, and Japan make a joint intervention with armistice proposals supported by the British, Italian, and Benelux governments. There is bitter recrimination and controversy within the United States. Partly out of fear of escalation, partly in response to almost overwhelming domestic and foreign pressures, the President agrees to a cease fire. This is not accepted officially by the North Vietnamese, who insist that the United States evacuate their country, but a *de facto* cease fire takes place between regular units. The irregular war that has sprung up in the rear of the United States' invasion army continues. The belligerents are unwilling to reach any formal agreement, but *de facto* cease fire hardens into a partial truce during which the United States in effect falls back to an enclave strategy, holding a forward area, logistic lines of support and two hostile cities, Haiphong and Hanoi. After a further period of international and domestic controversy and of violence and inconclusive counterguerrilla counterterrorist campaigns in Vietnam, the United States begins a staged withdrawal as part of a secret settlement with the North Vietnamese. There are cease fire arrangements for South Vietnam as well, leaving about 90 per cent of the countryside (and one-half of the population) to complete and open Viet Cong control and only the cities, the areas immediately around them, and a few rural enclaves in addition to Hoa Hao, Cao Dai, and Catholic areas under the control of the government. It is a situation of precarious balance and obvious impermanence, but for the present neither side is willing to move.

The Soviet Union, despite its role in achieving this settlement, does not get off well. Many partisans of North Vietnam argue that Russia acted to save the United States from a choice between debacle and further escalation, and that it did this in excessive fear of the latter possibility, thus preventing the former. The Soviet Union is also scorned for its inaction during the months in which the United States besieged Hanoi. The Soviets did "nothing" for the "heroic defenders." The Chinese, at least, intervened at the last moment, and in many quarters are given major credit for the degree of success the North Vietnamese finally achieved.

Mr. Johnson decisively loses an unprecedentedly bitter 1968 election to a right-wing Republican candidate who accuses him of folly and defeat in Vietnam. A leftist third party draws two and a half million votes, a sizable defection of Democratic votes (and even more Democrats prove to have voted for the Republican). The new President's policy is to cut foreign commitments, above all to end land commitments in Asia while enlarging the American nuclear force in the region and threatening China with massive retaliation if there is further Communist aggression.

NATO in 1969 is allowed to continue as a formal alliance but all *ad hoc* and other provisions for precrisis ground force integration are suspended, the Europeans arguing that such integration is no longer needed (and in fact wishing to dissociate themselves politically from the United States). The United States leaves two divisions in West Germany and the Soviets reduce their garrison from twenty-two to something between five and ten divisions. In the meantime, a series of agreements are negotiated between the Soviet Union and separate European countries, and accepted by Germany, that constitute a provisional settlement of the German problem on the basis of continued partition, including ratification of the Oder-Neisse line. While United States divisions are left in Germany, the United States is effectively excluded from these negotiations and has little or no influence on them. As a result there is vast disillusionment and hostility toward Europe among many in the United States, and much clamor either to withdraw all troops or to regain leadership in some unspecified but dramatic way. But the new administration refuses to act, fearing to lose its residual influence in West Germany. Germany concludes a separate treaty of mutual defense with France that implies a French nuclear guarantee. While most West Germans are unwilling to rely on this guarantee, preferring even an attenuated United States guarantee, it gives them a political and military hedge in a difficult situation.

By 1975, the post-Ulbricht East German government announces that it is prepared to consider reestablishing a qualified multiparty system in return for legalization of the Communist party in West Germany. Czechoslovakia has announced radical changes of economic decentralization and political organization to make the Communist party consultative and to institute "internal democracy." Yugoslavia, Rumania, and Greece establish a limited Balkan Common Market that envisages eventual association with the European Common Market and includes a system of political consultation and cooperation. Hungary applies for associate membership in the EEC.

In Moscow, the Kosygin-Brezhnev government has been replaced by a younger group oriented to action, national prestige and international assertiveness, and reacting against the fairly frank East European repudiations of Communist internationalism and rapprochement with Western Europe. One of the firts acts of the new regime is to attack the new East German concessions and to launch a political and propaganda campaign against West Germany. It warns the East German people of counterrevolutionary elements in their leadership who are willing to compromise with West German "revanchism." The response is East German defiance, a West German approach to Poland asking a treaty of friendship and economic cooperation, and a French invitation to the Poles, East Germans, and Czechs to discussions on European military cooperation, to include mutual assistance and mutual military inspection. These accept, and although the results are modest, as are the continued German steps toward reunification, the Soviet propaganda campaign is dropped. A new Soviet attempt is made at reconciliation with China; it is rebuffed. The subsequent Soviet policy is one of almost extreme isolationism—of national self-sufficiency and defense of the homeland in a hostile world; the national mood is sour and intraparty tensions are notably on the increase.

By the late 1980's the Soviet Union is an isolated power with a disoriented ruling party practicing a doctrine that everywhere else has either been abandoned or transformed into something that hardly resembles the Communism of Russia. Eastern Europe is frankly part of a European community. Czechoslovakia and Yugoslavia are genuine multiparty states; the other Communist governments remain one-party regimes but are highly consultative and pragmatic. Two Germanies remain but with certain common institutions. Europe as a whole cooperates on a rather wide range of external issues, is the predominant influence in a passive and troubled Africa, and has extensive links to Latin America. Otherwise it is inward-looking and politically prudent.

The United States, meanwhile, is largely isolated, troubled, and politically immobilized by deep internal divisions, especially on racial and social issues aggravated by American international setbacks and internal alienation. The administration is very conservative, tends to ineffective measures of repression and retaliation against its critics, and is not very successful. GNP growth has fallen off, and United States exports have steadily declined—in part because of the pressure of European competition and the political hostility of the Third World.

The Soviet Union has similar problems arising out of a growing disaffection of various national minorities and the intelligentsia and youth. Perhaps more important, there is an increasing impatience and hostility toward the regime among various managerial, professional, and scholarly groups. The claims of the now bitterly divided Communist party to universal expertise as well as a monopoly on political wisdom is regarded more and more with open contempt.

Clearly the above scenario could lead to any of the inward-looking worlds (variations three, four, and five) we described, to a most plausibly, perhaps, dynamic Europe and/or Japan.

I. FRAGMENTARY SCENARIOS FOR A DYNAMIC SOVIET UNION AND/OR A DYNAMIC COMMUNIST MOVEMENT (EITHER INWARD-LOOKING OR GREATER DISARRAY WORLDS)

1. Renewed Communist dynamism can be conceived of as coming about (a) through a renewal of vigor and ambition in Russia, presumably under a new generation of leaders; (b) in reaction against Soviet loss of prestige

and of bloc leadership, after some economic political crisis; (*c*) out of some new sense of threat from abroad; (*d*) because such current trends as extensive investment in and other encouragement of agriculture, "Liebermanism," thaw in internal politics and regulation of cultural activities, detente, and the like, eventually produce a new stability and progress. One sequence of events that could follow, or precede, such a renewal of dynamism would be a series of domestic crises and stalemates in China following Mao-Tse-tung's death that would cause China to lose its reputation as an effective radical power. A Sino-Soviet reconciliation might follow, substantially on Soviet terms, and perhaps a voluntary recommitment to the bloc of East European elites under the stimulus of efficient and intelligent new Soviet initiatives.

2. A scenario in which Russia leads a renewed Communism can also be constructed out of a Vietnam outcome in which Russia provokes a United States-Soviet confrontation and a United States backdown—perhaps by providing Hanoi with air force units and air defense troops. Russia might then exploit West European distrust of the United States by proposals that influence Europe toward a neutral position in the United States-Soviet rivalry. This might be followed by a qualified Sino-Soviet reconciliation. The United States might turn to neoisolationism, or alternatively make West Germany its chief foreign ally and follow an aggressive interventionist policy in Europe and elsewhere with the result that Germany and the United States come to seem a new and aggressive rightist force in the world. Old strains of pro-Communist, anti-American, and anti-German sentiment might then converge with new left and peace-movement trends to give Russia renewed prestige as the leading "peace-seeking" or "antifascist" power.

3. A second type of dynamic Communist movement could arise from China's gaining leadership of Third World radicalism, perhaps in the aftermath of a Vietnam outcome that seemed a defeat for the United States and a victory for the type of Communism preached by China. Such a movement probably would be anti-Soviet as well as anti-Western and would be strengthened if the Soviet Union continued in its present preoccupation with domestic affairs and either was reconciled with Western Europe—accepting a role as "bourgeois," "satisfied" world power, or if it suffered a series of East European repudiations or other setbacks which further diminished its international reputation. In this scenario the Chinese-sponsored Third World Communism might gain further in influence as many of the naïve expectations of the non-Communist new nations were dashed by economic crisis or developmental failures. The Chinese almost certainly would have to limit their attempt to direct or exploit this movement—which would mean a Chinese policy notably different from their present foreign political program —but with discretion they might enjoy sizable political gains. Such a sce-

nario might envisage a series of national liberation wars in Asia and Latin America, essentially indigenous but helped with Chinese arms and counsel, and attacking Western and especially American political and economic positions in ways exceedingly difficult or expensive for the established powers to contain. At the same time Russia would find its own European brand of Communism outflanked to the left in a series of Third World countries, and perhaps a Fourth International of Afro-Asian-Latin Revolutionaries would be created, its members professing a "Jacobin" Marxism, helped by China, loosely allied, and successful in leading much of the Third World into hostility to the advanced powers and most of all into hostility toward the United States.

4. Dynamic non-Soviet Communism could occur with even less of a role for the Chinese. Such a "dynamic Communism," or more properly "dynamic radicalism," could emerge as an undisciplined alliance of leftist groups including a wide range of neo-Marxist and Jacobin movements. It might have little interest in classical Communist formulations and Communist internationalism, but would express a sense of shared revolutionary purpose and moral objectives. Especially if it were treated by its enemies as a unitary phenomenon—simply as "Communism"—it might be expected in many ways to behave tactically as if it were united, and to establish meaningful ties to Soviet Russia and Communist China. Again, assuming that either or both of these powers had the discretion to support this movement without attempting to control or dominate it, they might gain considerably in their immediate rivalry with the Western powers, although in the longer term they could expect new problems of rivalry and struggle within the new radical movement. China—as a have-not power—is more plausible than Russia as an ally of this kind of radicalism, although China has thus far demonstrated a political inflexibility that contradicts the individualism and eccentricity of this new leftist current.

Such a bloc—ideologically linked but without much of a common international program—could rather effectively isolate the United States and the conservative European powers. Its material resources would not be great, but it probably could hurt the economies of the anti-Communist states, and if the Soviet Union were astute enough to cooperate with this bloc, and used its military power position to provide it with appropriate (and maintainable) guarantees of security, the Russians might succeed in mobilizing a dramatic and important challenge to the United States and Western Europe. With or without Soviet leadership there undoubtedly would be African converts and allies to the movement, and perhaps enough sympathy in Europe to bring neutrality, or even conversion, of one or two of the European nations, especially if there were conditions of economic or political crisis.

5. One could add to or vary any of these four scenarios, but particularly the last two, by having large leftist gains in Latin America despite—or helped by—American military interventions, leading to radical governments in such important countries as Brazil. One might also add to any of the above scenarios world economic crisis or Third World famine, driving states into even deeper opposition to the prosperous and conservative. An American decline might be accelerated if the American temper became excessively isolationist, markedly hedonistic, if the United States withdrew from the world or suffered major and continued domestic unrest on racial and social issues, or if American defeats or setbacks caused a loss in morale or self-respect.

J. FRAGMENTARY SCENARIOS FOR DYNAMIC EUROPE AND/OR JAPAN (AGAIN FOR EITHER INWARD-LOOKING OR GREATER DISARRAY WORLDS)

1. Several of the preceding scenarios could have easily included the emergence of Japan or one or several European states as independent political powers in a world of some disarray or potential menace. The prospect of a "threatening Europe" is not an implausible one for several reasons. The material resources exist in Western Europe to create a superpower rivaling the United States in economic and military power and out-ranking the Soviet Union. There are obvious questions about whether these resources could be coordinated in support of a single political policy, and whether they are likely to be devoted to producing military weapons and forces. But if a scenario is written that supplies affirmative answers to both questions, we have a Europe fully capable of "threatening" actions. Secondly, Europe includes the principal unresolved territorial and political issue in the world today. Germany's present status is that of a "revisionist" power—a power with formal claims to territory now incorporated into other states, one of them Soviet Russia. That the other European powers would unite with Germany in pressing such territorial claims, or indeed that Germany would regard these as more than legal claims to be bargained for political concessions, is doubtful in the extreme. But whatever Germany's territorial objectives, the provisional character of the present status of Germany—of the two Germanies—remains an unresolved issue that could produce "threatening" actions and events within Central Europe.

It must be added that Germany, even a united Germany, would not today enjoy the power predominance it did before 1939. There have been significant economic and demographic changes. Poland, Hungary, and Yugoslavia are advancing industrial powers with considerable military resources. France's population is increasing more rapidly than Germany's. France also has a modern nuclear technology and deterrent force, as does Britain. Thus a future Europe with a "threatening" character is not so likely to derive from German revisionism—except possibly as a source of instability generally or even of a precipitating incident—as from the dynamism of a partially or wholly united Europe. The plausibility of such a Europe must be considered in the light not only of the stability of the last twenty years but also of the larger European record in modern history and the factors we have noted in Section E, above.

2. Japan is the other candidate to become a dynamic Third (or Fourth) Power in international affairs. According to how the calculation is done, the Japanese have or soon will become the third-ranking industrial producer in the world. Her growth rate is larger than that of any other large country. We have remarked (in Chapter V) that the Japanese also possess a technology that could rapidly provide a sophisticated nuclear rocket force. While Japanese politics have been stable for the last twenty years, as we have noted Japan's last century of Westernization has demonstrated marked instabilities. A Japan as dynamic third power in the world seems to be a very clear possibility as a reasonable outgrowth of present trends. A prospering Japan dependent on world trade could increasingly assert itself in Asian affairs to stabilize the region and develop Japanese economic interests; the rivalry of China might also be a stimulus to political activism; such a Japan would plausibly strive for an independent status rather than follow United States leadership, probably attempting to maintain good relations with the United States while counterbalancing American influence and trade by developing relations with Russia, Europe, and perhaps China. In this scenario Japan would be active, independent, but a conventional factor in world affairs, probably concerned chiefly with the military defense and economic advancement of Japan.

Other scenarios, however, can be written in which latent instabilities within Japanese society manifest themselves in a foreign policy of acquiring Asian clients and asserting Asian leadership, or of cooperation with China— perhaps implicitly in an effort to dominate China.

K. FRAGMENTARY SCENARIOS FOR GREATER DISARRAY WORLDS

1. First Scenario: NATO's Collapse

The conflict between France and the United States over the future of NATO remains unsettled, while Britain, under financial pressures, steadily reduces its troop commitment in West Germany. While the United States and

West Germany no longer have the close relationship of the 1950's and 1960's, NATO slowly evolves into a United States-German alliance. Anti-German sentiments grow in France and elsewhere in Europe, allied to existing anti-American, antinuclear, pro-Communist, and "peace" trends in public opinion. The United States-German relationship is spoken of as the "new axis." The French see in this situation an opportunity to take European leadership, try to exploit it, but the complex diplomacy of de Gaulle becomes, under his successor, a frankly anti-German and anti-American program. The United States and Germany slip into a nuclear strategy approximating the massive retaliation of the Eisenhower years. American officials and many of their experts again speak of "quality weapons," and deterrence by brinkmanship. France actively competes for influence and allies among the East European states. Western Europe is close to losing the character of a pluralistic security community.

2. Second Scenario: A Nuclear Exchange and Aftermath

The United States makes a limited invasion of North Vietnam, possibly landing at Vinh to cut off about fifty miles of North Vietnamese territory. It is attempting to accomplish the following objectives: (1) retaliate against North Vietnamese violations of the Demilitarized Zone; (2) make a threat of further escalation credible; (3) create a hostage (the occupied territory); (4) cause a partial blockade of the Ho Chi Minh trail, and (5) satisfy some internal United States and South Vietnamese pressures for escalation.

The Chinese then carry out a limited intervention with "volunteers" who join North Vietnamese forces in trying to drive the United States out of North Vietnamese territory. The United States in retaliation conducts a limited conventional attack on Chinese nuclear and other military facilities. The Soviet Union makes a strong diplomatic intervention. Despite this the United States fleet bombards some Chinese coastal installations. China, overly confident of the Soviet need to lend support and overestimating United States inhibitions (possibly because, in spite of most United States opinion, our own included, they are indeed irrational), makes a mostly symbolic nuclear attack on the United States fleet. This is unexpectedly successful, sinking two United States carriers. China emphasizes the defensive character of this escalation, but threatens retaliation against both United States mainland and United States Asian bases if the United States strikes back. They also warn of the Third World War.

There are heavy pressures for the United States to retaliate sharply, but in the short pause that occurs while the United States considers what should be done, the Soviets, while condemning the Chinese, also deliver a strong but ambiguous warning to the United States not to retaliate with nuclear weapons. They privately stress to United States officials that while the

Chinese action was wrong it was understandable, and retaliation would put the Soviets under intolerable pressure to retaliate in defense of China.

The United States retaliates anyway and airbursts two small nuclear weapons over two Chinese installations, causing almost no nonmilitary casualties. The Chinese immediately drop a nuclear weapon on a Formosan air base and threaten strikes against other United States bases and the continental United States.

Both the United States and the Soviet Union have now gone on alert status. The Soviets intensify their warnings that they will retaliate for further attacks on China. In the meantime a Franco-British-Romanian proposal for mediation and cease fire is delivered to China, the Soviet Union, and the United States. The first two accept but the United States officially refuses. However, it does not retaliate against the attack on Formosa except by a large conventional attack on Chinese bases. It also announces a large grant to the Formosan government for military and economic aid.

The United States has, in effect, suffered a very severe "Cuban missile defeat." It acted far more weakly than the world expected. The first, "tit-for-tat," retaliation by the United States seemed to make the Chinese equal to the United States in status. Then, by retaliating with conventional weapons against a Chinese nuclear attack, the United States seemed afraid (or insufficiently motivated) to retaliate equally against a nuclear weapon dropped on a United States ally. The grant of aid funds to Formosa (to "buy off" Formosan recriminations) suggests that the United States feels it can always buy its way out of obligations. This undermines the effect of other United States guarantees and weakens greatly the position of those inside allied nations who would rely on United States support (even though some of these argue persuasively that the United States could not allow this to happen a second time and therefore that in some sense United States guarantees have been strengthened).

The Soviets at this point call (informally) for a conference on European settlements to which they invite the United States as an observer. They indicate that Soviet-European cooperation to contain Chinese and United States irresponsibility should be followed up by new and formal arrangements to end European tensions. This is not only desirable in itself but it will lessen the possibility of European involvement in future non-European crises and increase European influence as a force for peace and sanity. The French express interest, simultaneously making a preliminary offer to West Germany of a French nuclear guarantee.

The Germans indicate a willingness to discuss both this, if it can be accepted without jeopardizing the United States guarantee, and all-European negotiations. While they set conditions on East German participation, they indicate privately to the Soviet Union that they are open to negotiation on this issue. This "reasonableness" by the West Germans is concealed from the United States and other Europeans. The United States denounces the Soviet conference proposal. While some of the small NATO powers accept the initiative, under United States pressure the British, West Germans, Italians, and the Benelux nations finally decline the initiative. The result, however, is a strong reaction against the United States in Europe and a widespread opinion that an important opportunity has been allowed to slip away. The British subsequently announce extensive trade and credit agreements with the Soviets. A nonaggression treaty with the Soviets is discussed in the press. France, meanwhile, flatly demands a West German choice between the United States and Europe. It reiterates its offer of a French nuclear guarantee.

While opinion remains high against the United States, even in West Germany (for one thing many West Germans had feared that the Soviets would retaliate against them for the United States bombing China), the West German Chancellor not only turns down the French offer but in a bitter speech denounces his European allies both for their recent actions and their general anti-German prejudice. In the weeks that follow French and British military cooperation with Germany is terminated, and the German government either (1) falls, and is replaced by a "European" coalition, or (2) recommits itself to the United States in conditions of expanded military integration, increased West German consultation in United States strategy, and rumors of a bilateral nuclear force.

Given continued bad luck and bad judgment, this scenario could lead to extensive nuclear proliferation (including to West Germany), excessive risk-taking by an overconfident China, further deterioration in the United States political position or an isolation of the United States, and—in the case of the second version of Germany's line of action—West German estrangement from Western Europe and creation of an *ad hoc cordon sanitaire* against Germany by its neighbors.

3. *Third Scenario: A Soviet Political Offensive in Europe*

At some point in the second scenario after the United States invasion of North Vietnam or the first Chinese nuclear strike, the Soviets might demand that the West European powers disassociate themselves from the United States, giving weight to its demand by reinforcing its East German garrison. The United States could mobilize to reinforce the 7th Army. The Warsaw Pact could then mobilize. Civil disturbance might begin in both East and West Germany—spurred on in the latter by a fear that the Soviets might act against them. France might propose an emergency plan of withdrawal of all foreign troops from the two Germanies in order to ease tensions, linking this proposal to European acceptance of political disassociation from the

United States. Under intense public pressures and with Russian acquiescence the two German governments accept.

The United States withdraws from Europe. The two Germanies subsequently are unable to reach terms for unification; in fact a period of bitter inter-German cold war follows, gradually breaking down the restraints that had been enforced by the United States-Soviet occupation. The other European powers regroup defensively. Russia extends a new defensive alignment that incorporates Poland and Czechoslovakia, tacitly breaking the agreement on which Europe had obtained United States withdrawal. Hungary allies itself with the East German government. A Franco-British military entente is reestablished, but it is unconvincing in power and authority and the Soviets begin to exert new pressures on non-Communist Europe—perhaps to the point where major West European states begin to seek the role of a Sweden or Finland vis-à-vis Russia.

4. *Fourth Scenario: Soviet Bloc Renewal*

Romania quits the Warsaw Pact, timing the move to coincide with a Soviet party congress. An aggressive new Soviet leadership is unexpectedly nominated in conditions of tension and excitement; this group issues a condemnation of Romania as counterrevolutionary and Russia moves troops to the Romanian border. Disturbances break out in Poland and are put down by Polish security forces. Russia begins reinforcement of all its East European garrisons. After ten days of growing tension throughout Eastern Europe, the Romanian Premier is overturned and arrested by dissident members of the Romanian Communist party. A new governing coalition revokes the Warsaw Pact withdrawal. Troops have to be used to quell public demonstrations in Bucharest. As a result of this reassertion of Soviet authority (and perhaps a previous change in Chinese governing personalities), the Sino-Soviet dispute is provisionally halted and a new military cooperation agreement is signed. The reformed and purged Romanian Communist party then calls for reestablishment of the Comintern and for a new revolutionary discipline and austerity within the Communist bloc. The Russian, Chinese, and Polish parties commend this proposal and announce measures of domestic party reorganization and rectification.

5. *Fifth Scenario: A Left-Wing European Union*

NATO comes to an end in 1969 as an integrated organization, although the alliance remains in existence as a defense pact. United States forces in Europe are steadily reduced under pressure of commitments elsewhere, and in 1969 are almost entirely withdrawn except for two skeleton divisions, a logistical command controlling stockpiles and facilities in Germany, a Berlin garrison, and a tactical air detachment. German and French military cooperation is quietly extended and in 1970 Germany makes a sizable financial and technological commitment to the French Nuclear Force.

Western Germany slips into an economic recession as a result of a world economic crisis and dollar and pound devaluations in the early 1970's. The Socialist party comes under new leadership, campaigning for a policy of compromise and reconciliation with East Germany, the promotion of all-German economic cooperation, and political neutrality. The socialists are elected; the two Germanies jointly ask negotiations to withdraw from both NATO and the Warsaw Pact, voluntarily renouncing nuclear weapons; and West Germany severs its ties to the French Nuclear Force.

The world recession continues. Germany reunifies by stages, with the dominant political force of a new left-socialist force comprising national Communism and Socialism. Post-Gaullist France meanwhile has lost initiative and fallen into internal divisions; a socialist group patterned on the German emerges, calling for European unification to create a socialist world power repudiating the "obsolete" capitalism of the West and the equally "obsolete" bourgeois communism of Russia. With success in France this group leads the EEC into a confederal union. The French Nuclear Force is now reconstituted and expanded as a European deterrent force. Individuals within this European Socialist camp begin speaking of the historical "inevitability" of Poland and Hungary joining this greater European union.

6. Sixth Scenario: United States Overcommitment and Withdrawal

Military stalemate in the Vietnam war and intense international pressures produce a settlement in 1968 that is much short of United States' objectives. The administration that signs this agreement barely survives the ensuing election but a right-wing Congress is elected. Major disorders break out in Brazil and there is a leftist coup; the United States is asked to intervene by the loyalist government and it does so in force. The combined Brazilian-United States forces overthrow the rebel regime in heavy fighting and install a military government. This success redresses much of the administration's credit at home with the right but produces an intense reaction among liberals in the United States and throughout Latin America. Chile, Mexico, and Bolivia withdraw from the OAS. Subsequently the United States accepts an invitation by the Venezuelan government to send forces to prevent a coup there. A coup is attempted anyway, more or less by accident, but United States forces are present in force, and with only token Venezuelan representation arrest or disperse the revolutionists. There is an explosion of protest. Although the government remains in power, there is extensive guerrilla and terrorist resistance to the American and Loyalist Venezuelan forces.

With detachments still in Brazil and Venezuela, the United States becomes involved in another Latin American intervention. Unrestrained criticism in Europe, including from the German and French governments, makes European "ingratitude" a major issue in the 1972 American presidential campaign. The United States abruptly withdraws its forces from Europe. The Soviet Union offers German reunification in terms that insure the survival and influence of the East German Communist leadership. France counsels rejection. German opinion is deeply divided with the rightist parties favoring reunification and arguing the unreliability of all allies.

Extended Disarray-World Scenarios

Two of our colleagues contributed the following two pairs of scenarios, in which they work out the evolution of various disarray worlds in some detail, in accordance with their own views of what the world may be like. They would like us to emphasize, no doubt, that these are speculative, not predictive.

A. A PAIR OF RELATED, PESSIMISTIC SCENARIOS,
by Raymond D. Gastil

1. Introduction

The responses that men and nations make to new material possibilities and demands, and to the struggle for power over these, are likely to make possible a more desirable life in the year 2000 than we have today. There seem to be trends toward more civil liberty, or at least toward the kind of freedom that equality of opportunity brings to both capitalist and communist nations. There seems to be a growing consensus against the use of nuclear weapons as a tool of policy, and thus against any big war—and by extension against direct confrontations of any kind. Perhaps the heart is even going out of the ideological struggle. If so, then at least as far as the developed nations are concerned most issues are those of detail, or of guarding against freak accidents that might lead to major war or disastrous social change. In this view of the future the primary job of the next thirty-three years becomes that of preserving the rich while uplifting the poor.

Yet beneath this happy prospect there are countercurrents, counterpossibilities. I believe these are *less likely* to become reality during the next thirty-three years than the balmy future in which problems of allocation and technological development are all important. I also believe that these darker possibilities must be considered as perhaps more important than more probable alternatives; for the disutility of these possibilities considerably outweighs the significance of the argument that their probability is fairly low.

Let us, then, specify the following three trends as of particular interest:

1. Toward crass materialism and hedonism in which all emotions and feelings become superficial.
2. Toward completely centralized decision-making, a world in which people as thinking individuals with private desires and values become superfluous. Only the thinking of a tiny minority at the top is considered any longer as being socially desirable.
3. Toward catastrophic and/or continual warfare.

It is particularly ominous to notice one basis of Orwell's world—that is, continual, indecisive warfare that little disturbs the life of great nations but gives governments a myth that might provide powerful legitimization for a system of totalitarian control. On the other hand, there is a growing isolationist trend in American thinking today. Should this tendency once again become dominant, it might well lead through withdrawal to a disastrous "return." It is significant that many of the great wars of history seem to have grown out of a pattern of this kind.

Today the United States is involved in a policy of meeting international challenges that seems plausibly to accelerate movement toward the dangers that I have been describing. By and large I personally approve of these policies, yet I believe they contain real dangers in the context of those other tendencies that many believe they find in our world. 1984 is clearly too close for Orwell's vision. And an even faintly "rational" nuclear war in which the United States is involved would take decades of change. But it seems to me that current policy can lead to distinctly undesirable long-term trends that go quite beyond the immediate issues of international policy.

Below I will discuss how the following two dangers may come to occur: (1) major nuclear war, and (2) totalitarianism in America. I will write short narratives for each of these perhaps unlikely but surely important possibilities, and then take up some consideration of what I have attempted to do—of the methodology involved. In developing these narratives, I have used the four-year period of the presidential term as a salient unit of measure, realizing that this tends to overemphasize the role of the President and of presidential elections.

2. The Road through Isolation to War

Let us first imagine that the problems of Vietnam are insoluble in our terms, and within the restrictions we impose on ourselves. The Vietnamese war might then move to the point where the United States had five hundred thousand or six hundred thousand men involved—and a positive result was not forthcoming.[14] At the same time the United States might become in-

[14] The issue here is not how many men are "needed" to accomplish our goals. I assume only that our generalship in Vietnam might conceivably be so bad and the dedication and leadership of the Vietcong and North Vietnamese so good, that we accomplish little with such a large force.

volved in the defense of Kashmir, or in a parallel problem elsewhere. In this case one can visualize a United States President coming to power in 1969 who has promised to reduce United States overseas commitments. In the present version the President is of the party in power, representing a general fluctuation in national attitude. The United States will withdraw its forces as North Vietnam withdraws its, but all the United States has saved is "face." The South Vietnamese government will include elements of the N.L.F. In addition, there will be a federal government in the South, with certain areas under governors appointed by the N.L.F.

By 1972 it appears as though the result of "bringing the boys home" is a growing expression of dislike of America by past friends and enemies. Even those who have been urging our withdrawal from Vietnam seem to take this withdrawal as a sign of weakness. Southeast Asia becomes more friendly to the Chinese and Russians, with Indonesia and Thailand developing especially friendly relations with Russia and with rising European states, such as France and Germany. Simultaneously hostility between China and Russia grows and incidents occur in Manchuria, Sinkiang, and elsewhere. In Latin America hostility against the United States becomes stronger, as it does in the Middle East after the United States increases its commitment to India. The United Nations admits Red China to the Security Council seat of China. Taiwan is offered a seat in the General Assembly, but it decides to leave the United Nations in protest. The United States and Britain invoke the veto to avoid action against the British at Gibraltar.

In the elections of 1972 the opposition candidate convincingly argues that the United States is still too involved in unrewarding international affairs. We have brought home the boys, now let us bring home the dollars. The more we have given a country, the less likely it is to support us today in the United Nations. Military intervention overseas has proved unrewarding and costly. We have little support and often criticism from our more wealthy allies. Unfair laws discriminate against United States investments in Europe, investments that have made possible its modernization. Most underdeveloped countries do not have the administrative ability or motivation to use aid effectively. This candidate believes the real security problems of the United States have been solved by deterrence. Therefore let us give only limited humanitarian aid overseas, but stay uninvolved. Since economically 1971-72 are bad years, this isolationist's appeal is effective and the opposition comes to power.

The draft is cancelled in 1975.

The period from 1976 to 1985 is marked by general worldwide economic growth. The United States, Europe, and Japan look inward. Increasingly European nations and Japan trade among themselves. The rest of their trade is largely with the United States and the older Communist states. The establishment of left-wing or Communist party governments in much of the developing world is not seen as threatening. These states are weak and we and the Europeans have the deterrent. Moreover, the new Communist states occasionally skirmish with one another. There are recurrent threats of war between China and Russia, but a war never gets under way. A Nationalist-Communist GDR is recognized by Euro-America, while Berlin achieves the status of a Free City. Although there is a good deal of oppression in the new Communist states, it is reported that their administrations are more efficient than those of neighbors, and they certainly seem cleaner. In the United Nations only a few states outside of Western Europe vote with the United States (for example, Australia, New Zealand, Union of South Africa, Argentina, and Canada), but United States political leaders do not take the United Nations seriously.

By 1985 the number of nuclear armed states in the world has increased. Let us imagine these to include India, Pakistan, Indonesia, Brazil, East Germany, and West Germany.

Following a few years of economic recession, and because Canadian business is increasingly falling into United States hands, a radically anti-American, leftist government achieves power in Canada in early 1986. Confiscatory taxation of foreign businesses and extensive discrimination against United States products leads to steadily worsening relations. The United States is accused of fomenting communal unrest in Canada to bring down the government, and some incriminating evidence is publicized. Canada reveals in 1987 that in two years it will have nuclear armed missiles with a one thousand-mile range. It is charged in the United States that much of the detailed technology for this force has been "stolen" over the years from the United States. (The Canadians actually have legitimate access to much of this today.) In 1988 the United States is asked to remove all bases, radars, and so on, from Canadian soil—and we comply.

But the request and our acquiescence serves as a final jolt to the United States. Although militarily the bases had long been of insignificant value, Americans suddenly feel insecure and begin to look about them. The opposition nominates a candidate in 1988 whose primary concern is foreign affairs and national security. He convinces the country of the dangerous drift in our affairs. He points particularly to the wide disparity between the defensive systems of Euro-America and those of the Soviet Union—in addition to the fact of the gradual reduction in the size of the United States deterrent.

The national security picture does not look reassuring, although the United States budget for national defense has been averaging about forty billion dollars a year for the last decade. Most of this money has been spent on research, development, and maintenance of advanced systems for nuclear and conventional war. Thus, although 1988 finds a good "mobilization base" for the rapid procurement of forces, there is little "in being." For example, the army consists of five hundred thousand men with only six combat divisions. Soviet and Chinese armies both number in the millions. The United States has only two hundred to three hundred tactical fighters. The United States has only two modern ABM batteries deployed, about as many as China or Japan. Twenty-five earlier batteries deployed against China in 1970 have come to be regarded as essentially worthless. The Soviet Union has about one thousand ICBM's and the United States an equal number—China about one hundred: in spite of the fact that our experts feel the Soviet ABM is of doubtful quality, the Soviet government relies heavily on its ABM capability in its military planning. Although it is all nuclear powered, the American Navy of 1988 is about half the size of the 1965 Navy. Polaris-type submarines carry about five hundred missiles, and more advanced Soviet systems an approximately equal number.

The opposition candidate is elected in late 1988. In Canada this is followed by the outright confiscation of some United States properties. A two hundred billion dollar defense appropriation is then pushed through Congress. (Although a large amount, this is less than one-eighth of the GNP for that year.) The draft is reinstituted. These actions are in accordance with the emergency measures envisaged by the mobilization base concept adopted in 1975. By 1992 the United States should have twenty modern combat divisions, one thousand new ICBM's and one hundred deployed modern ABM batteries (providing several types of coverage).

In 1987 a struggle breaks out in Mexico between the Communist party and the leftist government. Although Mexico has increased in wealth, the gap between the rural poor and the urban wealthy remains. Fifty per cent are still living in essentially rural areas. At first the communists achieve relatively little success, although there is widespread terror. Their base of operations now shifts to the countryside. By 1989 Brazil, China, Cuba, and the Soviet Union are competing in providing aid to the communists, and large areas of the North and extreme South fall into communist hands. Hard-pressed, the Mexican government asks for United States aid and aid is promised. As the United States begins to act Chinese volunteers are arriving in a fleet of high-speed commercial ships (recently purchased from Japan). The Chinese reason that they may be able to bring the war quickly to a conclusion by destroying the weak and corrupt Mexican army before the United States can give substantial aid on the land or enforce a blockade. With the United States now alarmed, more careful policies are more apt to fail. Not until most of the North is controlled by the rebels and the Chinese have landed forty thousand men are United States troops committed and an effective naval blockade begun. Although it is a little war, smaller than the Vietnamese war of the 1960's, in view of our other fears and responsibilities, it is difficult for the United States to commit as many as four combat divisions by the end of 1989. Russians urge on the struggle in an attempt to distract both China and the United States from Asian and European affairs.

But the communist forces, whether rebel or Chinese, have been built up faster than their supply base. Communist troops begin to fall back due to appalling shortages of food and munitions. China's top leaders then come to feel both that China's political investment in this struggle is jeopardized and that they themselves are being criticized for risking China's position in such a foolhardy adventure. Fearing replacement if they fail, they now decide on reckless tactics. They judge that if the war becomes nuclear the United States will accommodate enough to allow the Chinese to save face. They do not see how the United States can go into a nuclear war, even with China, with its major cities undefended. However, to attack a United States city directly might lead to an irrational response. United States leaders must be given time to think. The Chinese "anonymously" use a nuclear weapon against the United States disembarkation area at Veracruz in an attempt to scare us out of the war. Ten thousand American soldiers are killed or wounded, and fifty thousand Mexican civilians. The United States is now thoroughly enraged, our leaders angry. We conclude correctly that the weapon was Chinese and decide to retaliate. But for fear that the Chinese might fire all of their ICBM's on warning, we avoid a general counterforce attack and use only two weapons to destroy their two largest nuclear weapon production facilities. We threaten the destruction of China should any more nuclear weapons be used.

Meanwhile, Communist East Germany occupies Berlin, hoping to get away with this move in the period of crisis, fear, and attention elsewhere. There are only five hundred United Nations troops in Berlin, and the occupation proceeds without firing a shot.

China's leaders desperately push on. For while the second echelon of the party blames them for bringing disaster closer to China, the country as a whole is filled with the bravado and hate that has been instilled in it for decades in preparation for this moment. China uses another nuclear weapon against United States troops in Mexico, and a submarine missile to block Panama. To maintain their position in the Communist world, the Soviet leaders warn the United States not to attack China again.

The latest Chinese move and Russian support makes sense to some United States leaders only if Russia is secretly behind the whole chain of recent catastrophes. These leaders accept the latest intelligence estimates of a small group within CIA-DIA that has collected indications that there may be a carefully laid-out Communist plot to surround and destroy the United States. These considerations lead the new President to threaten Russia as well as China with retaliation in a speech to the world. Secretly we also extend the suggestion to West Germany that it take energetic action against East Germany. We promise aid. Although the United States is still the strongest nation in the world in terms of many indices, the attitudes of

United States leaders are in some ways reminiscent of those of Austrian leaders in 1914. The United States course has suddenly become intransigent, bitter, and fatalistic. Although unprepared for immediate large-scale conflict, United States military leaders have come to believe it is now or never.

The first inclination of the older Soviet leaders is to negotiate any reasonable conclusion, to get out, to make China alone suffer. Yet as the crisis drags on, the United States builds up its Army, Navy, and nuclear offenses and defenses with fantastic speed. At German request United States troops arrive in Germany in early 1990, and the Federal Republic demands the reestablishment of Berlin as a Free City. The United States occupies large parts of Northern Mexico on behalf of the Mexican government. A Brazilian cruiser landing supplies for the communists is attacked and sunk by blockading United States ships. The unexpected strength of the United States response and our radical demands lead many communists, and even Russians, to feel that it is better to risk a global conflict now when the United States is relatively unprepared and the Soviet Union has great superiority, especially in ABM, than to settle on United States terms and watch the United States and its West German allies grow in power once again. For this purpose a long war will not do—the Communist victory must come quickly. The Soviet Union also hopes for the destruction of Chinese power in the process.

This is the context for major war. It may not go that far, but let me suggest two ways it would. First, the Soviets and Eastern Europeans might use their superior conventional forces to press forward rapidly over Europe. This might increase our desperation, leading us to use tactical nuclear weapons. But the Soviets do not scare easily, and simply meet every escalation in kind. Another possibility is that the Soviets are so confident of their abilities that they try nuclear attacks and threats in Europe to break our allies away one by one. As this works we decide we can no longer respond only outside Russia, and our counterblows begin to cross the Soviet border. From here on there are many possibilities, from early resolution, low casualty wars to wars of exhaustion.

Unbelievably aggressive policies for a nuclear armed world? In 1967 terms, yes, but there are many in the world of 1990 who have not lived through a major war among civilized states. For many, a boring life has suddenly gained interest in the burst of events and possibilities on the world scene.

3. The Road through "Victory" to Totalitarianism

Let us go back to Vietnam. In 1967 the United States commitment in Vietnam is involving more and more soldiers, but also a rising tide of internal dissent. One characteristic of this dissent is to strengthen the identification in the minds of many people of our leftist intellectuals with anti-

Americanism, and even with the Communist party. There is today probably a closer policy identification of the radical part of the university community with the radical left wing than at any time since the 1930's. And since foreign affairs is more important today in our politics, and key issues are foreign policy, the identification is probably more "treasonable" than it has ever been.

Let us imagine a series of ferocious battles in the Vietnamese highlands during 1967. The United States commitment goes to five hundred thousand men. We finally decide to occupy an area fifty miles into North Vietnam to serve as a pledge for Viet Cong good behavior, and incidentally to cut some supply routes. This area is rapidly occupied by United States troops after a very heavy destruction of railroads and other supply routes in North Vietnam is carried out. There is a tremendous outburst of antiadministration feeling in the United States. Whole universities demonstrate to express this feeling. Individuals resign from the government. As Chinese Communist troops intervene, and as they move into North Vietnam, a group of North Vietnamese officers stage a coup. They then place troops in front of the Chinese and agree to an armistice involving the withdrawal of United States troops to South Vietnam and the return of North Vietnamese troops to the North, and the return of any Viet Cong who wish to leave the South. All other Viet Cong are to surrender. During 1968 Viet Cong actions almost come to an end, although sporadic fighting goes on as Saigon wipes out some Viet Cong hamlets and reestablishes control in fringe areas. These latter operations lead to incidents between United States and South Vietnamese troops and officials and a decision is made to keep one hundred thousand United States troops in South Vietnam to enforce both southern and northern adherence to the armistice. In addition, a United States military-economic aid program of five hundred million dollars a year provides considerable leverage. Nevertheless, this is a costly United States victory and the anger at those Americans who were both wrong and "traitorous" at the height of crisis will harm considerably the ability of Americans to accept free speech in similar situations in the future. In particular, the disclosures by the new North Vietnamese officials of the degree to which the former leaders were misled by false hopes that the United States peace movement would succeed, turns many otherwise mildly liberal Americans against those who inspired such hopes in the enemy.

A radical government achieves power in Pakistan in 1968, vowing the recovery of Kashmir by any means. Pakistan leaves the United Nations, takes on the complexion of Sukarno's prerevolution Indonesia, and small actions begin all along the Chinese-Indian border; and along the cease-fire line in Kashmir. After a year the Nepalese leaders take the Sihanouk position in regard to Communist China—in order to avoid guerrilla activity in their own country. The Nagas are exploited as an important part of a fairly large-scale Communist guerrilla effort in Assam. Violence on a lesser scale spreads to other parts of India. The guerrillas exploit local loyalties, lack of growth, food shortages, and the growing participation of the United States in attempts to alleviate these. They also attack birth control as a white colonialist plot—a position taken by the Pakistan government as it threw out its American advisers. The result of these external and internal challenges to India is to make the Indian government more and more dependent on the United States, thereby increasing criticism. As this criticism is suppressed more and more harshly but ineffectively, the size and dedication of dissident groups within India is magnified. Of course, the external danger solidifies the Indian mass to some extent, yet there is not a clear frontal war. Increasing numbers of United States advisers and counterinsurgency experts finally become field units. The situation drags on with about one hundred thousand United States troops permanently stationed in India. United States-Arab relations are hurt every time Muslims are killed by American soldiers. Yet the economic position of India begins to improve and the United States can point by 1970 to frankly pro-American governments in India and Japan, a peaceful South Vietnam, a largely anti-Communist Indonesia. There is a good deal of internal and external left-wing criticism, but the United States has come to accept this and to see the *Machtpolitik* as paying off—in fact the only available answer.

In 1967 it becomes apparent that only internal quarrels within the Philippine Communist party and the Huk field command have prevented a resurgence of the Huk movement. Once these are resolved and hostilities renewed, the Philippine government seems to be able to solve neither the problems of its own internal corruption nor the military problems of suppressing armed dissidence. United States aid is requested. Twenty thousand United States troops are sent, and stay. They manage to reduce but not eliminate the threat.

In Latin America, the tactics of guerrilla buildup generally fail. But in Brazil an organization finally begins to build in the Northeast, with gradual extension to the whole country. Increasing numbers of leftists become involved with the rebels. The Brazilian left has come to feel that neither elections nor the usual Latin American machinations will give them another chance. More than in any other case since Vietnam, the Brazilian revolt becomes a worldwide leftist cause. When the United States comes in, the Soviet Union makes United States intervention a major international issue, and reignites fears over the Berlin question. European fears, ideology, and anti-Americanism unite to make this intervention a severe strain on Euro-American relations. In the United States there is widespread opposition as the United States again intervenes on behalf of an avowedly right-wing, military government. Nevertheless, the United States intervention breaks the back of the revolt, both because of the revolt's localized nature and the difficulty of getting aid for the rebels through a United States naval blockade.

By 1972, then, there are United States troops stationed at many points all over the world. Superficially this is a successful United States policy. We have, of course, kept taxes fairly high, lost quite a few soldiers in ways not meaningful to all, and maintained draft calls at a fairly high level. There is increasing federal control at home; increasing centralization of decision, especially in the defense department.

Internal opposition is voiced by three groups: the left which feels that the Great Society goals have been abandoned in favor of imperialism, and which feels the United States suppresses legitimate rebellions; rightist isolationists who feel that our adventures are wasting United States lives and money, and leading to the loss of freedom through overcentralization; and international businessmen who fear that United States business is being excluded from markets unnecessarily, and may soon be excluded from Europe. Unknown to a confident administration, all that is needed is a man who can mold these very different groups into one supporting mass long enough to be elected. The man is found.

In the election of 1972 a truly Jeffersonian candidate manages to unite the antiwar feeling of the left with the antibig government feeling on the right to elect a modern but noninterventionist Republican government. With all good intentions, this government serves for eight years of increasing erosion in our international position. Because of the heterogeneity of the President's backing, his domestic programs cannot be accomplished. Yet there is a leveling off in centralization, and the budget is reduced. Troops are gradually withdrawn from overseas. With an increasing success of a new "détente," repeal of the draft is made a campaign promise in 1976, and repeal occurs in early 1977.

In late 1978 a full-fledged regional revolt breaks out in a major African state (say, Nigeria, Sudan, Kenya, or the Congo). The rebels and the government are both radical left-wing movements on the Nkrumah pattern. The United States does not intervene, but the United Nations does. When the United Nations fails to stop the fighting, the Soviet Union steps in by sending one hundred thousand troops at the request of the United Nations General Assembly. Soviet forces do not take sides, but serve only a peacekeeping function. They successfully settle the revolt in 1979. In the world press there is a great deal of discussion of the Soviet Union now taking on its worldwide responsibilities. To the leaders of the internationalist Republicans and Democrats who supported the war in Vietnam, this is only the last in a series of frustrating, humiliating blows to the prestige built up in 1964-1972.

In 1980 the choice of the Democratic party is more fortunate than the

Republican. The Republican coalition breaks up over the inability of the party to understand the Great Society goals of the left-wing. A wave of contempt for the recent "small-power politics" of the United States sweeps the nation and an internationalist, "big power" Democrat is elected. The new party makes an issue of government efficiency, especially the use of modern techniques of administration. It comes in pledged to live up to the "world-wide responsibilities of the United States." We attempt to engineer a coup in Communist Syria in 1981, fail and are thoroughly unmasked. Criticism within the United States is slowly repressed by a frustrated administration. The theme of danger to the United States and its life is continually stressed in the news media. A new draft law is passed. In a few cases it is used to draft protesting students. This leads, in turn, to further internal criticism. India feels emboldened by the new United States administration and attempts to bring its continuing frontier guerrilla war to an end by attacking guerrilla staging centers in Azad Kashmir in 1982. The Pakistanis and Chinese believe that this is the time to move to a more general war. This is because Soviet relations with the new administration are extremely cool, and the United States is only now building up from the nadir of its relative military abilities, which was reached in 1980.

The United States nevertheless intervenes after a general Chinese-Pakistani attack from three sides on Ladakh. Because of their failure to seize or exploit control of the air early enough in the contest, the Indians lose Ladakh. Sikkim and Bhutan are then occupied by the Chinese.[15] The Indians then counter with a general offensive to recover the latter states and other frontier points in Chinese lands. Poorly planned, two Indian divisions are led into a trap and largely annihilated. The war rapidly escalates as a coup in Nepal turns that country over to the Chinese. As the war proceeds there is growing danger of Soviet intervention. Berlin is isolated completely, except for the airlift, and some East German firing is done on airlift planes. There is a real danger of a two-front war for the United States and little to back it up in the way of military capability.

The President declares a "national emergency" in order to avoid the kind of internal opposition that seems to be building up. In the hysteria of the times most people remember with horror the internal "traitors" during the wars in Vietnam and Brazil. The theory is urged that thousands of Americans died because protests in those wars continually encouraged the communists to believe that America was going to get out, and therefore

[15] There is a great deal of dispute over the real performance of the Soviet forces in World War II, of Chinese forces and logistics in Korea, and of the Viet Cong in Vietnam. I do not wish to resolve this here, but I think a good argument can be made for considerable capability in those wars allowing for the improvement of logistic routes between 1966 and 1983. I believe that the relative success I grant these forces in the 1980's is a reasonable possibility, particularly if United States generalship is not clever.

caused them to continue to fight. As war and the national emergency drag on into 1985 any internal opposition to the United States government comes closer and closer to being considered treasonable. Soviet moves over Berlin reduce the size of the isolationist opposition, already reduced by the apparent "failure" of isolationist policy. Opposition to war in universities leads to public outbursts; student leaders of these movements are dismissed from several colleges. Faculty members protest. Several protesting instructors without tenure are given notice. College administrators become careful. A "new standard of freedom" applicable during emergencies is developed by (and for) the "loyal intelligentsia."

Fear of nuclear war leads to a stablilization of conventional violence as the norm along the whole Indian border. It is not a little war; China maintains three hundred thousand troops in or near the zone of combat, with two hundred thousand reserves further back in Tibet and Sinkiang. Transport within the battle area is largely by Chinese jeep, pack animal, or impressed Tibetans. The United States has five hundred thousand troops in India engaged in antiguerrilla war and anti-Chinese position defense, with the reconquest of Bhutan and Sikkim as the first priority of a tedious offensive in the East. Our long-term strategy is to capture Lhasa, thereby cutting most of the supply routes to the Eastern front. For this purpose we are training special airborne and mountain divisions. It is hoped that a Tibetan revolt might accompany a general assault. The Chinese fight the war in four ways. First, they train and arm Chinese special forces and indigenous dissidents throughout all countries in Southeast Asia not allied with them. Second, they infiltrate regimental-size units along minor trails of the Ho Chi Minh type from Vietnam to Kashmir using both local logistics and coolie supply trains. Third, they use a fluid defense in depth for most front areas in which the United States commits large numbers of men. Finally, conventional means are used whenever appropriate. The Chinese have to replace their forces on Southern and Western fronts at the rate of one hundred thousand a year. But Soviet aid in training and equipment makes possible their indefinite replacement.[16]

East Pakistan and the southern part of West Pakistan are occupied by United States and Indian troops, Afghanistan by Russian troops. The United States is beginning to build up a general offensive in the West, although the successes are limited. Eventually Pakistani forces will become totally dependent on the Russians as they fall back on Peshawar. Widespread conven-

[16] The assumption that the Soviet Union and China would cooperate is, of course, doubtful. Yet one can imagine many reasons why this might occur. In addition to the opportunistic reasons suggested here, one might imagine both Communist hierarchies controlling internal disaffection by the maintenance of ideological war and a friendly rivalry in aims. It is also assumed that China and the Soviet Union have developed clearer ideas than in 1967 of their future spheres of influence: they have for the time being divided the world.

tional bombing is used, but not on major Russian or Chinese cities. In the Middle East United States policy becomes more and more pro-Israeli as the Arabs turn against us. Finally, when the Suez Canal is closed by the United Arab Republics, it is occupied by United States and Israeli troops. There is repeated firing into and around Berlin. Berlin is no longer economically viable, but is maintained by airlift as a dependency of West Germany (many people are gradually evacuated).

In 1985 fighting spreads to Iran where a United States-Soviet front is established roughly across the middle of the country. Since the United States and India are the only non-Communist countries actively engaged in the East, and since no communist homeland seems threatened because of evident United States fear of getting close to the kind of threat situation that might mean nuclear war, the hostilities are kept up at a conventional level by the communists in hopes of eventually bleeding the United States into accommodation. By the beginning of 1986 the United States has one and a half million men on the ground in Asia, from Suez to the Philippines. The Chinese have five hundred thousand in Manchuria and Korea, five hundred thousand opposite Taiwan, five hundred thousand opposite Vietnam, and five hundred thousand engaged in Tibet, Sinkiang, Ladakh, and Assam, with two hundred thousand reserves. There are now additional roads into these areas and expanded airlift with giant Russian planes. In addition to supplying China, the Soviet Union has one million men in Iran, Afghanistan, and Northern Pakistan, with one million men in reserve on the Southern front. There are large numbers of Russian and American troops in Russia and Germany, but both sides fear direct contact.

At home our national emergency is maintained. The election of 1984 was little more than a formality. United States foreign policy is increasingly seen as the key issue, and there is little open opposition to the war policy. After this election the Republican and Democratic parties join for the emergency to become the Democratic-Republican party. In 1988 there is only one major candidate for President.

Paralleling these developments the technology and use of modern devices for analysis and monitoring spreads. Although the period 1973-80 saw a concerted attempt to limit the invasion of privacy for public safety testing, medicine, and entertainment, the growing inexpensiveness of a myriad of electronic eyes and ears, and the public apathy that comes with familiarity has undermined the spirit of the limitations.[17] At the same time emphasis

---

[17] The 1950's saw such a movement toward increased regulation for the use of wiretapping, concealed microphones, and other advanced electronics. However, the early 1960's saw a burgeoning use of these devices as a great private market opened up. Cf. Alan Westin, "Wire Tapping: The Quiet Revolution," *Commentary*, April 1960, and his "Science, Privacy and Freedom: Issues and Proposals for the 1970's," *Columbia Law Review*, June and November 1966, pp. 1003-1050, 1205-1253.

upon mental health in both government and private industry has led to an increasingly paternalistic regard of administrators for understanding the "whole man." By 1980 it is standard practice for hotel rooms, college dormitories, and offices to be monitored through listening devices—and in some cases hidden television. At first the purposes of such monitoring are simple enough—to protect the public. Social scientists gradually begin to have access to the tapes or films produced, and then to the devices themselves. These studies and the records then produce evidence of deviance of a personal and social nature. The individual can discover, but is unlikely to destroy, such devices. It is better to leave the devices alone, because destroying them will merely lead to others being installed elsewhere, and to increased surveillance of those individuals who thereby reveal interest in avoiding monitoring. "No decent American should fear monitoring." Only 10 per cent of rooms need have such devices to make all fear that theirs does. Because of the psychological-sociological emphasis of the culture, many of the expressions of discontent formerly considered "political radicalism" are now realized to be primarily "developmental" or "structural" in origin. While political deviation is not always to be condemned in a free society, insofar as this deviation is due to personality disintegration, or social factors such as anomie, the "rebels" should be treated from the strictly medical point of view, and the social system corrected where it is in error. Friendly persuasion in psychological conferences becomes widespread. These conferences often follow certain kinds of indications that show up in the monitoring process. In some cases military discipline allows a better context for treatment. Structural malformations are treated according to the problem. For example. family members may be educated to play their roles more adequately. Adolescence is given new meaning by work and study programs sponsored by industry and government.

Let us then leave this picture about 1990. None of the events will occur as described, but trends like these do not seem out of the question.

4. Discussion

I have attempted to sketch two dangerous forms of interaction among future events. In doing this I do not mean to condemn most of the decisions that I ascribe to future leaders, or to imply that either isolationism or widespread military involvement in the 1970's necessarily, or even most probably, lead to losses of American values. But I think there is a chilling degree of plausibility to the accounts.

Let us review a few assumptions that I made in taking these possibilities seriously. First, I believe that given more favorable circumstances and better leadership, the isolationist, anti-"big government" forces are capable of recapturing control of American policy. They might do this through an alliance with an anti-imperialist left wing, or simply by capitalizing on growing dissatisfaction with foreign adventures. Second, I believe that the great Communist nations will be willing to sacrifice a considerable amount for world domination, and will be able to operate part of the time in at least quasialliances. States as different as the Soviet Union and the United States cooperated in war in the past. Third (for the second scenario), I believe that the general suppression of opinion, a strong turn toward totalitarianism, is plausible in this time span in America. This is a hard case to make, so let me make some heuristic conjectures. First, in 1966 perhaps 50 per cent of Americans might be willing to suppress the opinions and rights of others, as long as theirs were not suppressed. These people are found all around us, among war resisters, civil rights groups, the John Birch society, authoritarian personalities everywhere. The difficulty is that the 50 per cent seldom comes close to a majority on any issue—therefore, they are willing to accept the consensus of the culture, and the opinion of the other 50 per cent that civil liberties and privacy are worth defending, even for those with whom we disagree. In truly national wars, however, this consensus tends to break down. An overwhelming majority is formed which, for the period of emergency, is willing to restrict some liberties. If this majority is 95 per cent, little seems to happen. But if it is only 80 per cent, with a vocal minority, the evident oppression may become a part of our lives. What I am suggesting is that if war were made a continuing state, and were aided and abetted by more adequate technological means of control, a new cultural consensus might develop that a far-ranging security system is necessary to keep dissidents under control (or treatment).

Let us, then, consider the scenarios in methodological terms. I see reasons to fear certain future dangers, on the basis of intuitions or certain signs in the present context and current trends. To explicate these dangers I have developed two stories as to how they might develop. But in the process of developing these stories I have made a number of choices that were not necessary for the development of the themes. Let us note a few of these areas of variation:

1. It should be reasonably obvious that I might have selected different causative events with the same results. Thus each particular statement is arbitrary, revealing perhaps the limits of my imagination. For example, long-term United States involvement in imperialism might have nothing to do with India—Latin America, Africa, or Southeast Asia might generate the trend as well. The length of time between events is, of course, generally arbitrary.

2. I chose an irregular movement toward the objective rather than a direct buildup. This was done partly because this is often the way of history. But more important I wanted to point out that basic tendencies might go in quite different directions than short-term surface indications would suggest. The record of the years before the First World War has always been my favorite example—assuming there was a kind of inevitability in that war.

3. I chose to separate trends toward a big war from those toward totalitarian issues. I might have joined them, for they could easily reinforce one another, both before and after a nuclear catastrophe.

4. The projection of future history above passes through a number of "nodes of transition" that are not spelled out. At each of these nodes possibilities fan out in a number of directions, several of which might lead in the general directions that I have spelled out here.

B. 1975, 1985 ERODED DEMOCRACY SCENARIOS, by Frank E. Armbruster

The following scenarios attempt to examine a world in which most of the reasonable liberal programs have been fulfilled and in which many more radical proposals—espoused today only by fringe groups—have also been implemented. These scenarios logically extrapolate certain tendencies present in contemporary American society and world politics while, at the same time, ignoring the complexities of liberal politics and ideologies that would counteract such extrapolations. None the less, even though they are highly improbable, such extrapolations are not impossible or even necessarily implausible.

1. *1975*

Europe: As a result of the deepening détente in Europe, Communist parties west of the Iron Curtain have become more and more respectable. While Soviet nuclear capability remains high, the British become decreasingly interested in nuclear defense and—for that matter—even in conventional forces. The French, after years of attempting to lead a third force, actually find themselves supporting the Soviet Union more often than the United States on foreign policy issues. The Italian Communist party is now in such a powerful position that the government, though still a coalition, is strongly influenced by it in the realm of foreign affairs. The Germans have long since approached the east with economic aid and cultural exchanges to bring about a realignment of the satellite states that might eventually lead to German reunification. This policy has led to a lack of opposition, in West

Germany, to the strengthening of the East German government, and has resulted in the recognition of East Germany by all states in Europe except the Federal Republic.

West Germany attempts to maintain the international status of West Berlin despite the British, French, and American troop withdrawal. It is understood by most West Germans, however, that this is a losing battle; and, as anyone knows who wishes to bring personnel or matériel to Berlin through the East German area, the East German political offices that were set up in West Berlin as part of an international control group are really the center of power in that city. Abandoned by their allies, the West Germans put stress upon the increased prosperity that did result from the increased trade with the Communist countries in the East; they rationalize their foreign policy as being the only realistic way to approach the problems of the East. In sum, Europe almost has become a large Finland. This is so not so much because of the existence of a military threat to its security as because it lacks the will to wrestle with the difficult problem of designing and implementing foreign policies that are contrary to the desires of the still dynamic ideological force east of the Iron Curtain.

United States: Something similar to this has been happening in the United States, where—since the conference of 1968 agreed to the initial partition of South Vietnam (under the guise of a Popular Front government in which Viet Cong forces continued to exist as a private army and in which the National Liberation Front was a nominally equal, but actually dominant, member of the coalition party)—the national will and morale has been on the downgrade. In fact, in response to the takeovers in Laos and Cambodia, the United States has done nothing more than make protest in the United Nations, which, in turn, has refused to put the items on the agenda. The United States can no longer rally enough votes in the United Nations to get an item on the agenda over the opposition of the Communist powers. Over the last year, in fact, most of the United Nations' time has been taken up in debates over the existence of United States bases still remaining on Okinawa, in Spain, and in a few other scattered areas. At the same time, the unresolved problem of equal rights for Negroes and other minorities in the United States has become a key item on the agenda of each meeting, placed there by the solid vote of the uncommitted and Communist nations. The United States defense in the United Nations is becoming weaker as demonstrations in the United States against United States bases on foreign soil are joined by large groups of students and civil rights organizations.

The current debate at the moment revolves around a demand put on the agenda by several "uncommitted" nations that United Nations observers be sent into Mississippi, Alabama, and Georgia to supervise anticipated elections. It appears that the United States can muster its former allies in Europe and even some of the uncommitted states to oppose this measure on the grounds that the internal sovereignty of a nation cannot yet be completely ignored. At the same time, while voting this way, these nations make it clear that they want to put on record that they have done so only because the United States has made solemn promises to rectify its situation; and, if the item should come up again, they would have to reserve judgment on how they would vote, depending on how much progress had been made in the South.

Because of the lack of European, Indian, African, or even Latin American support for United States attempts to oppose wars of national liberation elsewhere in the world, the United States brings its foreign policy into line with the general "trends" around the world. This is supported by liberal and humanitarian groups who urge that each nation be allowed to work out its own destiny. Reporting of events is reasonably accurate, although sympathetic to these developments. Those who oppose these trends are viewed as reactionaries (even Birchites) or alarmists. They are ignored by the public and eventually by the news media. Their point of view is then regarded as prejudiced, in some quarters as dishonest, and by much of the press and many academicians as not respectable.

The inability of the United States government to master enough support at home to take a stand against Communist subversion has led many underdeveloped countries to assume a posture similar to that of Cambodia in the mid-1960's. They believe that their only chance to prevent Communists in their own countries from causing chaos and possible civil war—as these parties become increasingly bolder as the United States withdraws from confrontation throughout the world—is to follow "neutrality" not unsympathetic to the Communist bloc. United States foreign policy is dominated by those influential people who believe that the world is in the midst of a social revolution that seems to be going badly—and against the United States in certain areas—because we are not pushing the "Kennedy policy" of winning the hearts and minds of men quickly enough. The net result is that larger and larger amounts of foreign aid are being poured into Latin American and other underdeveloped countries while more of these countries fall into line against the United States on almost all issues. Those who fully accept the idea that economic assistance and United States broadmindedness are essential to getting these powers into line on our side blame United States military assistance programs and errors in our carrying out the policy as the reasons for our failures. The result is that more and more military aid programs are canceled while the economic aid to these countries is increased. Our aid program administrators are belabored by the press for the stupid way in which they deliver the aid each time one of the recipients stands up in the United Nations and condemns the Americans as imperialists.

Slight concessions on the part of the Communist countries are construed as proof that the evolutionary process in the Communist countries—predicted for so long by liberals—is really taking place. The fate of West Berlin is glossed over, but the granting of entrance permits to West German students for tours of the Soviet Union is headlined. The constant increase of influence of Havana in Latin America through the activities of political cadres and guerrillas sent into these countries from Cuba is overlooked. But the visit of a group of folk dancers from Havana is touted as the beginning of a new era in Cuban-United States relationships and a sure sign that Castroism is "evolving." Many newspapers write editorials in support of groups of United States students and leftist organizations demonstrating for the United States abandonment of Guantanamo Bay.

2. 1985

At this time there are two types of nations in the world: the first are those with governments of relatively high morale, with a sense of direction and more or less stable situations within their borders; the second are those with internal situations ranging from chaotic to "unhealthy." With some notable exceptions there is a correlation between strong internally stable governments and one-party Communist totalitarian governments. There is also a general correlation between the chaotic to unhealthy nations and the non-Communist states. Nations, both Communist and non-Communist, still squabble with each other, but the nations with the mobs in the streets of the capitals, with the falling governments and the guerrillas in the back country are almost invariably those with the non-Communist governments. To be sure, even the Communist states have their differences of opinion and bitter quarrels with one another. Moreover, smaller Communist countries swing from one sphere of influence to the other within the Communist orbit.

Yet, just as the dynamism of the Western world in the seventeenth, eighteenth, and nineteenth centuries, once it was allowed to spread unchecked, took over other areas, so Communism in this time period—at least in its revisionist forms—has been allowed to become *the* great dominating force in the world. Democracy seems to be losing in its struggle with Communism just as at one time Moslem ideology proved the weaker in its struggle with Christendom.

Wishful thinking and rationalization reach a new high in many non-Communist countries, including the United States. These are intense outgrowths of the established articles of a foreign policy pursued for more than two decades: the avoidance of opposition, great or small by any country, particularly the United States (for fear of nuclear war); and the belief that Communist countries are showing signs of evolution because they are using an increasing number of Western technological innovations and even some of the products of the art forms (though few of the Western political developments).

Many nations are finding that the old democratic principles of the elected representatives of the people voting on legislation, and peacefully passing laws for social reform, and so on, are slowly eroding. In this era, anyone in the "free world" who desires to back a cause takes mobs into the streets carrying placards. This process of protestation has been going on for two decades and has been the principal excuse for motion after motion in front of United Nations and other joint groups to demand that the democratic governments cease their obvious suppression of the rights of their citizens.

The United States, incidentally, has several Communist powers very near her. Mexico has experienced a Communist coup which took over a popular revolution. It is now a totalitarian Communist state with the dynamism of a new Red revolution, replete with "advisers" from all of the old revolutionary states who poured in to assist in the new movement. Canada has assumed a role of neutrality. The Organization of American States is now dominated by the Communists who ceaselessly attack the Yankee imperialists. In the United Nations, the United States is unrelentingly assailed by the Communist Chinese and Russians who are competing with one another to demonstrate their anti-imperialism. A popular front government in Italy is dominated by Communists, while England has completely retrenched her worldwide commitments and counsels a similar "sane" policy to the United States. The Communist party in France is now so powerful that the country's foreign policy is dominated by it, although the coalition government supposedly is not.

There is a clamor for the return of the Panama Canal to "its rightful owners." The new Mexican Revolutionary government begins to talk, although not yet seriously, of the Mexican lands that were "stolen" by the United States. In the United States some liberal and humanitarian groups have gone so far in the rationalization of their thinking that their "transfer of loyalties" to international organizations is almost complete. To many liberals, these developments appear not as an erosion of the United States position but as part of the development of a democratic world order.

The constant harassment from the outside and the quarter of a century of increasing reliance on demonstration groups and street mobs to make a point—linked with the guilt complexes built-up in so many students— seriously weakens the social and political system in the United States. Without any government policy around which the average man in the street can rally and with the constant discrediting in the press of proponents of a weak version of containment, the United States is receptive to left-wing and student groups and they finally begin to have the kind of influence they have always wanted.

At this point the United States has lost most of its foreign military bases. Soviet and Chinese military aid groups and some bases have been set up around the world. Soviet ballistic missile submarines are now housed in ports in the Caribbean and Latin America, and Chinese ballistic missile submarines cruise off our West Coast. Large Soviet and Chinese forces are stationed in many of these countries just beyond our borders. The strategic position of the United States has obviously become serious; yet the prevailing climate of opinion views the changes in the strategic situation primarily as equitable redistribution and is hostile to any American actions that would "rock the boat" or increase the dangers of nuclear war.

Some of the most dynamic professors in our universities in this period are Communists and many more are sympathetic to Communism. The evolution of Communism into nothing more dangerous or complicated than a left-wing democratic club is taught as fact to students in the universities. At the same time, opposition to these tendencies is viewed as a vestige of reaction. The big danger, it is taught, is from the reactionary right's stopping the social revolution that is surely and directly leading to the fulfillment of mankind's destiny as free from want and as realizing full potentiality. Thus opposition to these trends is now viewed as academically unrespectable.

Under these circumstances, leadership of the opposition cannot and does not come from the intellectuals. It does not come, moreover, from the government. The average man in the street, depending heavily on public news media, finds that regardless of the issue, every demand made upon our government both internally and from abroad, is espoused by seemingly ever-present groups in the streets carrying placards condemning our own government. It has become difficult for the average citizen to determine exactly what is the right or wrong of any issue. The result of this is a deep fear in times of crisis from the portentous military threat, great confusion over each new issue that arises, and the gradual erosion of the political will of the populace. The pacifists truly see tremendous dangers at this point and hope to avoid them by internationally cooperative policies; the leftists find little difference between the "evolved" Communism and enlightened democracy (as they believe that it should be). Furthermore, the feeling of guilt in certain groups in the United States over past exploitation of peoples in underdeveloped areas makes it easy to accept these tendencies.

Since the most stable governments in this era are totalitarian, the constant debates going on in the international organizations, such as the United Nations, center around the chaotic democratic countries. The democracies find themselves constantly on the defensive in these forums while protestors at home stir up trouble faster than the difficulties can be solved. Despite enormous progress in these areas, the United States finds itself ceaselessly defending itself against charges of mistreatment of the Negroes and other minority groups in the United States. In fact, United Nations observers are now in the Deep South. The reports coming out are always conflicting, however, since the observer teams contain Communist members, and as a consequence the observer commissions can never get a clear opinion of improvement.

Threats of intervention under the auspices of the United Nations are made against states that continue to "oppose the social revolution for the betterment of mankind" that is sweeping the world.

In actual practice, every time there is a point at which resistance to Communist pressure is suggested, arguments burst from the left-wing groups stressing that "really, we aren't exactly as clean as a hound's tooth in this argument"; and the whole issue is confused in the minds of the decision-makers and general populace. A *coup de grace* is administered by those who interject: "Really, since we hold so questionable a position, why risk world annihilation because of it?" The Communist countries themselves then provide the threat of world annihilation—and the United States takes a further step backward.

By 1985 democratic countries in the uncommitted areas are subject to almost continuous internal strife and external intervention. Left-wing groups continue to agitate constantly; center groups are uncertain and concerned; and the constantly dwindling right-wing faction is harassed and belabored.

Meanwhile, votes in the United Nations have condemned the United States practices of restricting "strategic trade" with its potential enemies and the United States has bowed to the decision of this body. In addition, once again because of the voting in the United Nations and the World Bank, large amounts of American money are going to Communist countries resulting in a strengthening of their economies. Moreover, long-term loans stemming primarily from the wealth of the United States are being given through these international organizations, which the United States government—because of press opposition that would condemn a refusal to go along with their "humanitarian" efforts—cannot oppose. In fact, the press attributes every crisis that causes another country to go anti-American to American "feet-dragging" in giving aid. The result is that American wealth is made available to the Communist organizations while the morale of the United States sinks to a level below that of Britain in the early 1970's.

At this time there are several members of the House of Representatives who are confirmed Communists, though they are carrying party labels which do not say Communist per se, such as the Progressive Workers' party. It is now obvious to all those who have not rationalized their thinking that the United States is quickly sliding into a position similar to that of Western Europe. It is rapidly becoming a second or even third-class power, sick politically, with diminishing faith in its institutions and way of life.

CHAPTER VII

Some Possibilities for Nuclear Wars

A. INTRODUCTION

The scenarios we have discussed thus far—startling as some of them were —compare conservatively with the actual history of the first two-thirds of the twentieth century. They have stopped just short of major war, major upheaval in the international system, major and prolonged worldwide depression, major new totalitarian movements, or other catastrophic changes in the character of political life of the old nations and to some extent of the new ones as well. (See Table VIII, "Some Possible Causes of 'Surprising' Changes in the Old Nations," on page 24.) On the example of either the first or second third of the twentieth century, the optimistic bias of these scenarios for the century's last thirty-three years would seem so great as almost to exclude them from serious consideration—although some of them were extraordinarily pessimistic, compared to our hopes and even our expectations. Yet, as we pointed out in Chapter I, they include nothing to compare with World War I, the rise of Soviet Communism and the Comintern, and the Great Depression during the first third of the twentieth century; or, in the second third, with the rise of fascism, World War II, and the liquidation of colonialism.

We have argued that the next two decades may be free of events of this gravity—let alone of a series of them. It is not entirely implausible to expect the year 2000 to be reached without catastrophic occurrences. But it would be absurd and dangerous to ignore the possibilities of major war, depression, violent new political movements, or even of more unpleasant developments. Many people are emotionally or intellectually disposed to neglect such prospects (except for largely rhetorical references to nuclear

Armageddon.[1]) While there is some possibility that conditions today are in some way fundamentally and permanently different from those of the recent past, it should be remembered that optimism as a characteristic of Western intellectual and political life is facilitated by the tendency to believe that the catastrophes of the past—to the extent they are remembered at all—are aberrations rather than persistently recurring features of our history.

In any case there is at least some possibility of catastrophe in the world today. In this chapter, and the next two, we will consider some more or less plausible scenarios that explore this possibility. First, let us take the most obvious factor in the situation: nuclear weapons systems exist, and states other than the five that now possess them have the resources to create them. It would be absurd to consider the future without explicitly considering that these weapons systems may be used. Such a war might be accidental or irrational, or under some unusual circumstance might be both rational and deliberate.

B. NUCLEAR WAR SCENARIOS: COMMENTS ON OUTBREAK, WAGING, AND AFTERMATH

In the mid-1950's nuclear war did not seem at all implausible to many analysts. Many scenarios were written in which wars occurred either accidently or inadvertently, or even relatively deliberately but out of crises that had themselves arisen in a more or less accidental and inadvertent fashion. That a nuclear war could arise even out of a more or less deliberate crisis, as in the Cuban missile affair, seemed plausible to many. For a number of reasons it is extremely difficult to write credible scenarios for nuclear war in the mid- and the late 1960's or even in the 1970's, at least in any Standard and most Canonical World contexts. Probably the most plausible scenarios involve United States-Chinese wars, but these too would nonetheless be judged by most students in this field to be implausible.

Among the reasons for this change from the 1950's to the 1960's are changes in nuclear military forces themselves, which now seem to be much less accident-prone and much less vulnerable to surprise attack than before; this leads to the belief that decision-makers are more likely to be prudent

---

[1] To insist on thinking of any and all nuclear war as inevitably Armageddon may itself be a form of denial, one which renders unnecessary the serious assessment of nuclear war and the ways in which it could realistically take place—or be prevented. See the review by A. J. Wiener of *Psychiatric Aspects of the Prevention of Nuclear War*, by the Committee on Social Issues of the Group for the Advancement of Psychiatry, in *The International Journal of Psychiatry*, Vol. 1, No. 3 (July 1965), pp. 398-405, for a discussion of this syndrome.

and less likely to feel under pressure to preempt, in a crisis, for fear that the opponent will strike back. Another reason is that tactical and strategic doctrine has changed. Governments today no longer tend to think that nuclear weapons ought to be used more or less according to straightforward calculations of military necessity or advantage. It seems likely that almost any military request to use these weapons would be overruled by both the United States and the Soviet governments. Military services themselves seem to have sharply changed their doctrine to favor conventional over nuclear action. But the most important reasons for the change lie in the political context discussed in Chapter I, III, and V and in the widespread recognition of this political context.

It would be foolish to argue that because the staffs of organizations such as the Hudson Institute find it difficult to write plausible outbreak scenarios nuclear war is therefore highly unlikely. It can be argued that the *specific sequence* of events that produced the outbreak of World War I was most implausible, and that a scenario embodying those events would not meet current Hudson standards. Nevertheless it is hard to feel that a situation in which it is difficult to write nuclear war scenarios is not much more satisfactory—or consoling—than one in which plausible scenarios are easily conceived.

A "plausible" nuclear war scenario for the 1967-2000 period would probably assume a sequence not too different from that that preceded World World War II. That is, we would assume first an important change in the government of a major power (that is, something like the appointment of Hitler as Chancellor of Germany in 1933). We would then assume a sequence of events in which this government was increasingly aggressive and provided a series of warnings of impending danger (as with the denunciation of the Versailles Treaty, Germany's withdrawal from the League of Nations, the occupation of the Ruhr, the campaign against the Jews and liberal elements). Then flagrant warnings would come—as in the Austrian Anschluss and the Czech crisis in 1938. At this point it should be clear to all that war is too plausible. One might expect still another crisis, such as Munich in October 1938, and then, because war might still appear unthinkable to many, something like the occupation of Czechoslovakia in March 1939 to make the danger clear to all. A showdown would seem inevitable, or at least everyone would claim to believe in it. One would expect rearmament, an arms race, and then an incident in which, say, an ally of a major nuclear power is attacked or threatened under circumstances that cause the nuclear power to declare war but not yet actually to use its nuclear weapons. It, in effect, stands by while "Poland" is destroyed. (Because of fear of German retaliation the French and British even feared to bomb Germany in 1939.) One might imagine a period of conventional or "phony" war as both sides, terrified of escalation, probe, push, bargain, cajole, and threaten.

There might be limited actions and counteractions, reprisals, and finally escalation to one or another level of nuclear war.

It is clear that at any point this sequence might be interrupted and the situation restored to a more normal status. It also seems clear that the length of this sequence of events, due in the 1930's to British and French fears of war (war was almost as unthinkable to Daladier and Chamberlain as it is to Brezhnev and Johnson today), makes "Hitlerian" behavior in the future more practical. While the balance of terror is a great deterrent to "experimentation" and serious probing by conservative powers, to a reckless power the balance of terror and the caution it generates in others may look like an opportunity or shield behind which it can get away with a good deal. Thus it is possible to assume that a plausible scenario for the outbreak of nuclear war may involve "Hitlerian" behavior where the "Hitler" may have little in common with Adolf Hitler except a willingness to exploit everyone else's desire for peace to have his own way.

The scenarios that follow are not introduced by a five- or ten-year period in which the quality of international relations is grossly changed by the rise of Hitler. Thus the reader is likely to find them quite implausible, but they are hopefully as plausible as any brief scenario is likely to be. The first is drawn from *On Escalation: Metaphors and Scenarios,* by Herman Kahn. It is a more or less "standard crisis" scenario.[2] It is set in Germany, not because we necessarily believe that Germany currently is an area of unusual danger, but out of the conventional assumption that the division of Germany is the most obvious and plausible source of European crisis.

1. A Central European Outbreak Scenario

The following steps occur:

1. Unrest and precipitating incident of violence in East Germany or Berlin
2. A high level of popular agitation with street violence follows in East Germany
3. The East-West German border (or the Berlin Wall) is opened up at various points by East German insurgents
4. There is a limited but important degree of intervention by West German "volunteers"
5. The Soviets deliver a warning to West Germany and NATO

[2] A much more detailed version of a similar scenario, by Frank Armbruster, depicts events, motivation, and politico-military situations in a relatively minute fashion and mostly on an hour-by-hour basis (see HI-503-P, *East German Uprising Scenario,* Hudson Institute, March 1965). A less realistic but dramatized version of much the same basic situation is given in *The Seventh Day* by Hans Helmut Kirst (New York: Doubleday, 1959). Either of these fuller scenarios may carry more conviction than the bare outline above.

6. Limited evacuations in Europe and the United States
7. NATO replies to the Soviet warning with a warning against Soviet intervention
8. Violence and border crossings continue, with West Germans involved in large numbers
9. The Soviets intervene, launching a limited foray across the border or initiating other major violence, or perhaps making a nonlethal demonstration of nuclear force
10. Further exchange of messages
11. A cessation of or abatement in hostilities
12. "Armistice" is violated
13. More evacuations and the initiation of other emergency readiness programs
14. More border crossings by both sides
15. One side issues an ultimatum
16. Preparation and completion of emergency readiness programs
17. Either the Soviets make a limited attack on Western Europe, designed to display resolve and to split NATO (with the hope of gaining capitulation, or pressure for capitulation, by one of the major participants), or the United States makes a limited attack to deter the Soviets
18. United States announcement of open cities and a city-avoidance strategy
19. Similar NATO announcements of an open Europe west of the Rhine, with likely selective announcement of open areas in Germany
20. Either the United States or the Soviets make a large counterforce strike with very careful avoidance of collateral damage, simultaneously issuing either a further ultimatum or an offer for a peace settlement
21. . . .

This scenario needs little discussion. Many readers will doubtless find it implausible, since it is quite clear that in most circumstances this crisis would more likely be stopped at any given point in its development rather than pass on to the next point. Nevertheless it is a conceivable development, since real or imagined technical problems, official or unofficial sabotage, defiance or unauthorized behavior, misunderstandings and miscalculations, and so on, could interfere with attempts to arrest the crisis—and there would, of course, be significant popular and political obstacles to any decision that would be interpreted as causing a "Hungary" in East Germany. It could take more political courage or pessimism to stop the crisis than might be available in the bureaucracy. Indeed, there would undoubtedly be some officials who would see in the crisis as much opportunity as danger.

There are, of course, a large number of different ways in which this crisis could continue. Some of them are:

1. Local (preemptive?) surrender by either side
2. Local (preemptive?) accommodation by either side
3. Surrender or accommodation by the Soviets or NATO
4. Revolution or disarray in NATO or the Warsaw Pact
5. Cease fire—stabilized front
6. *Quid pro quo* settlement
7. Quick restoration of *status quo ante*
8. Sustained conventional fighting
9. "Pause"-type conventional fighting
10. Local victory and local retreat
11. Short tactical nuclear war
12. Sustained tactical nuclear war
13. Central escalation
14. Negotiated peace treaty

2. A Sino-American Outbreak Scenario

Let us suppose that Communist China intervenes in the Vietnamese war following a United States decision to invade the North. As the ground fighting intensifies, a decision might be taken in Washington to employ nuclear weapons, possibly against Chinese troops and lines of communications in Southeast Asia only, but conceivably against the Chinese zone of interior as well. Such a decision would seem implausible to almost all expert opinion today (and to ours as well) but it could happen. The decision presumably would be made to demonstrate the force of the administration's prior warnings to Peking not to expect a privileged sanctuary as in the Korean War. It could also grow out of a mounting domestic pressure to employ "quality" weapons against a large, growing, and feared enemy, in the hope that fear of further bombings would induce the Chinese to back down or even in the hope that the regime would be toppled. If Chinese strategic and/or critical industrial facilities are also hit, there may be an expectation of setting China back militarily and/or economically for many years. Rather paradoxically, such war might seem likely to discourage nuclear proliferation for a time, if it were thought that the United States decision to bomb China with nuclear weapons had been eased because China was itself a member of the nuclear club.

Alternatively, we may postulate a more complex case. There is a plausible American reluctance to employ nuclear weapons in the first instance, but a nuclear exchange grows out of the following events: a Chinese entry into the Vietnamese war that is intially successful; an American decision to counter Peking's pressure by mounting a punitive invasion of the Chinese island of

Hainan; a purely defensive Chinese first use of atomic weapons over the Hainan beaches and against the American invasion fleet.

If the Chinese attack were moderately successful, there could be a severe loss of American lives, both on the beaches and at sea. A United States nuclear retaliation would be likely and the major question would be of what kind. It might be directed mainly against Chinese nuclear installations and against military or economic targets that were especially selected to permit the minimization of collateral civilian damage. In this case it might be possible to damage China severely, possibly even to cripple it, and yet to keep Chinese civilian casualties in the low millions. This would be a large loss of lives by any past standard but substantially less than most people would expect for a nuclear war. If the United States made a completely indiscriminate bombing of China, then casualties could easily reach a major fraction of the Chinese population. Contrary to most assumptions, China is a "small" country in the sense that the great mass of its people live within a relatively small area east of 105° longitude. Given the radius of destruction of thermonuclear weapons, it would be possible for the United States to kill almost any determined portion of the Chinese population.

Presumably the Chinese would not start an attack unless they felt they had a credible deterrent threat against the mainland of the United States. In the case of a limited United States retaliation against military and economic targets they might or might not exercise that threat because of the prospect of a second United States retaliation against China as a whole. In the case of large-scale United States attack they would almost certainly do so.

Let us assume that in this second case they could damage four Western United States cities: Los Angeles, San Francisco, Seattle, and San Diego. The existence of this threat would probably be enough to deter the second type of United States attack (to the extent such an attack would not be self-deterred by American unwillingness to inflict tens or hundreds of millions of casualties). But the United States possibly might still be willing to risk at least a limited military and economic attack in the belief that Chinese retaliation would be deterred by threat of an even larger, perhaps total, attack against Chinese civilians. This is not to say that the President would be confident of his ability to do this or that he could find it a desirable choice, but only that when he examined his alternatives he might think of this as his least undesirable choice.

No matter what the scenario or tactics, nuclear war would not only have been demonstrated to be thinkable but would have proved the self-evident but often misunderstood proposition that two-sided nuclear wars need not necessarily end in mutual homicide (as, for example, has been virtually the consensus position since the mid-1950's with respect to any nuclear exchange with the Soviets). If the United States made a military retaliatory attack and the Chinese followed it with a city attack and the United States then destroyed China the opprobrium attached to America might be less than in the first instance: here China has not only made a first use, but was the first to attack cities; and the "victor" too would have lost a good deal. If the Chinese were to bomb Los Angeles, San Francisco, Seattle, and San Diego only with one 100-KT weapon per city there would still probably be between a few hundred thousand and a million dead. While these numbers are an order of magnitude less than general expectations, they are still of the same order of magnitude as the casualties suffered by the United States in World War II. If the Chinese had deliverable multimegaton bombs available to them, then the same attack could easily cause casualties in the five to ten million range. This is not a happy outcome, even for a victor, and the President could wonder whether the game had been worth the candle.

One consequence of a nuclear exchange with the Chinese might well be a *de facto* partition of China: the United States, having won its war, might occupy various coastal enclaves (such as Shanghai, Canton, and Shantung) as well as southern Manchuria, while the Soviet Union might move to occupy Peking and those regions of China (such as northern Manchuria and Sinkiang) adjacent to its own territories. In these regions the Soviet Union would be acting somewhat analogously to the way Stalin acted in 1939 when Hitler invaded and defeated Poland. Many believe that as the German armies advanced, the Red Army moved into Poland from the east in order to maintain a buffer.[3]

Such a China might then have three governments: a "democratic" one in the United States-dominated coastal enclaves, a Moscow-oriented government in Peking, and a "legitimate" Chinese Communist successor to the present regime in the remaining unoccupied regions. This would not, incidentally, be an unprecedented situation in Chinese history.

If, on the other hand, the result of this encounter between a large nuclear power and a small one was stalemate, the exchange ending when a few weapons had been detonated, then the possession of even small nuclear forces would come to be perceived as an immense boom. Let us suppose that the United States were to reply to the Chinese first use by destroying the Chinese plutonium and U-235 production facilities, together with some airfields and naval installations. The Chinese in their turn might destroy San Diego or even a smaller West Coast city such as Santa Monica, issuing a warning of further strikes. The exchange might terminate at that point—if the administration in Washington were to break under the Chinese threat. Nuclear weapons would indeed then seem the great "equalizer," like the Colt .45 of the Old West. One consequence would be a great stimulus to

[3] In fact, the German armies moved rapidly through the German "allotment" and then Germany demanded that Russia keep its bargain and occupy its "allotment."

proliferation. Countries such as Japan, West Germany, Australia, and perhaps India, which had been relying on United States protection, would doubtless make preparations to obtain nuclear weapons.

Doctrines of flexible response and intrawar bargaining enhance the possibility of such an outcome under the technological and strategic conditions that are likely to hold over the next decade or two and perhaps for much longer. Under current conditions prevailing between large and small nuclear powers, if it came to *"tout ou rien,"* there could be only one outcome: damage to the large state, annihilation for the small. But once the notion of limited nuclear war enters the picture—of nuclear responses proportionate to the "crime," of message-sending and bargaining between attacks—then, in a "slow-motion" or limited nuclear war, the intrinsic quality of the opposing *societies* and the nature of the leadership may become all important, dominating technological asymmetries. Suppose China in 1970 (granting it survivable forces) simply matched, or overmatched, the United States' strikes? The will of the American leaders might break sooner than the will of the Chinese leaders. Or China's strikes, though technically equivalent or even smaller in yield, might be delivered with far greater finesse, or be accompanied by more effective political warfare, than the American. One would not expect France, with or without De Gaulle, to trade cities with the Soviets; but what of bargaining tactics against a nation, and a military leadership corps, like Japan in its hysterical mood of 1941? A nation that organized a *kamikaze* corps and whose war cabinet seriously debated mass suicide after Hiroshima would be no mean opponent in an escalation bargaining situation. The notion of the mad leader—the nuclear Hitler, or better, Patrice Lumumba—is, of course, a commonplace nightmare. But has enough attention been devoted to the possibility of one society, even if relatively poor in nuclear weapons, testing its mettle—its cohesiveness, will, and elan—against another? Frankly one might suspect that if the Chinese were ever to mount a nuclear challenge against the United States, it would be on the basis of some such calculation; the Chinese as Communists and Marxists might calculate that *their* nation would not come apart; so they might launch an attack, or commit aggression against a neighbor, daring the United States to do its worst. One doubts this; but the possibility is there.

A Sino-American nuclear scenario—one that suggests the complexity of alliance politics in a nuclear proliferation world—is the following: United States fleet units are destroyed off Hainan by a defensive use of Chinese atomic weapons; the United States mounts a limited disarming attack on the Chinese mainland; the Chinese destroy American bases on Okinawa and threaten massive destruction to any ally of the United States (Japan, the Philippines, Thailand) that allows United States forces into their territory as staging areas or to mount strikes from their territory against China. If the threat were subsequently followed up with a civilian attack, destroying Kobe in Japan, say, or Cebu in the Philippines, the resulting pressure on the United States might be unbearable. In such a case if the United States did nothing, American prestige would fall; Chinese power and prestige would rise. If the United States reacted to this attack with a salvo against Chinese military or population targets, once again we would find ourselves in essentially our first scenario. Whatever the result, many nations would see possession of national nuclear forces as the best insurance against attack.

3. A Soviet-American Nuclear Exchange

Another scenario—a common one in discussions of nuclear war—is the war between two strong nuclear powers ending not only in mutual destruction, but in much collateral damage to other powers. One outbreak scenario is the one mentioned previously of Soviet invasion of Western Europe, perhaps precipitated by a German crisis, met by NATO conventional forces, and, after a suitable "pause," by an all-out "city-busting" strategic campaign. Although the notion that all humanity would be destroyed in this Soviet-American exchange cannot be supported by calculations, even allowing for uncertainties, and is no doubt an exaggeration, the vast physical—and social and moral—damage that such a war would entail cannot be discounted. Such an outcome as mutual destruction, or near-destruction, of the two superpowers would immensely enhance the notion of deterrence and self-deterrence in the postwar world. The result would probably be to slow down proliferation (for a time), and also possibly to lead to some degree of nuclear disarmament or even of world law as well. It could also tend to produce nuclear proliferation if the destruction in the Soviet Union and the United States were so extensive that middle-level powers could aspire to leadership or even world hegemony.

If two such strong powers as the United States and the Soviet Union were to exchange few weapons, ending the nuclear war early and without result, then the weapons would likely seem "useless," as so many contend today. It seems a fair "rule" that in these matters an actual outcome tends to be seen as an inevitable outcome; and what might have been in fact no more than the result of special conditions or of United States-Soviet incompetence or weakness of will might be seen as a "law of war." Even if the postwar bargaining and settlement led to a slight advantage to one side against the other, the value of nuclear weapons measured against the human cost and risks would not seem great. Nevertheless a parallel effect in some quarters would likely be to search for a qualitative superiority as a way out of the stalemate in the future.

4. Sino-Soviet Outbreak Scenario

A somewhat more plausible version of this scenario does not involve the United States at all but presupposes a Sino-Soviet war in the mid- or late 1970's. Here the Chinese, having built up a nuclear force sufficient to deter the Soviets from using nuclear weapons, or more plausibly, sufficient to stalemate a nuclear exchange at a relatively low level of damage, might employ the Chinese mass armies to recover "lost" territories along the Sino-Soviet inner Asian and Siberian frontiers.

The merits of this scenario are still dubious. The credibility of nuclear responses to a conventional provocation cannot accurately be evaluated *in vacuo*. The credibility of a strategic nuclear first strike in this situation is not too different from the credibility of American protection for overseas interests or allies. But it is far less likely that a power like the United States, the Soviet Union, or even France would shrink from using tactical nuclear weapons to defend its *homeland* against invasion. The probable Soviet response needs to be assessed in the light of a special history. Russians have exhibited a strong "territoriality" in their wars. Moreover, the elitest "centurions" of Soviet nuclear command might very well choose to make the "existential" choice of a nuclear response.

A possibility we are inclined to consider plausible is a war between two ostensibly "strong" nuclear powers such as the Soviet Union and China (in our time frame) in which many weapons are discharged at target *but unequal numbers are landed*. In this case the Chinese suffer a catastrophic defeat. This is a nuclear "Cannae" or "1940." In history equal damage sustained by parties to a war is less common than one might suppose. Wars often have ended in stalemate and negotiation; but crushing defeats of one great power by another are common enough too. Nuclear weapons alter much, but in both the nineteenth and twentieth centuries when two so-called equal forces met in battle, victory often tilted dramatically in a single side's favor—for example, in the Franco-Prussian War. It is at least plausible to postulate a significant technological superiority by one side over the other, though this superiority would not be certain until the actual outbreak of war. As Friedrich Engels put it in a letter to Marx in 1857: "Among other things I am now reading Clausewitz' *On War*. A strange way of philosophizing but very good on his subject. To the question whether war should be called an art or a science, the answer given is that war is most like trade. Fighting is to war what cash payment is to trade, for however rarely it may be necessary for it actually to occur, everything is directed towards it, and eventually it must take place all the same and must be decisive." [4]

---

[4] As quoted by Sigmund Neumann, "Engels and Marx: Military Concepts of the Social Revolutionaries," in *Makers of Modern Strategy* (Princeton, N.J.: Princeton University Press, 1941), p. 158.

Thus to project a mere ten years or so into the future, one might plausibly expect a war in which one side escapes with comparatively minor damage in this way: the victory is the result of some vastly superior combination of counterforce capability, ballistic missile defense, and civil defense preparations. Good strategy or tactics may also play its part.

5. A Large Conventional and Small Nuclear War

One of the important possibilities that grows out of discussions of the balance of terror is the possibility that a large and purely conventional war may again be fought. This possibility in its unusual formulation has probably been overstressed by some of the experts since it seems unlikely that nations would again be willing to escalate to Second World War levels without at some point introducing nuclear weapons. However, nations seem less likely to introduce nuclear weapons on a large scale when holocaust is risked than on a small scale when it seems possible to attempt to bluff or intimidate the other side into backing down or accepting a negotiated settlement. One can imagine one side firing one or two nuclear weapons on logistical targets to say, in effect, that it is desperate and that if fighting is continued there will be a large nuclear war. The attacker gives the opponent the chance to make the first large strike because it is confident that it can strike back equally heavily or at least heavily enough to make the opponent regret the escalation. It is difficult to see what the second side could do. It might collapse; it might be willing to accept a cease fire, or it might retaliate itself with one, two, three, five, ten—or many—weapons. Even if it retaliated with several weapons it would presumably still attempt to limit the retaliation enough to preserve some possibility for a cease fire and to avoid massive retaliation. It is also possible that after the tit-for-tat exchange had occurred neither side would be willing to retreat enough to enable successful negotiations to be carried through. In this case both sides, having tested the use of nuclear weapons and found the opponent unwilling to accept a settlement, might decide to go back to conventional war rather than to place further strain on the ability of nuclear deterrence to prevent nuclear emption under conditions of controlled reprisal. The subsequent conventional war could become quite large without triggering another nuclear testing of wills. Clearly both sides would be cautious about pressing gains earned on the conventional battlefield for fear that at some point they would touch off a nuclear riposte by the losing side. As we have indicated, such a nuclear riposte still would not necessarily be conclusive. Yet it would still be something that neither side is likely to want tested. Whether or not the war is settled at a first or second nuclear phase, or during the conventional phase, it would likely be followed by an arms race in which both sides sought a quantitive or qualitative superiority for any future test.

It should be noted that the concept of major conventional war in Europe is not so one-sidedly in favor of the Soviets as necessarily to make it a preferred Soviet tactic. The Soviets have allowed their conventional forces to erode in numbers and they have adopted doctrines that make their forces heavily dependent on the use of nuclear weapons. While there is likely to be a future revision of this doctrine, it is also likely there will be great pressures on Soviet leaders to intensify their search for national security "on the cheap." The role of nuclear weapons in offsetting mass armies and the advantages of deterrence over warfighting capabilities are—as the United States knows—seductive to government budget-makers.

6. Some Postwar Contexts

Different postwar worlds can be distinguished by such factors as:

1. Degree of damage suffered by:
   (a) United States and Canada
   (b) Europe
   (c) Soviet Union
   (d) China
   (e) Japan
   (f) the rest of the world
2. The degree of control the United States can expect over the above areas and the access it has to their resources [5]
3. Morale, élan, and psychological condition in the United States and other countries
4. The conditions of the cease fire or peace treaty
5. Attitudes and capabilities of other powers, and so on.

Many people believe that if the Soviets ever attacked the United States

[5] There has never been a serious study of recuperation that took account of the possibility of international trade. In particular, the very real possibility that United States stockpiles ranging from food to gold would be very important bargaining commodities and that we could get important items from overseas, such as steel from India and Brazil, automobile parts from Brazil, and so on, not to speak of Japan, Europe, and even the Soviet Union (if industry survives in these areas), is not considered. Everybody, of course, recognizes that food may be important, but few understand that the same may be true of gold.

It is often thought by Americans that gold is only of arbitrary value and would have no value in a postattack world. But history argues the other way. During troubled times people almost always cling to the belief that when recovery finally comes, gold will be valuable and that this is perhaps the only thing they can possess that has an assured value.

Gold has great importance in another way. If the United States won a nuclear war, it would be able militarily to dominate the world. This does not mean, of course, that it could or would want to take over the world in a kind of totalitarian fashion, but it does mean that we would have an immense authority, both moral and physical. Under these circumstances we could probably organize international trade so as to have a sort of price control system, and our gold could then be used to buy commodities at cheap prices.

with multimegaton bombs targeted on the settled part of the United States it would take many decades to recover in any meaningful sense. In one respect this estimate is clearly correct, since the environment would likely be more or less permanently (that is for ten thousand years or so), more hostile to human life than it would have been if, other things being equal, there had been no attack. (This would occur because of the long-lived radiation emitters, particularly Carbon-14 and, to a lesser extent, Strontium-90 and Cesium-137.) However, analysts who have studied these problems seem to believe, admittedly on the basis of uncertain and unreliable calculations, that the United States or the Soviet Union could probably recover from a thermonuclear attack as large, say, as two hundred to five hundred multimegaton weapons (directed mostly at cities, with an average yield of, say, five megatons). Depending on the detailed course of events and the prewar preparations, casualties might lie between two and one hundred fifty million dead in either country, but it is still arguable that the survivors could, if strongly motivated, restore—in an economic sense—something close to prewar living standards within five to twenty years. Nevertheless, of course, the damage would still be immense.

The usual view of thermonuclear war is, of course, of annihilation on an enormous scale in areas that include Europe, China, Japan, and sometimes even Africa, Asia, and South America—not to speak of Australia and New Zealand, even though it is difficult, strategically, to see why either the United States or the Soviet Union would divert many weapons to attacks on all (or perhaps any) of these areas and even though there are many reasons why they should not do so. Aside from moral and political considerations, it would be of importance to both sides (or to the winning side) that as much as possible be spared, since there is hope that the surviving participant in the war could draw on the rest of the surviving world for immediate necessities and for medium- and long-term help in restoring what had been destroyed. It actually seems likely that one or more of the above areas would survive a nuclear war almost untouched by direct effects, and would suffer only from the worldwide effects of radioactivity. Radiation damage is almost certain to be manageable if preparations are made, but of course it is precisely in the areas of Africa, Asia, South America, and Australasia that preparations are least likely. Fortunately, while there would then be much unnecessary damage and suffering, even then the radiation damage is not likely to be annihilating.

If A wins a war in the sense of destroying B's military capability, he might choose to spare as much as possible of B's industry, hoping either to confiscate it or to utilize its production (most likely *in situ*) to produce goods for him. Of course, to the extent that an aggressor hopes to utilize the surviving resources of neutrals and allies, or even of the enemy, to ensure or expedite his recovery, his opponent might actually threaten the extensive

destruction of resources as a deterrent to attack. Although this has a precedent in the burnt earth doctrine, its value as a deterrent is dubious unless
acquiring that productive capacity was either a purpose for starting the war
or a requirement for continuing it.

If the side that strikes first intends to utilize its opponent's industry and
wealth to aid in its recuperation, A must strike B relatively carefully, avoiding as much collateral damage to B's productive capability as possible. B, in
anger, could strike back countervalue and destroy as much of A's population
and property as he can. A is then likely to have a very stark threat against
B, and presumably could force B to surrender. Under these circumstances A
presumably would also benefit greatly if he had a large army to occupy B's
country, thus assuring his control of B's recuperation. But as we have suggested, A might act as other than a blackmailer and give an acceptable
quid pro quo. Nevertheless in this scenario large land armies and large
navies play an interesting, if somewhat unexpected, postattack and postwar
role.

One of the most important aspects of the postwar situaton is how strongly
motivated, disciplined, and socially competent the survivors would be. It is
often argued that psychological, and in particular sociological, effects of
thermonuclear catastrophe would be so overwhelming as to destroy the
social and economic fabric. Actually this might be greatly dependent on how
the war started, was fought, and was finished. The political sequence of
events of the war might be more important than the level of casualties in
determining the postwar psychology. In discussing postwar situations we
must specify the scenario and try to estimate the psychological, social, and
political effects of the particular scenario. Conditions would also, of course,
be affected by the terms of the cease fire or of the peace treaty. Indeed, if
there is only a cease fire it is possible that the war would start again, and it
is even conceivable, though somewhat unlikely, that survivors would be interested in access to foreign countries to renew the arms race. Here again the
question of credit and resources could be important. On the other hand,
cease-fire arrangements that are presumed temporary may prove permanent.[6] One reason postwar worlds should be studied is to consider the
importance of various peace terms. There are important trades even in a
thermonuclear war between the demands that are being made by each side
and their tactics, strategy, and bargain capabilities.

Finally, there is a question of the attitudes and capabilities of other
powers. A victorious country is likely, at least for a very short period, to
have large strategic forces, particularly if reasonable preparations had been
made to preserve capabilities in a postwar environment. But if preparations
had not been made or if mutual destruction had been great, or if it were

[6] The cease-fires of World War II were all surrenders. The postwar cease-fires
were not surrenders but still proved remarkably stable.

impossible to maintain strategic forces because of the low level of production and of other preparations, a victor in a nuclear war might find itself vulnerable to a second-rank national power. Other states will have some military capability and some demands and objectives in a postwar situation and will have to be dealt with. Some of the problems of international power are generally likely to exist in the postwar world as in the prewar world, though for a short period of time the victorious countries or the neutral powers may have the ability to dictate peace terms. Unfortunately there has been little discussion of the role of thermonuclear war as a transition from one state of international order to another, and even less discussion of plans for postwar worlds in which a country continues to strive to achieve reasonable national objectives.

(a) *Worlds Dominated by Raw Nuclear Power.* There are two kinds of reasons why raw nuclear power might be important in a postwar world. First, the balance of nuclear forces might be radically altered, leaving one country with a decisive nuclear superiority. Second, the use of nuclear weapons might weaken or destroy many of the psychological and political barriers to the further use of nuclear weapons and nuclear threats. If these two factors joined, a nuclear empire could be imagined. That is, a country, presumably the United States or the Soviet Union, that had achieved a great nuclear predominance in a war in which it survived much destruction and many casualties, might very well resolve to use its remaining nuclear power to control the world—if for no other reason than to prevent future wars.

While the one-power world seems the most likely form of a world dominated by nuclear weapons, it is not the only one. There might be a spheres-of-influence situation, in which the nuclear powers avoided one another and used their nuclear power to control nonnuclear countries, principally perhaps in efforts to restore their damage, but perhaps to prevent further proliferation of nuclear power.

(b) *Traditional Power Worlds.* Although in psychological and political terms it is difficult to believe that any strategic nuclear war above the barest minimum would not produce profound effects, it is quite possible to envisage wars in which the basic modes of power, and the basic relationships between states, were comparable after the war to what they are today. That is, nuclear power might be pervasively present yet most issues might be settled by a politics that is more immediately concerned with economic, psychological, or nonnuclear military force. These worlds are also ones in which people have not yet been able to solve the dilemmas of disarmament and world law and in which nations continue to conduct their relations with one another through variants of familiar techniques.

(c) *Radical Regime Worlds.* These are worlds in which nuclear war could lead to radically new institutions in international relations. Radical transfers of sovereignty to a world authority might be a possibility. The horrified survivors might turn their remaining forces over to one or a group of small powers, preferring the unknown dangers of an external arbiter to the already experienced costs of bipolar rivalry. While it is hard to believe that any radical regime created in the aftermath of a great war would survive without eventual challenge, it is quite plausible that there could be a dramatic international transition creating a "life-cycle" of quite new changes, evolution, and perhaps "counterrevolution," in the international system.

(d) *Destruction-Dominated Worlds.* These are the worlds most people are inclined to see in a postnuclear war world. The destruction caused by the war is the dominant factor in human affairs. It is impossible to know how much destruction there must be before such a point is reached, and harder still to predict the form such a world would take.

Somewhat more plausible, or at least easier to imagine, is a world in which the United States' role is dominated by the destruction it has suffered. Casualties and damage would cause us to be largely uninterested in international affairs, or unable to assert ourselves. In such a world we might be a victim of others, an outcast, or conceivably—at least temporarily—just another middle-sized power without too much national influence and with a peculiar economic structure and trading pattern. Another possibility is vividly portrayed by Walter M. Miller, Jr., in his *A Canticle for Liebowitz* (New York: Bantam Books, n.d.), in which a great simplification (in effect a reversal of the multifold trend) takes place. All scientists, scholars, technicians, and men of learning or education are eliminated, along with their works, in an attempt to prevent a recurrence of nuclear disaster.

CHAPTER VIII

Other Twenty-First Century Nightmares

A. INTRODUCTION

In the previous chapter we considered some of the ways in which a nuclear war might occur, and some of the possible consequences. In this chapter we shall comment briefly on some other possibilities for disaster, some of which may require more than three or four decades to become plausible. Indeed, to the extent that the issue arises out of assuming "surprise-free" projections, it follows that if the extrapolation of trends toward disaster is plausible, the disasters become increasingly plausible with the passage of time and in the absence of remedies or unforeseen countertrends. However, it should be noted that none of the scenarios are impossible *before* the end of the twentieth century; nor do they necessarily become more likely in the period after the year 2000.

B. BUSINESS CYCLE WORLDS

In these worlds the implied straight-line or exponential economic projections of the Standard and Canonical Worlds are interrupted by major vagaries in the business cycle. If a depression occurred in the late 1960's or the 1970's, causing serious decline in economic activity and much social and political unrest, our earlier projections would be much changed. Popular unrest could manifest itself in several ways, including new redemptive political movements in the advanced or semiadvanced states, or movements of the "primitive protest" type in less developed as well as the semiadvanced states.

It would seem important to have contexts in which there is a serious setback to what today promises to be, according to material criteria, a golden age for at least the established industrial nations. The two scenarios that both follow are admittedly inadequate, but they illustrate some of the possibilities. These are based, respectively, on sketches by Ellen von Nardroff and Gus Weiss of the Hudson staff (although neither is responsible for the present versions). Among other things, both scenarios illustrate the difficulty of conceiving the circumstances of worldwide economic crisis during the next few decades without either a series of coincidences or a series of drastic political mistakes.

1. *A Major Depression*

During the next decade there is an aimlessness in the political affairs of nations. A series of interim accommodations keep major problems from erupting, but none are "solved" or settled. The United Nations admits Red China, and as a result experiences even more difficulty than it has in the past. Agreement becomes impossible in the Security Council because of Chinese vetoes (there appears to be a deliberate attempt by China to wreck this organ). Conditions in the General Assembly become increasingly chaotic, not only because of Chinese intransigence but because of French, Soviet, and even United States and British attempts to limit its authority. One result is that available funds are barely adequate to finance the routine administration of the United Nations.

The various international economic institutions of the 1960's still exist but undergo no major improvements, and no important new institutions are created. No generally acceptable means of revising the international currency system is devised. The IMF functions much as it has from the beginning, and gold, dollars, and sterling still constitute the bulk of the international currency reserves. The General Agreement on Tariff and Trade is still observed, but there are no successful new negotiations. NATO atrophies; the Common Market continues unchanged; and the developed world, including Soviet Russia, drifts through a period of general prosperity and complacency.

There are, however, serious stresses in the system. The Common Market clearly becomes a restrictive customs union. It does not expand its membership and the effect of the common tariff barrier, when finally completed, is more protectionist than earlier estimates predicted. Both the United States and the EEC remain determined to protect agriculture. The efforts to provide the underdeveloped nations with preferential treatment in the Agreement of 1967 prove ineffective. In addition, efforts toward political integration of Europe are more or less abandoned, and West Germany, in particular, is unhappy. Her agriculture fails to respond to Common Market competition and the initial advantage her industry enjoys is soon largely eclipsed by the transformation of industrial production in France and Italy. Germany eventually claims that the mark was pegged upward as a temporary gesture of accommodation and that it should now be devalued. When her EEC partners fail to agree readily, she begins to intensify her pursuit of markets to the East and the numbers of trade agreements between West Germany and East Germany and other former Soviet satellites increases. Other EEC members insist that Eastern European nations are, in effect, benefiting from subsidizing trade with West Germany and that West Germany is seeking to establish a central European economic empire.

Meanwhile the underdeveloped nations experience acute growing pains. Functioning mainly under quasimilitary governments, they ruthlessly seek economic growth, and most experience a steady increase in both aggregate and per capita GNP. The chief problem is a lag in the development of sound political systems. Internally there is discontent about the distribution of wealth and political repression. External relations among the developing countries are characterized by nationalistic posturing, particularly on the part of those whose development has been less successful or has been achieved with increasing maldistribution of income. In the case of Communist China, this attitude is extreme. The welfare of the Chinese people has increased very little and Mao's successors, lacking both the weight of tradition as original revolutionaries and the will to innovate radically, have chosen increasingly to shift the blame for their failure to the hostility and sabotage of the outside world. The country, equipped with an impressive number of ICBM's, has solved its labor problems by becoming a garrison state. It is cautious only in its relations with Russia, which has replaced the United States as "the enemy."

A low unemployment rate in United States history is achieved in the mid-1960's. From then there is a slow but steady increase in unemployment with continued deficit and spending policies by the government; only leakage in the form of a continuing payments deficit prevents acute inflation.

By the late 1970's it is becoming more and more apparent that:

1. The world is saturated with dollars. The developing countries, while continuing to hold dollar reserves on hand, are now converting new gains to gold and the United States supply is diminishing rapidly.
2. The political consensus that prevailed in the United States in the 1950's and 1960's erodes. Conventional party labels lose their meaning and opinion is polarized around the radical right and the protesting left. The President finds himself the hapless heir to international overcommitment and domestic inflation and the leader of a shrinking "middle" group. There is little agreement about foreign policy, and effective agreement about one thing only in domestic policy: with a campaign one year away, there should not be a tax increase. The Fed-

eral Reserve Board is too intimidated by the Treasury either to raise the rediscount rate or to engage in open market operations. Therefore the tools to cure domestic and international economic ills simultaneously are lacking.

At this point, bickering between West Germany and other EEC members becomes open and vehement. Finally, Germany concludes sweeping trade treaties with the eastern European nations and Austria and defiantly devalues the mark by the full 10 per cent permitted by the IMF. At this point, although it is by no means clear what will happen to EEC, it is obvious that the dollar will be in trouble if other EEC nations indulge in retaliatory devaluation. Devaluation of the mark alone causes difficulties. The United States President knows domestic deflation is impossible but, nurtured in a tradition of United States noblesse oblige vis-à-vis Europe, finds unilateral international action in economic matters repugnant. He seeks a special session of the IMF Board of Governors, but this is a tragic mistake. The rest of the world concludes that the meeting is a prelude to devaluation and a run on the dollar begins. The European Central Banks do little to help. There is now no choice. The dollar is made inconvertible and the pound sterling follows. An orgy of disequilibrating speculation in the remaining hard currencies begins and exchange rates fluctuate wildly, strangling trade and the flow of productive capital. Inventories mount in export industries everywhere and output is cut back. Stock prices plunge. All developed countries invoke emergency exchange control measures and withdraw many tariff concessions. Acute panic is shortlived in the developed countries, but no nation or constellation of nations exists with the power to restore order to the international economic system. Capital flows, trade and domestic adjustment are hampered by doubts and uncertainty. In the United States recovery is the slowest of all. Isolationist sentiments in both the radical right and left prevail; the defense economy is hastily dismantled; government expenditures drop and the mustered-out troops further depress the labor market. An angry domestic politics, reminiscent in some respects of the 1930's, reappears.

In the developing countries, economies are devastated. Their currency reserves are wiped out and their export markets nearly disappear. Unilateral aid is abandoned and the IBRD and other development banks are handicapped by defaulting creditors and inability to market new bond issues. Development plans are scrapped and governments fall. They are replaced with indigenous forms of state socialism ostensibly dedicated to equitable income distribution but often really pursuing forms of state capitalism and rigorously supressing dissent. By and large the history of the Russian and Chinese revolutions is repeated. The new regimes seek to develop in largely closed economies with some technical assistance, little trade, and no outside capital. By the turn of the century a few of the best endowed of the developing countries have reachieved the level of GNP they had reached in the late 1970's, and the growth rates of the highly industrialized countries, after a long period of stagnation, begin to turn up again. The straight lines of our "Standard World" projections are set back by several decades.

2. An Economically Stagnating World

By the early 1970's the United States is heavily committed in Asia to a policy of containing Communist China through extensive ground-troop deployment. An uncomfortable pacification has been achieved in South Vietnam, but the United States sees few of its political aims fulfilled. Although NATO has declined in importance since the mid-1960's, United States security expenditures for West Europe have not been dramatically reduced. Foreign aid programs have increased roughly in proportion to the increase in United States GNP, but are still well below the requests of the less-developed world. However, private investment abroad, both portfolio and direct, has increased substantially as United States capital sought avenues of higher profit.

Domestically, the United States is prosperous, with unemployment below 4 per cent. A continuing creeping inflation, which has not been arrested because successive federal administrations chose to accept inflation rather than unemployment, persists over the decade of the 1960's and into the 1970's. In addition United States prosperity keeps imports (and especially foreign travel by its citizens) at record levels. This combination of factors maintains a flow of dollars into world reserves.

Despite inflation in the United States, exports continue to exceed imports because of world inflation, the technical and market prowess of the United States, and tied forms of aid. Also, by the early 1970's, the return flow of earnings and debt repayments to the United States is a substantial source of foreign exchange. However, the favorable current account balance and earnings inflow are not sufficient to fully offset the outflows caused by extensive United States commitments and external private investment.

Gold and dollars form the core of international liquidity. Sterling has fallen from favor following the 10 per cent devaluation of 1969 and there is constant talk of further devaluation. The economic performance of Britain is continually disappointing, with productivity increasing slowly despite investment incentives and the denationalization of some heavy industry. After devaluation, Britain is still not world competitive. In particular, it tends to suffer from wage inflation. England is thus following a path similar to that of postimperial Spain, and seems destined to economic stagnation.

The EEC has evolved into a semiprotectionist club with Britain excluded.

The EEC's relations with the United States are polite but cool. GATT has proved disappointing because of the use of new types of trade barriers in addition to tariffs.

Growth of world trade continues into the early 1970's, with Japan and East Europe substantially increasing their participation. The international Monetary Fund, by 1973, increases its quotas twice, but there are no major renovations in the international monetary mechanism despite numerous reports and conferences.

In 1970 the Soviet Union and France initiate talks about establishing a fully convertible ruble. The Soviet Union is anxious to peg the ruble to gold: Western analysts believe that the Soviet Union anticipates increasingly protectionist sentiments in the West and seeks convertibility as a means of enhancing trade in the face of forthcoming constraints.

By 1975 a major split develops between the United States and Europe over ruble convertibility. The United States, although anxious to find new sources of international liquidity and to relieve recurrent strains on the dollar, opposes convertibility because of political stresses still evident in Asia. The Europeans argue that convertibility is a species of "détente," a further step in the settlement of the Cold War. Many in the United States interpret the European position as an economic threat to the United States in the form of a Rapallo-like rapproachement in trade.

By 1980 world gold production has slowed. The United States manages to hold the gold price at thirty-five dollars, and at this price many mines are not profitable. Some gold has come to Western central banks from Soviet and Communist Chinese grain and machinery purchases, but this is not of significant impact. On balance international liquidity has increased largely on the basis of the availability of dollars from United States deficits and from an increase in the turnover of dollars.

In mid-1980, prior to the American presidential nominating conventions, the ruble is declared fully convertible at a price of eighty-eight cents. This change is immediately and blatantly denounced by Communist China. The Soviet Union announces a gold stock of six billion dollars, well above the then-current Western estimates.

By late 1980, the United States has entered a recession. High rates of interest, necessitated by the balance of payments problem, deter investment in housing and plant and equipment; by 1981, following the election of a rightist administration, the unemployment rate stands at 6.9 per cent, the highest in decades.

At this juncture United States policy-makers face the classic dilemmas of solving a domestic recession in the face of a persistent balance of payments deficit. With surprising swiftness, bolstered by its substantial election victory and a wave of neoisolationism, the administration announces cuts in aid programs, reductions in noncritical security forces abroad, and selected import quotas on both manufactured and raw material products. An interest-equalization tax is imposed on securities and loans abroad, and a tax is placed on United States travelers going abroad. No outright tariffs are announced. To support the thirty-five dollar gold price, all "cover" is removed by Congress from the domestic money furnished by the Federal Reserve System. United States authorities pointedly tell the emerging European-Soviet economic bloc that the viability of the world economic mechanism depends, to some extent, upon their actions, that is, their decision to claim gold or hold dollars.

The supply of dollars coming into reserves diminishes markedly. Deficits in payments develop around the world, and the less-developed nations especially suffer contractions in exports and incomes. As a consequence of the trade multiplier, world incomes fall and United States exports and trade income likewise decline. Defaults on some loans occur, but hard currency countries continue to meet their long-term debts to the United States as they come due.

Most countries receive lower incomes from their trade sectors, but not all are hit equally. Developed nations with high propensities to import—like the United States—and most less-developed nations are hurt.

The United States achieves partial success in halting its deficits. While payments do not achieve surplus, the magnitude of deficits is considerably reduced as a consequence of government policy edicts and reduced imports. The unemployment problem proves stubborn but does not reach depression proportions. Other developed countries witness lower rates of growth, while less-developed nations see much of their hard-won progress eroded.

The decline in world economic activity stimulates further political factionalization in Europe, while the United States reacts with world retrenchment and isolationism. Underdeveloped nations, still faced with problems of generating investment capital and the press of population become stagnant, demoralized, and vulnerable to extremist political movements.

C. A NEW PAN-EUROPEAN MOVEMENT

In conditions of developing world economic crisis or stagnation, as in the "Business Cycle Worlds," "Poujadist" protest tendencies gain strength among the small entrepreneurial and white-collar classes of Western Europe and the United States. They are seriously disruptive of parliamentary government and dramatize the incompetence or irrelevance of many of the existing parties and institutions of the West but remain a marginal force. Then the economic crisis forces a series of bank failures in Spain. An unexpected alliance is formed between these elements of protest and the Spanish working class with its tradition of anarchist and syndicalist action. A strong if unfocused antigovernment movement develops, jeopardizing the weak liberal regime that has succeeded General Franco. In this situation a group of young (and largely ex-Falangist) intellectuals issues a manifesto blaming Spain's—and Europe's—economic troubles and modern impotence on a twentieth-century surrender to bourgeois and "American" values. They condemn the bourgeois and commercial spirit. They preach a reformulation of European society that will incorporate all classes into an austere and disciplined movement of reform and European unity. Their manifesto involves a highly romanticized reinterpretation of European aristocratic and chivalric traditions but extends these to the masses of a newly classless Europe, adding to this a program of technocratic economic and industrial administration emphasizing new managerial and data processing techniques. They want rationalized state-control of industry, production "for human needs rather than profit," restored European military power and political autonomy, the cultivation of classlessness, the voluntary abandonment of privilege by the rich, a term of service in state social or military organizations by every citizen, and the "abandonment of selfishness."

This movement enjoys a dramatic success in Spain, and in power it establishes a level of government competence and energy unknown in Spain in this century. The Spanish economy still suffers from the world depression, but there is a dignified and egalitarian national program in Spain that includes highly effective social services, an impressively just distribution of goods, a brilliantly successful state subsidization of the arts and of intellectual enterprise. The romantic doctrine of the regime, reinforced by its humane social program, its cultural accomplishments, and its manifest success in restoring national morale and a notable standard of individual conduct in Spain, has an enormous impact elsewhere in Europe.

Over a five-year period the Spanish experiment provides the nucleus of an all-European movement that steadily limits or abolishes parliamentary government and the old political parties, integrating most of Western Europe and Central Europe into an economic union under a brilliant international technocracy, sponsoring European scientific enterprise, slowly but steadily disenfranchising bourgeois, "reactionary," and commercial groups and interests. Political discipline is enjoyed as a matter of self-subordination to the interests of the mass, but there is a real, if limited and intelligently conducted, repression of dissident elements within European society. There is nothing violent or vulgar about the new political oligarchy; the leaders are enlightened and incorruptible men. But the fact that they make up an oligarchy is unmistakable. Their policies increasingly turn from internal to external affairs. The developing foreign policy of this

Europe is intensely hostile both to Russia, as a discredited and exploitative tyranny, a "reactionary" state as Russia had always been perceived by Western Europe, and to the United States, preeminently the national society of bourgeois and commercial values and of human "vulgarization." All of Europe's grievances against the two super powers of the 1950's find gratification in this program, and the successes of the new Europe reinforce a policy that becomes increasingly aggressive in expelling foreign influences from the continent and in attacking American interests and political influence in Africa, Asia, and Latin America (where the new Europe is watched with enthusiasm, especially among the young and the intellectual elites).

Continued, this scenario would project a political hardening and increasing militarization of this Europe as the United States and Russia resist its influence. Perhaps there would be a Soviet-American alliance against it. Perhaps this Europe would undertake to reestablish European power in Africa or Asia. In any event conditions would develop in which conflict between this Europe and its old or new rivals would become increasingly harsh.

D. NEW MASS OR ELITIST MOVEMENTS

The discussion in this section only partly belongs in this chapter, since the range of new religious, ideological, ethical, and other social movements that may occur includes many that may not deserve to be described as nightmares. Some might seem threatening, but others might prove beneficial to mankind. In many cases, of course, the assessment will depend upon prevalent value systems and/or individual judgment.

The most difficult thing in examining current trends is to judge how many are actually significant and how many are transient, idiosyncratic, or simply more of the kind of thing that society recurrently experiences and that the established elements almost always view with raised eyebrows or alarm. We have referred to "beatnik," Bohemian, cultist, New Left, and other "dropouts" from society. Every society has its quota of "dropouts"; in some cases they are quite significant, the starting point for movements that eventually change society. In other cases they simply manifest factors of alienation or indifference of a kind that are nearly always present. We would argue that the fact that such large and significant universities as Berkeley today are in part affected by these movements, which enjoy the toleration or even the passive support of majorities in many student bodies, suggests that they may be an important trend within the United States. Beyond this country, we are disposed to believe that the next thirty-three years will provide fertile soil for new radical movements, some of which are likely to be emotional or irrational. Such movements are not likely to sweep any particular country before the year 2000, but we believe that there will be some reinforcement of these trends from many outside the movements; that the movements will enjoy a supportive psychological context. In the advanced countries, especially the United States, one can readily imagine a limited but very intense reaction against work-oriented, advancement-oriented, achievement-oriented gratification-deferment values in favor of new "cultures," some of which will emphasize aesthetic values and human companionship perhaps in addition to leisure and high consumption—perhaps instead of them.[1]

It is interesting to compare this "postindustrial" antieconomic Utopia with Marx's and Engels' ethical critique of bourgeois values, in the *Communist Manifesto:*

> The bourgeoisie, wherever it has got the upper hand, has put an end to all feudal, patriarchal, idyllic relations. It has pitilessly torn asunder the motley feudal ties that bound man to his "natural superiors", and has left remaining no other nexus between man and man than naked self-interest, than callous "cash payment." It has drowned the most heavenly ecstasies of religious fervor, of chivalrous enthusiasm, of philistine sentimentalism, in the icy water of egotistical calculation. It has resolved personal worth into exchange value, and in place of the numberless indefeasible chartered freedoms, has set up that single, unconscionable freedom—Free Trade. In one word, for exploitation, veiled by religious and political illusions, it has substituted naked, shameless, direct, brutal exploitation.
>
> The bourgeoisie has stripped of its halo every occupation hitherto honored and looked up to with reverent awe. It has converted the physican, the lawyer, the priest, the poet, the man of science, into its paid wage-laborers.
>
> The bourgeoisie has torn away from the family its sentimental veil, and has reduced the family relation to a mere money relation. . . . All fixed, fast-frozen relations, with their train of ancient and venerable prejudices and opinions, are swept away, all newly-formed ones become antiquated before they can ossify. All that is solid melts into air, all that is holy is profaned, and man is at last compelled to face with sober senses, his real conditions of life, and his relations with his kind.

Of course, the poisoning of values and relationships that Marx and Engels attributed only to the bourgeoisie seems to be present in any industrial, economically striving society, whether socialist or capitalist, and to be absent only where economic criteria have little or no effect on the values people place on each other and on the society as a whole. Thus as we suggested in Chapter IV, if the postindustrial society deemphasizes economic

---

[1] Perhaps in the spirit of Keynes' "reactionary" or "fundamentalist" description of life after the "economic problem" has been "solved," quoted on page 215.

criteria then there should be a return to many of these preindustrial values or an advance to their postindustrial equivalents.

A less utopian view of the postcapitalist age is provided by such historical and social philosophers as Danilevsky, Spengler, Toynbee, Schubart, Berdyaev, Northrop, Kroeber, and Schweitzer, all of whom—as we pointed out in Chapter I—seem to think of civilization as experiencing three phases. An early phase, which might be Sorokin's Ideational, Schubart's Ascetic-Messianic, Kroeber's "religiously dominated," Northrop's "dominantly aesthetic," Berdyaev's "barbaric-religious," is one in which the crucial issues are man's relationship to God or the supernatural or to ethics. There is little or no interest in individualism, in hedonism, in the ego. A second "mature" or "summer" phase, which corresponds to Sorokin's Idealistic, Schubart's "Harmonious," Berdyaev's "Mediaeval-Renaissance," and so on is a mixture of what one might think of as nineteenth- and early twentieth-century pragmatism and secularism with the earlier ideational, religious concepts. Literature and art, instead of emphasizing the supranatural and suprahuman concerns, focuses instead on great men and important events—usually in an idealistic, heroic, or "uplifting" fashion. These authors also tend to agree on a third phase of decline, disintegration, "autumn," or "winter." This is Sorokin's "late Sensate," Schubart's "Heroic or Promethean," Berdyaev's "Humanistic-Secular," Northrop's "theoretic," and Kroeber's "secular, intellectual-artistic culture, and it is free from religious domination." In this final stage there is an almost complete secularization of the culture and then a polarization. On one side there is a revival of religious and/or ethical attitudes and activities, and on the other of egoistic, hedonistic, and sensate attitudes and activities.

Since Classical Culture is one of the important sources for these ideas the analogy of this view of the postindustrial culture with the early Roman Empire is once more apt. All kinds of new religions swept the early Roman Empire. To us, of course, the most interesting is Christianity. Epicureans, stoics, and even traditionalist Romans were much bothered by and contemptuous of the "irrationality" and "emotionality" of these new movements, including Christianity. In much the same way the emotion and irrationality of the New Left, the hippies, and other such movements bother many in the United States today.

We do not wish to lay inordinate stress on historical theories, themes, and analogies; but the works we have mentioned do give rise to the hypothesis that these movements could be both a sign and a cause of approaching anarchy and yet lead eventually to a new religiosity.

One characteristic of many of the more interesting new American movements is a concern for personality and relationships with others that is relatively new to American secular intellectual life of the last century. Thus the New Left talks in nearly religious terms about "commitment," "bearing witness," "self-realization," "confrontations," and so on. Another important theme is the need for companionship and a sense of belonging. In some cases this suggests the classic characteristic of mass movements by which an individual escapes from himself by surrendering to an all-embracing ideal in which he can submerge any inner contradictions in the certainty, unity of purpose, and action of the mass movement and its ideology. In some cases it seems simply a desire for the kind of warm personal relationships that most societies have supplied as a matter of course but which have often been relatively lacking in our own society, in part because of the breakdown of the extended family and settled community, in part because of the substitution of contractual—that is, economically calculating —relationships for traditional and familial relationships.[2]

This desire for closer emotional relationships and support is very evident in such a group as Synanon which, while it is a specialized group dealing with drug addicts, has a technique for creating a familial community. Synanon places an addict in a house with about fifty other people, all of whom are part of his new "extended family." Once or twice a week they play so-called Synanon games that are related to psychodrama and psychotherapy. Members of this community feel themselves in a warm, human, and sympathetic milieu. It is not expected that the individual will leave the "family" when cured; rather he will live in Synanon the rest of his life, not because he has to but because he prefers it. Synanon is now attempting to recruit nonaddicts to join this way of life, which is no doubt better for those who need it. Some of the "hippy," LSD, and free-love cults attempt to supply similar values, presumably with less permanent success, at least for most recruits. At another level, the creation of a "familial" community is used by such movements as the Black Muslims and the Soka Gakkai, but now in a way that furthers the adjustment of their adherents to those values that make middle-class "bourgeois" cultures so successful economically.

If there were new large movements of this general class in the postindustrial future, where might additional recruits came from? In the United States one might think of the following as among the rather likely sources of candidates. First, and perhaps foremost, is "small town" America, a population group that tends to be lower middle class in its attitudes (though in many cases its members have achieved quite substantial incomes), that is often nostalgic for the values of the vanishing (and idealized) culture, and that is intuitively convinced that the current sensate drift of American society is profoundly subversive to its values. It is common to ridicule

---

[2] This need for more intimate relatedness may be in some conflict with the theme of anarchistic individualism and the "hang-loose" ethic.

the nostalgia of these people and the political doctrines they often support; but in the context of this discussion one must feel a certain sympathy for them, if not for the cures they often choose.

Another group of potential recruits consists of the socially uprooted, perhaps those who have moved from rural to urban areas but who have not yet achieved a satisfactory urban adjustment. A third group consists of various racial and other minorities who already often feel alienated from the United States government, the United States establishment, and United States values generally. The militant Black Power movement often seems eager to create their kind of alienation. If there is a marked loss in charisma of white society, they may yet succeed. Another likely source of recruits are the children of successful middle-class people who feel guilty about their affluence, especially as contrasted with the poverty of the outside world. These people often feel that their parents must have "sold out" to have acquired so much for so little. Affluent adolescents often also feel alienated from United States culture because they feel it offers little significant challenge to their capabilities or significant ideology to explain their longing. Another vulnerable group consists of middle-class suburban women who, according to many accounts, often feel they lead an inane and frustrated existence. In general any group that feels it has an unsatisfactory degree of usefulness, worth, or prestige because of current trends is likely to furnish recruits to old or new emotional or messianic movements. It seems quite possible that there will be many such in the next thirty-three years. This possible development may reinforce the social controls problem discussed in the next section.

E. SOCIAL CONTROLS

We shall begin with an extrapolation of some of the technological innovations noted in Chapter II and some of the possible changes in the international system discussed in Chapter V. Neither the data nor the social science theories exist that would permit such complex and long-term extrapolations as those that follow to have any reliability or any more certain basis than informed intuition. Thus to the extent that anyone takes seriously the speculations that follow it will necessarily be a matter of intuition, ideology, or indeed of imagination, rather than documentation and deduction. The implausibilities seem inescapable, however, in part because any other extrapolations would also be implausible—including assumption of a continuation of present social forms, mores, and values. Technology is changing and population increasing so rapidly that the fundamentals of social life and the human adjustments to material and social environment will, by the twenty-first century, have many aspects starkly different from anything we know today. In this sense, the following cannot be considered bizarre. It is bizarre in some normal sense; but the real future is likely to be bizarre in that sense—indeed it almost must be. The seeds of what we suggest are already present, even if they never come to fruition, in the world we inhabit today. To recognize their less desirable potentialities may be a necessary, though not a sufficient, condition for avoiding them.

Much has been said about social controls by gifted novelists and essayists —Aldous Huxley and George Orwell among many others. (See especially Huxley's essay *Brave New World Revisited*.[3]) Only until now their anti-utopias have been regarded by many as merely imaginative—that is, as imaginative in the sense that technological and social preconditions for them could not easily be envisaged. Today, many of the technological developments required to produce their worlds can be extrapolated from existing progress in the sciences. Huxley's Alphas and Betas would still be scientific marvels; but recent advances in genetics, with specific reference to the unraveling of the DNA code, show them to be within the range of future possibilities. Many of the scientific developments of the future may be even more consequential than nuclear fusion, less controllable by current techniques, and more inconsistent with existing social institutions and cultural values.

One standard cliché of strategic literature emphasizes that complex societies are more vulnerable to disruption than simple societies. The complex society has both greater instantaneous and long-range flexibility than earlier societies, but it also has less redundancy and more bottlenecks that could affect the whole society. Thus it may be more affected by major interruptions that overwhelm its instantaneous or short-run adjustment capability and that occur too suddenly for the long-range flexibility to get a chance to work; since simple societies are less dependent upon interrelations with other sections of the nation, local "breakages" and "outages" are often less total in their effect. The modern industrial society is highly differentiated and therefore requires great integration in order to function. A disrupted complex society may not, under at least some important conditions, be able even to sustain the low level of productivity that is normal to a simple society.

Greater wealth and improved technology give us a wider range of alternatives; but once an alternative has been chosen, much regulation and imposed order is needed. Thus with geometric increase in the complexity and organization of modern life, corresponding, even if not directly proportional, increases in the scope and complexity of human and organization controls will become necessary. One need not assume the triumph of the police mentality, or the intrusion of motivation denigrative of human dignity, to foresee

[3] New York: Harper and Row, 1960.

this. Each restriction will have its valid and attractive rationale, which may even be libertarian. Federal safety regulations for automobile manufacturers and tests for drivers today increase the "freedom" of the license-holding driver to drive in safety. Coercive treatment for the mentally ill raises the probability that they will be able to lead freely constructive lives. Plastic hearts may replace real ones and damaged brains may be linked to computers. Therapeutic abortions, through the death of the foetus, increase the freedom of the mother. And the biological adaptation of man to his ecological niche in an extremely complicated and overpopulated society will increase his freedom to live a satisfying and useful life.

We have, of course, omitted the crucial qualification, under the existent conditions. It is still possible that the terminus of the process may be inconsistent with anything we would regard as freedom or dignity, or even human. The evolution of society may produce the devolution of man. The adaptability (and superiority) of man has heretofore consisted in his lack of specialized adaption (as in the case of the lesser animals). Man may, in the not-too-distant future, be adapted in a specialized sense, while society through the control of genetic science maintains its general adaptability by fitting men to the varying tasks that time and environment provide. (Thus the survival of the fittest may be replaced by the fitting of the survivors.)

Consider a few of the factors that will facilitate and seem to justify a controlled society, and then a few that will make it feasible—although the two categories are neither necessarily nor entirely distinct. Overpopulation and organizational complexity have already been mentioned. The greater susceptibility of society in general to disruption could create opportunities for deliberate intrasocietal attacks accompanied by blackmail, to say nothing of organized crime on a novel scale. When nuclear weapons become subject to criminal access (miniaturization will help to bring this about [4]), and when criminal or political conspiracies can bring civil government to a halt through disrupting the computerized networks upon which it will depend, the only alternative to a new feudalism (without the mitigating social features of the old) may be forms of surveillance and control far surpassing any now in existence. Access to places of amusement and museums may have to be rationed, food substitutes developed, access to new forms of socialized housing (mile-high community units) regulated, scarce medical facilities (replacement organs, esoteric remedies, very skilled surgeons, and so on) allocated. Some humans may have to be adjusted to environments different from the earth's surface. It would be clearly erroneous to compare man to the lemming, but every known animal species on which the experiment has been carried out is dysfunctionally disorganized by over-

[4] See the paper on "Nuclear Weapons in Internal Politics" by Lewis Bohn in *Selected Papers From the Hudson Institute*.

crowding. Rules governing mutual adjustment (whether social or legal) will inevitably be very stringent. There will be a strong emphasis on adjustment (other-directed orientations) in place of individualism. Resort to drugs, other worldly religions, delinquency, crime, and mental disease (as a way of "opting out") could increase significantly, requiring medical, social, and criminal sanctions to prevent or contain those forms of disturbance that are excessively dysfunctional for the social and political systems. The consequences of dislocations and mistakes in the production, logistics (distribution) and control functions of business and government are likely to be so huge that the facilities for coping with them must take precedence over civil liberties or private pursuits and property. The Eastern blackout of 1965 only suggests what can go wrong in the future. (That particular disturbance need not have occurred with proper systems design, including cutoffs and redundancy, with their concomitant costs—but that is the problem. On the one hand, there could be extremely sophisticated and prudent system designs or, on the other, there could be extensive control and supervision to avoid the possibility or consequences of relatively far-fetched disasters.) Needs for control and surveillance will develop to utilize (or as Parkinson might say, "expand to fill") the technological capabilities that are present in the system. Technological developments will, in addition to meeting environmental requirements, produce needs to satisfy technological capabilities.

It is already possible to monitor conversations by the disturbances they produce on window panes and to photograph documents through windows and at great distances. TV monitors both indoors and out may become common as the techniques become cheaper. As we pointed out in Chapter II, voices and faces may be checked immediately by advanced computers working through nationwide banks of identifiers. Quite apart from credit needs, the means to maintain continuous checks on the entire population and to scan them automatically for disturbing words or phrases will be available by the year 2000. It may turn out that only those with enormous resources will be able—and in even these cases only partly and perhaps only by bribery or political manipulation—to avoid some monitoring or to interfere with transmission of the data. At the minimum, if the monitoring exists, new code languages will develop in efforts to evade some of the consequences.

There are cases today of individuals kept biologically alive in an attempt to avoid testamentary consequences, by bizarre and uncomfortable medical techniques long past the point where the physician, the individual, and his family would otherwise prefer a natural death. As facilities for replacing human parts increase, including artificial stimulation or substitution for certain brain functions, court cases will almost inevitably arise on the issue of when a man ceases to be himself. (Consider, for example, the case of a man who has had most of his intellectual capabilities replaced by a computer or even a transplanted brain.) Ultimate resort to these techniques would come under government regulation. If overpopulation and means for increasing longevity increase to some as yet unspecified limit, the right to bear children and to resort to longevity techniques could be controlled by government. How these issues, which are so politically potent, could be handled presents a challenge to the imagination. If such issues arise, then the consequences for what we now regard as civilized human standards are obviously enormous.

Drugs and other behavior controls may be available by the year 2000 to produce personality changes at will, to reward activities by hormonal flows (perhaps by remote control) in ways that overcome rational or egoistic (or super-ego) objection to continuation of the activity, and to punish other activities. Alternative techniques include radio waves, ultrasonic impulses (that cause uneasiness), induced hallucinations, and various forms of educative devices operating from infancy. These may be so effective that continuous control techniques would be superfluous, although available for obdurate cases. Much of this may even be available or imposed under the rubric of mental hygiene, simply because such intrusions on individual freedom are not likely to occur except for highly persuasive reasons. It is not difficult to understand that a dictatorship—even a benevolent one— would use such techniques. The Soviet Union has already sent some of its important literary men to mental institutions; the United States sent Ezra Pound to one, and did so as an act of kindness. It is difficult to accept that such techniques would be used widely in the United States until one recalls the extent to which such techniques are already legitimized. We also note that hundreds of psychiatrists were apparently willing in 1964 to lend their names to the conclusion that Barry Goldwater was mentally unsound without examining him. Our culture is attuned to the concept of mental illness and its cure: the modern concept is to rehabilitate rather than to punish criminals because crime results from mental illness. Delinquents are guided by social workers. Disturbed school children are treated by guidance counsellors. Parents read psychologists to learn how to raise their children. The rhetoric of our time—and most of it is, of course, genuine and functional— is the rhetoric of mental adjustment and treatment. Our national pastime is self-medication with tranquillizers and other drugs that affect the psychological condition of the individual. Rather than doubting that Americans would use the most advanced techniques that become available and as systematically as possible, there is reason to doubt that there would be much effective resistance. We do not need the rationale of a political ideology justifying control of the masses. We have our own myth of adjustment and mental balance; and antisocial behavior as determined by the received truths of the day is sufficient to indicate the desirability of treatment. Even some of the New Left—self-proclaimed rebels against societal conformity—have advocated (perhaps too seriously; perhaps not) placing LSD into dormitory food to free the mass of students from their "false"—and hence also "sick" —beliefs. Even those of us who criticize this abuse of terminology often enough think of some of the New Left or other social rebels as "merely sick." As antisocial behavior becomes less tolerable as a result of the increasing complexity and crowding of society, are we not likely to treat what we cannot tolerate? No doubt if we were ever presented with this kind of future and the present as systematic alternative choices, we would not opt for the future. But even if this future is the true future, it will not be presented as a matter of effective and coherent choice. Each new technique will provide a marginal change, and each marginal change for the most part will be desirable on a cost-benefit basis.

The ethical problems caused by learning to produce man or variations of man in the laboratory are unlikely to occur until after the year 2000. Laboratory men who are indistinguishable from ordinary men would, we hope, be granted the rights of natural men. Specialized laboratory-created beings that differ from natural men, but that do possess an ability to reason, are more likely *not* to be granted full rights (a decision we would deplore today). Questions might be raised about the rights of adapted and specialized natural men who are indistinguishable from manufactured adapted and specialized men. In any event, the scope and variety of restrictions upon full natural men will be enormously increased. This problem may arise if bionic computers are made that perform many of the tasks of men and develop creative capabilities. As the distinction between man and lesser creatures and machines begins to shade off, the uniqueness of man and the rights that are attributed to this uniqueness may begin to attenuate. The vulnerability of the political system to shock and disruption may tend to reinforce arguments for the restriction of man based upon the substitutability of manufactured men and bionic machines. A creature that is superfluous as well as dangerous may appear difficult to defend. If even the artistic functions of man are duplicated, a further criterion for man's distinctiveness will have been attenuated. Bionic computers, for example, may become able to produce real art. Even now, some popular music (and even some classical) records are produced as much by equipment and artificial interventions in the performance as by "natural" performance with "normal" instruments.

If athletes begin to make use of prosthetic devices as well as drugs to improve their performance, we may gradually produce almost entirely artificial athletes, for whom bionic robots might eventually substitute. By the end of this general process man's confidence in himself and his role in the world may be seriously undercut.

A variety of strange religions would likely spring up in an effort, that would probably fail, to reexplain the universe. Such religions may attempt to glorify man in ways that repudiate the rational and scientific interpretations that have flourished since the renaissance; or they might be masochistic and denigrative of man. More likely both types would flourish under the suggested conditions.

Perhaps many (most?) men would be kept in a permanently drugged state (pacified?) and adapted to the ecology to which they are assigned according to some computerized calculation. As always the central government would so likely be swamped by the problem of keeping the system functioning properly that it would be concerned only with marginal and immediate problems rather than with the increasing repulsiveness of the entire system or with other basic issues. In any event there may be no rational or moral (whatever these terms mean in such a twenty-first century) feasible solution that does not reject the modern technology or condemn billions of surplus humans to death or deprivation. The twenty-first century would no more be able to return to the world of the twentieth century than the Hellenistic world could return to the "golden age" of Pericles.

Efforts to control the situation would doubtless occur—perhaps as desperate measures. For instance, the political and intellectual elite might distribute contraceptive drugs through the food supply that could be counteracted only by other drugs restricted to the elite. The rationalization could be persuasive: with bionic automation, production would not be disrupted and population might drop to tenable limits that permit humane standards. The problem would arise whether the cure was not itself more brutalizing than the problem. In any event this "cure" assumes that a technocracy, or "aristocracy" or oligarchy, controlled the political system. As technological innovations are made and as biological manufacture and reproduction intensifies, the legitimacy that invests political democracy may deteriorate and the political bases from which these encroachments can be resisted be undermined. If at the same time the system becomes so complex that it can be worked only from the vantage point of control of the central computer and memory banks of a national or worldwide computer system, political and military capabilities would in fact be concentrated in one (if not monolithic, at least centralized) control center. Particularly if creative bionic computers and mancomputer feedback circuits are involved in this central apparatus, control may pass from man to machines, in which case, although population may be limited since it serves no useful function, to the extent to which humankind is permitted to persist it may be kept in a perpetually drugged and/or subservient state. This would prevent rebellion and disturbance or other "undesirable" interference. By determining what information to feed back to the computer-linked controllers and by manipulating the logic of the problem, the computers may gradually gain control of the entire system. This may result not from some analogous organic urge to control or even to destroy, although the possibility that this complex might enter a condition equivalent to madness can hardly be dismissed, but from an effort to reinforce stasis—since the linked humans are defective both emotionally and logically.

Because of the enormous importance of the national computer networks for planning and control, even apart from the possibilities adumbrated above, access to and control of the computers would become the focus of politics, conspiracy, and intraelite *coups*. Quite possibly these efforts might themselves disrupt the computer functions at least temporarily and produce crises or disturbances that affect the operations and prognosis of the system. Advanced weapons systems that operate on a computerized basis would make consensus of the population and support within the armed forces almost irrelevant. Some types of weapons could be individualized and could, in effect, "home in" on voice and sight patterns of particular individuals who have been identified from the national population register as enemies. Others would be used against large groupings but would themselves not require any human agency other than programming the computer. These weapons would use advanced surveillance techniques to find and destroy their targets or alternatively to incapacitate them. Again, the patterns they would home in on, whether group or individual, would be transmitted from a central registry. Pickup of prisoners would be automated.

But even the computers of this period are likely to have limitations on the storing and reasoned use of information. Thus it should be possible for those with sufficient resources and connections to attain partial cover from surveillance.

F. CAPTURE THE FLAG

Six of the boys stopped at the near end of the playground, next to the schoolhouse, and set up the flag just behind the machine gun, which they began assembling and loading with clay bullets. Meanwhile, at the opposite side of the field, Johnny Matthews, the seventh-grade captain, was inspecting the bayonets on the ends of the clay-shooting rifles his forces were carrying. In spite of strict orders, every little while one of the boys would hone his plastic bayonet to a deadly sharpness.

Of course, in Capture the Flag the bayonets were seldom used, since the machine gunners and automatic riflemen guarding the nest usually held off the charge. So the game was mostly an exercise in keeping low, using cover properly, and crawling under barbed wire. Occasionally, though, an accurate sniper would pick off a machine-gunner, or the riflemen would get close enough to use a little mortar or even to lob in a clay grenade, and if communications were snappy a charge would overcome the men left in the nest, and the flag would be captured. Then there would be plently of work for the eager stretcher-bearers and the giggling girls with the antiseptics and dressings.

"You know," Miss Allison ventured, as she and Mr. Hawkins watched the proceedings with fieldglasses from the hill just above the midfield stripe, "I really think these children are old enough to handle bazookas or long-range mortars. Why with bazookas . . ."

"Can't get the appropriations," Mr. Hawkins snapped, holding the glasses to his eyes with one hand and his cigar with the other.

Miss Allison had been a little nervous about the visit of Mr. Hawkins, the District Superintendent of Schools. He had dropped in on her class unexpectedly and had sat all morning in the back of the room. She'd put the class through their discussions and practice exercises on Tables of Organization, First Aid and Human Renewal, Psychopharmacology, Introductory Cybernetics, Civics, Tactics, and Calisthenics, and everything had gone smoothly. Of course, she had to admit, many of her questions had been about yesterday's work, just to make sure they wouldn't fumble too much. Mr. Hawkins had watched them store information through Programmed Problem-Solution. She was *so* anxious that they make a good impression on Mr. Hawkins, and now she could hardly help beaming at them as they got ready to play Capture the Flag. Sometimes she wondered if she might not be a little overindulgent. She had been taught the dangers of that! But they were so winning, just approaching adolescence, and taking themselves so seriously, so eager to learn and to do the right thing.

At the near end of the playground, Johnny was directing his staff command and control girls, a stenographer, first-aid people, and a scattering of observers with radio-telephones. He was standing in front of a contour map that his staff had prepared, showing every bush, hill, trench, and pit, and indicating just which areas were inaccessible to the machine-gun fire from the other side. Now as the rat-tat-tat of the machine gun and intermittent cracks of rifle fire began to echo sporadically from the schoolhouse wall, Johnny was directing the coordination of several squads, so that there were always some drawing fire, some covering, some advancing, and so forth. The machine gunners were firing cautiously, managing only to slow down the infantry's steady advance, since their ammunition had been calculated to last until the end of the hour only if they were prudent.

In a little while the infantry had advanced almost close enough to use their grenades, but not close enough to overwhelm the nest in a charge, and the really tense part of the action began. Several boys and girls were wounded now, and Johnny skillfully drew fire away from the corpsmen as they brought them back to the base.

Suddenly Mr. Hawkins almost dropped his cigar. Johnny had given an order to charge! Dozens of children were dashing crouched across the field, firing from the hip, and falling under the withering machine-gun fire. But at the same time a small figure appeared in a second-story schoolhouse window. He had been hiding inside! Then he leaped, bayonet first, toward the nest. As he fell three of the riflemen defending the nest turned to meet him, and he was spitted on their bayonets. At the same time the grenades in his belt all went off, and the nest flew apart, amid screams. The charging infantry was under the barbed-wire and over the sandbags, and with a few final bayonet thrusts the flag was captured.

"My God," said Mr. Hawkins. "I've never seen anybody try *that!*" The game was over, and the medical group rushed to the machine gun nest and bore the seriously wounded to the school infirmary, while the less serious powder burns, clay wounds, and bayonet gouges were given Human Renewal on the spot.

Miss Allison and Mr. Hawkins went to the infirmary to check on the condition of Bob Jameson, who had jumped from the window. He was expected to live, and several of the boys defending the nest were already well-sedated and being fitted with polyethylene prosthetics. Johnny was there too, congratulating and encouraging them.

"Come and see me when you're through here, son," Mr. Hawkins told him. Then he and Miss Allison went back to the playground and watched the clean-up, mop-up, rebuild operation.

Johnny came running up and stood awkwardly in front of them, grinning, his face flushed with excitement.

Mr. Hawkins spoke slowly and gently, in fatherly tones. "Johnny," he said, "haven't you been taught that we must always avoid casualties unless they are absolutely necessary?"

Johnny's grin vanished. "Yes, sir," he said solemnly.

"I suppose you thought these were necessary." Johnny's face grew redder and he stared straight ahead, almost beginning to pout. "I guess I did, sir," he said.

"You wanted to put on a good show for me. That's it, isn't it?"

"Yes," Johnny croaked miserably, and looked at the ground. For an instant Miss Allison had a wild fear that he might burst into tears.

"Johnny," Mr. Hawkins continued, "you've had classes in Emotional Adjustment and Hygienic Relationships, haven't you? And you've studied the Threat of Deviance, and Personality Disorganization and Entropy?"

"Yes, sir."

"What you did this morning was very Creative. Have you ever thought about the resemblance between Creativity and the Threat of Deviance?"

"No, not much, I guess." He was beginning to look frightened.

"Well, you have to be very, very careful not to get them mixed up. I want to tell you some things about Principles of Practical Realism because I think you're smart enough to be trusted with the ideas. But I don't want you talking to the other boys about it. Is that clear?"

"Yes, sir."

"Suppose two men each get a new idea about how to do things. One of them is Creative, which is good, providing he knows how to use it. But the other is just plain Deviant, and that's dead wrong. The trouble with the Deviant is that he doesn't practice Systems Analysis. In other words, he doesn't have the Big Picture. He's off on his own. Way off, maybe even in left field. Do you follow me?"

"I think so, maybe," Johnny said. He was staring open-mouthed. Even Miss Allison felt a little nervous about this kind of conversation, especially in front of a child, and she hoped Mr. Hawkins would take all the responsibility if anything went wrong.

"Okay, now," Mr. Hawkins continued. "Now what's this Capture the Flag really all about, in the Big Picture?"

"I know what you mean, Mr. Hawkins, sir," Johnny said eagerly. "This is only practice for the real containment actions, so there's no sense wasting men in practice. No sense letting the death rate go up, same time you're tryin' to raise the birth rate in order to meet worldwide responsibilities. The canon is 'Men Are Worth Money,' " he concluded triumphantly.

"Terrific. You're a smart boy. Now what about the Containment Interventions? Why do we keep running a high Gross Annual Adjusted Casualty Rate?"

"Why, men become casualties because of loyalty, sir." Johnny drew himself up stiffly.

"Yes, yes, but try to go beyond that. As you know, loyalty is the same as obedience, so that if a man's told to get killed, naturally that's what he'll do. But I want you to think more on a policy level. You see, it's part of the Big Picture: 'Death is a Fact of Life' as the canon says. Certain members of the group are expendable, for the good of the group. From the point of view of Systems Analysis, it's a matter of allocation, of marginal utility, as you've learned. But what about the men on the other side?"

"They're butchers and murderers, revolutionaries and fanatics, puppets of various aggressor regimes."

"Of course, of course. But there's more to it than that, at least for those on a leadership echelon. Though you shouldn't talk about this to people who aren't smart enough to understand it. Have you ever thought about the *enemy's* policy?"

"Of course not!"

Mr. Hawkins laughed indulgently. "A leader can think about it, long as he keeps his thinking sound. Of course, they've got either Atheistic Dialectical Materialism or some kind of Revisionism, whereas we have Practical Realism under God and the First Amendment. Their governments are totalitarian, while we are Actively Loyal to the Cabinet and Congress of the Bipartisan Coalition, and to AHA, the policy of the *Ad Hoc* Alliance. On a strategic and tactical level, it sometimes seems there's not so much difference between us. After all, enemies always have to learn from each other. But of course it's the ethical element that makes the real difference!

"Now keep this stuff to yourself. Not everyone can grasp all the principles of Practical Realism, so the canon is 'Truth Must be Stratified,' the same way authority is. You wouldn't expect an officer to let his men in on all the information he has, or the government to open its affairs to the public, do you? Well, ideas are the same way. You'll get more of this stuff in college, of course. Come around and see me when you're ready to go, maybe I can get you assigned to my old school." He winked proudly at Johnny. "I, uh, know some of the officers up there very well. We served together in a whole series of Actions. The Brazilian Missiles, the South African Massacre, the Italian Civil War, the Himalayan Secession. You've studied them all. I just might be able to pull a few strings for you. Well, goodbye, Johnny."

"Goodbye, sir. Thank you, sir."

"Yessirree," Mr. Hawkins whispered to Miss Allison, "that boy'll go far. And don't you start worrying about these policy problems. They're a little out of your field."

"Oh, I know that, Mr. Hawkins. I stick to my job, and try my best to do that well." She knew she was fishing for a compliment, but Mr. Hawkins only grunted.

Johnny was standing looking out over the playground, which by now had been completely cleaned up. A quick job, Miss Allison noted with satisfaction. Everything A-O.K. and All Systems Go. Nobody could say her pupils didn't have Know-How. "Know-How is Point number A-One of Practical Realism," she repeated idly to herself. She watched with a warm glow as Johnny squared his shoulders and squinted speculatively into the distance, looking as if already he were beginning to feel himself a man of vision, a man of responsibility in the American future.

G. DISCUSSION: INTERACTIONS OF DOMESTIC AND INTERNATIONAL POSSIBILITIES

We have already speculated to some extent about domestic and international interactions, especially in the scenarios by Gastil and Armbruster in

Chapter VI. The "garrison-police state" formulation of Harold Lasswell[5] and his many followers, and the related dystopias of Orwell and others, are well-known hypotheses or warnings about some of these possibilities. A. J. Wiener's short story above is another attempt to speculate about some of the prospects. It was intended not as a prediction, but as an experiment in "fictionalizing" a "scenario"; thus it makes free use of exaggeration and parody. To the extent a substantive intention exists, it is to suggest something of the impact possible future patterns of international relations might ultimately have on ordinary citizens, and something of the interplay that might take place between traditional traits of American character and culture and features introduced by the new situation.

H. CONCLUSION

Not only is it difficult to make projections forward from the present, but it is also difficult to draw helpful inferences for the present from the rather bizarre future possibilities that we have described. Yet clearly it is desirable to have some concept of the alternative futures toward which policies may tend before the policies are formulated. Otherwise points of no return may be passed without any conscious awareness that the panoply of choices is so great and the future so uncertain. If these be speculations or nightmares then —as they are—rather than science, prognostication, or, except with respect to limited aspects of the problem, technological extrapolations, they (or something similar but better) ought nonetheless to be part of the intellectual equipment of modern man. "Wild" speculation is needed to provide an imaginative perspective within which alternative choices can acquire a deeper, if not necessarily more exact, meaning. They are heuristic and propaedeutic methods for studying the future: a future that will be upon us whether we will it or not, and sooner than we like to believe. If it is all of thirty-three years to the year 2000, it is but a mere twenty-one years since the conclusion of the Second World War—an event that changed the lives of many of us. If we are as intellectually unprepared for events at the beginning of the twenty-first century, and lack as much understanding of the issues as we did in 1929, 1941, and 1947, we are not only likely to be subjected to some very unpleasant surprises, but unnecessarily to exacerbate and prolong their negative consequences—perhaps to the extent that desirable institutions and values will be irrevocably overwhelmed.

[5] First advanced in Harold Lasswell, "Sino-Japanese Crisis: The Garrison State versus the Civilian State," *China Quarterly*, III (Fall 1937): 643-49; and discussed by Lasswell in many subsequent articles, notaby in *National Security and Individual Freedom* (New York: McGraw-Hill, 1950), Chap. II, and recently, "The Garrison State Hypothesis Today," in Samuel P. Huntington, ed., *Changing Patterns of Military Politics* (Glencoe, Ill.: Free Press, 1962).

We have described in this chapter some of the issues that come up when one desires to be intellectually, emotionally, and—let us use the word—morally prepared for the various possibilities. It is a curious comment on our current milieu that the invocation of the language of morality is almost completely restricted to the intellectually unrespectable extreme right or left. No doubt this is because abuse of moralistic exhortation has made it embarrassing to the more sophisticated; yet it may be this very characteristic of our times that makes plausible some of the possibilities we raised.

In the next chapter we turn to some of the dilemmas and opportunities that international changes may ultimately pose.

CHAPTER IX

The International System in the Very Long Run

A. THREATS TO THE STABILITY OF THE SYSTEM

Many analysts hold that the potential instabilities in the current international system and environment make it difficult to imagine that this system can last indefinitely. President Kennedy gave expression to this view in 1961:

> Today, every inhabitant of this planet must contemplate the day when this planet may no longer be habitable. Every man, woman and child lives under a nuclear sword of Damocles, hanging by the slenderest of threads, capable of being cut at any moment by accident or miscalculation or by madness. The weapons of war must be abolished before they abolish us.
>
> Men no longer debate whether armaments are a symptom or a cause of tension. The mere existence of modern weapons—ten million times more powerful than any that the world has ever seen, and only minutes away from any target on earth—is a source of horror, and discord and distrust. Men no longer maintain that disarmament must await the settlement of all disputes—for disarmament must be a part of any permanent settlement. And men may no longer pretend that the quest for disarmament is a sign of weakness—for in a spiraling arms race, a nation's security may well be shrinking even as its arms increase.
>
> For 15 years (the United Nations) has sought the reduction and destruction of arms. Now that goal is no longer a dream—it is a practical matter of life or death. The risks inherent in disarmament pale in comparison to the risks inherent in an unlimited arms race.[1]

This kind of statement obviously is not a comment on any given short-run strategy. It concerns the basic structure of international relations even to-

[1] Address before the General Assembly of the United Nations, New York, September 25, 1961.

359

day: independent countries, many of them armed with weapons of mass destruction, each its own judge of how far it is willing to escalate in any quarrel. The result is a situation that could well "blow up" in the long, and possibly in the short, run.

In the late 1950's many intellectuals, and most informed audiences in the United States, would nod approval to any speaker who assumed or asserted the inevitability of the demise of the (armed) nation-state system. Believing that the current system of competing nationalisms was dangerous and obsolete and would necessarily pass, they would sometimes go on to ask why anyone should be willing to risk his life to preserve it. This was a reasonable position—though a nation might be willing to risk war, as individuals might be willing to risk their lives, in order to "vote" on the system that replaces the current one. Today, however, some of the arguments for a catastrophic change in the current system are not so widely accepted. It may be useful therefore briefly to examine some of the arguments for catastrophe and the reasons for at least a developing skepticism. Not so much despite as because of the seriousness of many of the concerns, a judicious skepticism seems more likely to lead to useful reforms than an excessively apocalyptic or rhetorical view of the issues.

1. *The Arms Race*

"If the arms race is not halted, there will be a nuclear war that will destroy the human race." If the word "ultimately" is inserted, the proposition becomes plausible—though not yet a theorem. In any case, we can certainly agree with the deep concern that is being expressed. A "classical" literature has emphasized the possibility that arms races produced wars. Historians have long held this point of view and Lewis F. Richardson gave a mathematical theoretical foundation to it.[2] By simple extrapolation from views concerning these earlier arms races, a nuclear arms race will produce a nuclear war; and a nuclear war will, as other wars are supposed to have done, entail the use of the full panoply of existing weapons. Both the historical and theoretical generalizations, however, are insecure—at least as generalizations. There have been arms races not followed by wars and there have been wars not preceded by arms races. And of the cases where arms races had preceded wars, it is by no means clear that the arms race was the—or even a major—cause of the war.[3] Finally, it seems increasingly unlikely, despite much expressed disbelief, that if nuclear weapons are in fact used they are going to be used from the start in a reckless and unrestrained fashion without concern for the consequences. The simple picture that every

[2] Richardson, *Statistics of Deadly Quarrels* (Pittsburgh: Boxwood Press, 1966).
[3] Samuel P. Huntington, "Arms Races: Prerequisites & Results," Carl Friedrich and Seymour E. Harris, eds., *Public Policy*, Yearbook of the Harvard Graduate School of Public Administration, Cambridge, Mass., 1958.

decision-maker with access to a button is, once the nuclear threshold has been crossed, going to press every button becomes an increasingly indefensible position. Nations are more likely to back into, or to be dragged into, a nuclear war than rush into it.

Nor is a spiraling arms race very likely. In the mid-1950's, the United States spent one-seventh of its GNP on defense. Today, in the midst of the Vietnamese war, it spends about 10 per cent. The Soviets have gone through a similar or larger reduction during the same period.

Most arms races tend to dampen themselves, particularly if the defense has an advantage over the offense, or if there are political, doctrinal, or budgetary restraints, or even if it is just good sense—and recognized as such—on the part of the two rivals to prevent a spiral. However, one is not likely to increase the possibility of good sense on the part of both rivals by unilaterally overstating the likelihood of spirals (empirical studies indicate that these are most uncommon) or the likelihood of immediate blow-up. Rather, the opposite would seem more likely to be true.

One may have the gravest apprehensions, as we do, about the long run and still maintain that it is important to keep one's head in the short run, precisely because one is interested in having a "vote" on sensible long-run policies. A number of recent crises have indicated the extreme reluctance of the United States and the Soviet Union to cross the nuclear threshold, or even to get into a nonnuclear crisis too deeply. One does not advance the cause of peace by agreeing with the position that is often held by some of the more shrill leaders of the Afro-Asian nations that any Afro-Asian crisis is very likely to create World War III; and, therefore, it is only the good will of these leaders that prevents this war from occurring.

We indicated in Chapter II that the weapons technology of the future may be horrendous, indeed. Further, it seems quite clear that some of this technology may become available to quite irresponsible governments.

Theoretically it has been urged by Arthur L. Burns that arms races will tend to dampen themselves if the defense has an advantage over the offense. Burns has also argued that in a nuclear missile arms race the stability of the system against accident or provocation is increased with larger numbers of missiles and that above some numbers, the quantitative arms race tends to dampen itself. Moreover, even were this not true, other constraints—particularly budgetary constraints—at some point in the arms race would tend to serve dampening functions. Even in the absence of a continuing nuclear arms race, however, those that might occur could conceivably be disastrous to mankind.

On the other hand, official American defense strategy rests on the assumption that even if nuclear weapons are used in a central war, their use *may* be kept limited. The Cuban missile crisis showed the extreme reluctance of the United States and the Soviet Union to cross the nuclear threshold. It is true that in the future nuclear weapons can—and likely will—enter the military arsenals of a number of nations in addition to those now possessing them. Should such weapons fall into the hands of irresponsible and shaky governments, they might well be used, although it is extremely unlikely that world destruction would be threatened. Such diffusions of weapons would create problems for political management on a regional or a world scale. They do not, however, necessarily or even likely spell disaster —and we are extremely lucky that this is the case, for proliferation remains a strong possibility. It seems most unlikely that the current situation, in which only the major victors of the Second World War possess nuclear weapons will continue for fifty-five years after that war has been over (for this purpose we are counting Mainland China as a victor of that war). In fact, it is rather surprising that this situation is still true more than two decades after the end of hostilities. Speculations about the year 2000 must take into account the possibility that the twenty-first century will begin with a reasonably large number of nations possessing nuclear weapons and address themselves to the issue of what to do about this.

2. Human Aggression

"If man does not curb his aggressive instincts, he will destroy himself." The view that large modern wars have been initiated because of the aggressive instincts of man reflects at best an extremely partial truth: a *capacity* for aggression exists—and presumably always will. It perhaps makes slightly more sense than the speculations of Ludwig von Bertalanffy, the biologist and founder of general systems theory, to the effect that speech causes war because only animals with speech go to war; and it would perhaps be as radically difficult to eliminate speech as to eliminate man's potential for aggressive behavior. If either were the sufficient cause of war we could only give up in despair. However, it is obvious that wars also require certain forms of social organization, such as a system in which nation-states command individual loyalities; they also require certain kinds of situations, in which the decision to use force appears to be necessary or justified.[4]

The problem is, as indicated in the previous section, to improve the inherent stability of the situation, decrease the occasions or proximate causes of war within the system, and decrease the destructiveness and other disutilities of any wars that actually occur. One may also wish to add to this list, "decrease the cost of defense preparations," but we would argue that this should take a rather low priority to the first three objectives. Human aggression affects all of the above, but so do many other human qualities. The solution of the problem may or may not involve decreasing sharply

[4] Kenneth Waltz, in *Man, the State, and War: A Theoretical Analysis,* (New York: Columbia University Press, 1959), has provided an interesting comparison of theories of causes of war.

human capacities for aggression. We certainly hope that it does not since, as indicated earlier, we believe that this requirement would make the problem most difficult.

3. *International Anarchy*

"If the present international anarchy continues, the international system can only blow up." The view that the international system is one of anarchy stems from the fact that those centralized legislative or judicial organs that exist in the international system have very limited power, and that most nations remain, in some sense, judge, prosecutor, and jury of their causes. This picture of international politics, while having important truth, leaves out much that is equally important. It ignores entirely the self-regulative mechanisms and rules of behavior that can arise in and be maintained in informal organizations. The constraints that maintain regulative behavior in such informal systems may stem from the immediate interests of the participants, when confronted with the countervailing interests and actions of the other actors in the system, and from the indirect interest in maintaining the system insofar as it is a system consonant with the needs and interests of the participants. Most of the nineteenth century was characterized by limited wars and reasonable—as well as reasonably observed—rules of international law. Violations of the law are always more prominent in the eyes of the beholder than the observances. This is particulary true in international political systems and largely accounts for the belief that the system is anarchic. But the evidence shows that the system worked more often than it failed and even that many of the so-called violations of international law were in fact more like unilateral legislative enactments that were acquiesced in by other states because they satisfied the needs of the members of the system under changed conditions. The loose bipolar system also evolved recognized standards of behavior including some that were general and that came to be explicitly stated and including others that were relatively particular and remained tacit,[5] for example, the United States' decision not to bomb Manchuria during the Korean War and perhaps the reciprocal decision of the Chinese not to bomb our staging areas at Pusan and in Japan.

Simplistic talk about international anarchy seriously oversimplifies the problem we face. The problem is not whether we replace anarchy by law but whether the kind of international system we now have provides as much order as we need or the right kind of order. Harangues about international anarchy mislead us in a serious way, because if we are to improve the order we possess, we must know what the nature of the order is and what institutions and mechanisms sustain it. If we do not understand this, then we attempt to legislate from ignorance.

[5] See Morton A. Kaplan and Nicholas de B. Katzenbach, *The Political Foundations of International Law* (New York: John Wiley, 1964).

To call the present system a "war system" is to substitute rhetoric for analysis. One might as easily call this system a war-limiting system or even a peace-producing system, for the system both limits wars and produces periods of peace. The rhetoric holds out the hope that we can somehow escape from this "war system" into a "peace system." Such a perspective turns our attention away from the order-sustaining as well as the disorder-producing aspects of the current international system and thus detracts from our understanding of the system and hence of the ways in which the system can be managed, changed, or even transformed.

How much is the current system likely to change? How much should we want to change it? Will a system of nation states persist? The weakening of NATO, the growing polycentrism of the Communist bloc and the nationalisms of many of the new nations would seem to indicate both the strength of nationalism and its reinvigoration. On the other hand, requirements of scale of economic organization in the modern world make it difficult to believe that nation-states, particularly those of European (or still worse, African) scale, are viable in today's world. If nation-states persist, then it is not unlikely that they will do so in changed form and with changed functions and within the framework of more comprehensive organizations. Will regional organization be a prelude to, or eventually inconsistent with, world organization? Will world organization, if it develops, produce the end of war or will it produce a variety of civil wars more deadly in extent and scope because of increased weapons capacity, the automatic involvement of the entire globe, and the confusion stemming from the lack of territorial organization? Obviously we do not know the answers to these questions, and while we speculate about them here, we feel that the discussion presented is all too inadequate; yet these are exactly the kind of questions that speculations concerning the year 2000 must take into account.

4. Economic and Developmental Disparities

"If development does not take place, wars will occur between the 'haves' and 'have-nots.' " There can be little doubt that problems of development constitute a serious economic and moral concern. The elite of the under-developed nations take their models not from the histories of the developed countries—that is, from slow progress from the stage of underdevelopment to the stage of development—but from the advanced countries' present stages of development. This sets a standard so high that even effective development policies are likely to prove disappointing in many respects. Unsuccessful policies may lead to stagnation or to retrogression. These may lead either to apathy or sloth in the underdeveloped countries or to radical political movements. Yet this probably does not imply any serious confrontation between the halves of the "dichotomized world" (see Chapter III) in the twentieth century, for the underdeveloped countries, even in concert, are unlikely to possess the resources, either economic or military, to wage serious military campaigns against one or more developed countries, provided the latter follow reasonably prudent military policies and do not suffer from disastrous moral uncertainty or weakness in such a confrontation. But the possibility exists for the twenty-first century—certainly if some of the predictions of Chapter II are realized. In the nearer future, however, one or more underdeveloped nations might engage in an irrational attack upon another, as a response to its domestic insecurities, or make a suicidal attack upon one of the developed countries. The fear or threat of such developments might create a climate of opinion necessitating control over the military establishments of the underdeveloped countries. This is quite feasible; it would also be a catastrophe in terms of human values. Yet it is not clear what can be done to prevent such an eventuality—or sequence of events. Many of the necessary measures might smack of neocolonialism to the underdeveloped countries. Indeed many of these nations perhaps now believe that if neocolonialism persists to the year 2000, then north-south wars will occur. Yet, even doing nothing has an impact on the weaker systems and the very availability of the stronger systems as a source of aid or as a potential danger also exercises a strong influence on the weaker systems. Integration within the world community would not solve this problem, unless the smaller and underdeveloped nations were in some fashion extended voting pluralities. It is difficult to see on what voting could be based —all the obvious systems, such as one man one vote, one nation one vote, one dollar one vote, have serious and obvious defects—as do combinations. However, we will discuss some possibilities below.

Partly for the above reasons, there is currently less fear of catastrophe, though that fear is still widely held, than there was in the past. There is a somewhat lessened fear of the short-run arms competition—a tendency to regard it as an arms "walk," a "sport" restricted to a few powerful or ambitious, but prudent, nations, rather than an all-out arms race in which all nations enthusiastically and vigorously compete. It is becoming increasingly understood that most countries have more to gain—certainly if economic issues are dominant—from domestic growth than from foreign expansion.

Of course one can hold such a view of the next thirty-three years and still believe that the system will be unstable or at least will not endure in its present form for much longer than thirty-three years. But if one believes that the system will not last, one must also believe that it will change and if it changes, it will be different. While this would seem to follow inescapably, surprising numbers of intelligent people agree the system will not last, but cannot conceive of it's becoming something different, as a realistic possibility. Even those who have given the subject serious attention often think in quite hypothetical terms about general and complete disarmament, or world government, without considering seriously how one might get from here to there, or even what "there" would really be like.

But if there is a reasonable probability of international change, certain questions arise: How might the change occur? What would be some plausible scenarios? Is the change likely to be peaceful or violent? How violent? In what direction? Can we influence the change deliberately? In what direction should we try to influence it? What risks and costs are we willing to accept to influence the likelihood of alternative destinations?

B. MINOR MODIFICATIONS OF THE CURRENT SYSTEM

It seems worth examining briefly some characteristics of a twenty-first century in which current trends continue and only minor modifications in the nature of the international system take place. A chart follows which, although it is not intended as exact, does indicate some alternation of periods of limited and total wars in history.

TABLE I
Eras of Limited and "Total" War in Western History

Approximate Date	Characteristic Wars
1000-1550	Limited War (Feudal, Dynastic)
1550-1648	"Total" War (Religious)
1648-1789	Limited War (Colonial, Dynastic)
1789-1815	"Total" War (Revolutionary Nationalist)
1815-1914	Limited War (Colonial, Commercial)
1914-1945	"Total" War (Nationalist, Ideological)
1945-	Limited War (Cold War, Revolutionary, Proxy)

As this chart suggests, a return to limited wars after a period of total wars has ample precedent, quite apart from the invention of nuclear weapons—and it does seem plausible that a return to limited war after the Second World War would have occurred at that time and that nuclear weapons only amplified a trend that would have otherwise occurred. This retreat from total war could endure into the twenty-first century (but presumably unless there are system changes not indefinitely). But nations may for a time become increasingly cautious, careful, and skilfull in avoiding nuclear conflict and even nuclear-prone conflicts—and even be careful and restrained if nuclear weapons are used. Within this system it is possible that the current system of deterrence, defense, national egoism, and occasional wars—nuclear or otherwise—will continue more or less as it exists today.

While many people accept the argument that a modern thermonuclear war is not foreordained to be the end of history, it remains true that the weapons and tactics for a genuinely suicidal thermonuclear war can and may be developed and used. To give an extreme example, it is technologically possible to make a Doomsday Machine [6] though this does not mean that such machines will in fact be built or, if built, used. Short of Doomsday Machines, it is conceivable that the international system could "accept" a series of nuclear wars—though one must point out that a sequence of "lesser" nuclear wars could easily set civilization back to a devastating degree even though no single war itself exceeded a "tolerable" level of intensity. And survival does not, of course, exclude profound tragedy for mankind. But the fact that a certain prospect is not easy to contemplate does not mean that it will not occur. It may well be that the next century will see one, two, or even more periods of large-scale nuclear warfare; and there could be even more periods of relatively limited nuclear war, limited either because the number and size of states engaged were small or because the participants chose to accept certain restraints and conventions. Under these circumstances only a relatively minor modification of the current system might result. Each nation could remain the sovereign judge of the justice and practicality of its causes and of the methods by which it chose to forward its interests as it saw them. There might be fewer than ten (as in some kind of bloc system) or more than two hundred (we have today about one hundred thirty-five) independent sovereignties. While the international system might make use of many institutions to alleviate and regulate international conflict, in the final analysis cannon (nuclear or conventional) could still be "the ultimate argument of kings."

Whether the cannon would be nuclear or conventional could depend on factors other than the technical or economic. We can fairly assume that by the twenty-first century most nations as far as technological or economic constraints are concerned, will have access to nuclear weapons. These weapons will be easy to make from widely available plutonium (itself a byproduct of power reactors) and possibly from other easily available materials. Most nations will also have access to missiles. They may be able to buy high altitude and satellite-launching research missiles—or even commercial missiles for other purposes—on the open market, and these can be modified for military use, or military missiles themselves may be available for purchase. And of course the competence to manufacture missiles is certain to be much more widely shared than it is today.

---

[6] A device that could destroy all human life: suggested as a *reductio ad absurdum* in criticizing certain notions of massive retaliation. See Herman Kahn, *On Thermonuclear War* (Princeton, N.J.: Princeton University Press, 1960), pp. 145-149.

However most nations are likely to continue to exercise caution and distrust zeal, although one can assume that some nations may try to use "sophisticated" nuclear tactics to achieve their ends, and extremist movements may develop that are willing to run considerable risks. There will be frustration, dissatisfaction, and rivalry in the world even if favorable growth rates are maintained in the underdeveloped areas. Disparities among nations will still be great, and growth itself tends to be an unsettling process. All of these suggest that nuclear weapons may be used again.

The next use of nuclear weapons might not be against one of the developed powers that could retaliate, but by a developed power against a smaller or less developed power, or by smaller and/or underdeveloped powers against one another. It is an interesting precedent that the first great battle between modern ironclad ships with modern guns and fire control systems occurred between China and Japan in 1895—the two nations that were last to acquire these ships.

The effect of establishing a precedent of nuclear use is hard to gauge, but it seems reasonable to expect that if two small nations fought and suffered great damage, as we discussed earlier, the rest of the world would probably be confirmed in caution. Under these circumstances there might be strengthened stability in the international system, or there might be pressures to reform the system so as to prevent such an event from occurring again. If, however, a large nation used nuclear weapons against a small power and suffered no serious material or political aftereffects, there might be a strengthened tendency for the larger nations to threaten or coerce smaller nations, which in turn would undoubtedly accelerate a nuclear arms race among smaller nations—and ominously deepen and embitter international rivalries. A similar effect would occur if one small nation successfully used nuclear weapons on another small (or large) nation. In any case, the next nuclear use is likely to be of momentous implications for the twenty-first century, and if on balance it seems to have succeeded, benefiting the state that resorted to nuclear war, other nuclear uses would be likely to follow, and possibly a profound and enduring estrangement between the nuclear and nonnuclear states. The trends toward world empire and "institutionalized warfare" discussed below might be set in motion, and the century could be one of great violence and disorder.

C. THE INSTITUTION OF ALL-OUT WAR WITHERS AWAY

Even if international relations continue to be based on independent national sovereignties, strong restraints on the use of violence might well develop, and not only might the all-out war system *seem* to wither away, the use of weapons of mass destruction seemingly abolished, but the system of restraints might be both fairly effective and reliable—at least for a time, perhaps for decades.

There are many different ways, at least in principle, by which worlds could develop in which there is little or no threat of international war. In "Gallois Worlds" this tends to occur when every state has nuclear weapons (even though small wars may occasionally occur, the result will be a warning to others). The system is thus supposed to maintain itself. Indeed General Gallois has written:

> Contrary to popular belief, the further we advance into the ballistico-nuclear age, the more possible it becomes to outlaw violence, even if the aggressor nation is stronger and more richly supplied with combat means than the nation it threatens. . . .[7]
>
> To humanity, it seems absurd that the very omnipotence of these new weapons can, at least temporarily, create a form of peace that would be more stable—and more advantageous—than any ever known. . . .[8]
>
> If this must be the direction of the development, and if the movement is as irreversible as the one which culminated in the generalization of firearms, it would be better for the Western nations to reach an understanding . . . by distributing its weapons among the cooperating states.[9]

So sober an observer as Winston Churchill indicated some agreement with this thesis. Churchill said: "Then it may well be that we shall, by a process of sublime irony, have reached a stage in this story where safety will be the sturdy child of terror, and survival the twin brother of annihilation." [10]

The position was also argued by Nikita Khrushchev in a speech delivered on January 6, 1961:

> The task is to create impassable obstacles against the unleashing of wars by imperialists. We possess increasing possibilities for placing obstacles in the path of the war-mongers. Consequently, we can forestall the outbreak of a world war . . .
>
> A word or two about local wars. A lot is being said nowadays in the imperialist camp about local wars, and they are even making small caliber atomic weapons for use in such wars; a special theory of local wars has been concocted. Is this fortuitous? Of course not. . . .
>
> There have been local wars and they may occur again in the future, but opportunities for imperialists to unleash these wars too are becoming fewer and fewer. A small imperialist war, regardless of which imperialist

[7] Pierre Gallois, *The Balance of Terror: Strategy for the Nuclear Age* (Boston: Houghton Mifflin and Co., 1961), p. 113.

[8] *Ibid.*, p. 167.

[10] Winston Churchill, House of Commons, London, England, March 1, 1955.

[9] *Ibid.*, p. 229.

begins it, may grow into a world thermonuclear rocket war. We must therefore combat both world wars and local wars. . . .

Now a word about national liberation wars. . . . Liberation wars will continue to exist as long as imperialism exists, as colonialism exists. These are revolutionary wars. Such wars are not only admissible but inevitable. . . .[11]

Khrushchev, of course, specifically points out that the absence of international war does not mean the absence of conflict and violence. There is still opportunity for murder, assassination, sabotage, terror, and subversion. But all of these are tolerable by comparison with modern thermonuclear war.

Recently there has been discussion, notably by Lewis Bohn, Arthur Waskow, Kenneth Boulding, Walter Millis, and others, of the possibility of a relatively peaceful world in which an attrition of the weapons systems themselves took place. This is perhaps harder to understand or to accept as plausible since the argument of an enduring system of multilateral deterrence assumes deterrence working well—and this presumes the existence of deterrent forces. But Kenneth Boulding, in particular, has raised the possibility that the twenty-first century could initiate what he calls the "postcivilization era." He argues that war is an institution of the era of "civilization," which he identifies as beginning about 3000 B.C. and ending about 2000 A.D. He says that in the pre- and postcivilization eras war was not and is not likely to be a normal institution of human society. Boulding makes his case by amplifying the line of argument we have noted concerning the lack of aggressiveness characteristic of most nations today.[12]

A number of mechanisms could consciously be used to buttress such a trend. They include the following possibilities and tendencies:

1. Warfare continues but is limited by
   (a) instrumental considerations, or
   (b) agonistic restrictions.
2. Conflicts that previously erupted into war are sublimated or resolved by other methods of conflict resolution and competition. In particular great power competition is primarily expressed in
   (a) acceptance of *faits accomplis* or the verdict of internal war,
   (b) "potlatch" wars, or
   (c) very limited "contests."
3. Even escalation is unthinkable because of
   (a) a rule of law and peaceful arbitration, or
   (b) the existence of a worldwide pluralistic security community.

It seems likely that there will be increasing acceptance—at least among the old nations—of the notions and concepts of instrumental war—war con-

[11] *New York Times*, January 18, 1961.
[12] See *The Meaning of the Twentieth Century* (New York: Harper and Row, 1964).

ducted with an eye toward profit and loss and the avoidance of disaster—with restraints based upon rational calculation. Objectives are limited because of fear of escalation, and both sides bargain, negotiate, and threaten, but are always in reasonable control of their commitments. There is limited use of force, but enough restraint so that the escalation "never" erupts. In this situation a residual fear of war (or eruption) must continue to exist since it plays an important role in enforcing prudence, agreements, and limits on demands and tactics. The system may also exploit various thresholds, conventions, and customs of the kind we discuss below to make restraint more reliable.

If instrumental war and politics last for any great period of time, the "rules" are likely to acquire an ethical or agonistic value. That is, the rules would begin to lose some of their instrumental quality and take on an independent value, becoming ends rather than means. The new rules for the new values may be related to current religious concepts, or to considerations of chivalry, honor, or ethics. Transgressions then would be perceived as immoral—as outside the rules, even if their consequences were otherwise acceptable or even greatly desired.

It is incidentally noteworthy that almost all vertebrates, including fish, seem to have agonistic rules; fights between members of the same animal species are rarely fatal—animals do not usually "fight like animals." [13] Conflict in fact is often highly ritualized and more nearly resembles a tournament than a mortal struggle. If this were not the case—if losers were killed or seriously injured—fighting might threaten the survival of the species. Thus two rattlesnakes will wrestle without biting one another. According to Lorenz, when two wolves fight the loser bares his throat to the winner—the winner does not then seize the loser's throat but accepts the act as a sign of submission and releases the defeated foe, who then leaves the victor his prize.[14] When two elk fight they tend to charge each other head-on, and occasionally fight to the death in this manner, but if one turns and presents its flank to the other, the opponent will not charge it. This would almost always be lethal. Similarly throughout most of civilized history when two human groups have recognized each other as civilized they have generally acknowledged agonistic rules limiting the tactics and objectives of war. The exceptions almost always involved a denial by one side that its opponent is civilized—that is, the exceptions have been ideological wars, religious wars, or wars against, by, or between, "barbarians." Total war between civilized people is largely an invention of the twentieth century; yet even in our secular world one can imagine a return

[13] See Eibl-Eibesfeldt, I., "The Fighting Behaviour of Animals," *Scientific American*, December 1961.
[14] Konrad Lorenz, *King Solomon's Ring* (New York: Crowell, 1961).

to agonistic restrictions—in part because of the knowledge that total war has become so self-defeating as to be "unthinkable."

Of course, over a lengthy period of time, as arms continue to develop and become widely available, or as "outsiders" come into the system who do not understand or who do not choose to obey the rules, the system may collapse. Nevertheless it is still possible that in our current international system, in which there are really no outsiders, all who have access to nuclear weapons may learn, even if by trial and error, the need for agonistic codes of conflict, and eventually a worldwide ethic might develop that either restrained all nations or worked well enough so that a few "outlaws" would be unable to exploit successfully evasions of the code.

A "withering away" of war might also come as the culmination to a worldwide trend toward what Karl Deutsch and his associates have called "pluralistic security communities"—such as that between the United States and Canada, where war no longer is "thinkable" in a dispute or conflict. We have already suggested that Western Europe (and perhaps eventually all of Europe) will develop or has developed a similar "pluralistic security community" [15] and that serious conflict between France and England or France and Germany has become "unthinkable." It is possible that special and regional pluralistic security communities may gradually enlarge so as to cover almost the entire world, and nations that are excluded will find it impossible to challenge the community—even in the absence of enforceable world law. (There may be many special institutions and customs for coordination and cooperation and for carrying out important international functions.)

The possibility of a successful pluralistic security community, with or without other methods of conflict limitation or resolution, would be enhanced if international legal and arbitration procedures were increasingly resorted to in dealing with conflict. One can imagine a gradual "legalization" of international relations, comparable to the development of law and arbitration in resolving conflict within nations. This trend would be greatly enhanced by the likelihood that many specialized functional agencies will develop in response to the complex requirements of the international postindustrial world.

Many readers will argue that this is wishful thinking. Perhaps; but the historical record suggests that such systems may develop and function successfully, at least for a time and to a degree. As indicated by Table I, this does not really require human nature to change; there are reasons in both history and present conditions for at least a qualified optimism. We have mentioned several times the lack of interest in territorial aggression in the

---

[15] See Karl Deutsch et al., *Political Community in the North Atlantic Area* (Princeton, N.J.: Princeton University Press, 1957).

world today, the awareness that imperialism no longer is clearly profitable. The two nations that have prospered most in the postwar world—Germany and Japan—were defeated in war and have no colonies. It is also possible that by simple factors of carrot-and-stick, disorderly or revisionist nations may be restrained, while the powerful nations are self-restrained—as well as the majority of other nations. If this majority of peace-desiring nations preserve at least a modicum of military capability, or the ability to mobilize such military capability rapidly, and if these nations are sufficiently cohesive and unified in their desire to preserve a peaceful world and willing to accept losses in this cause, the result could be a stable system.

We believe that there is enough ambiguity in most cases of aggression, and ambivalence in attitudes toward peace and world unity, to make total achievement of this result unlikely. We would also put emphasis on the force of ideology—the self-righteous and idealistic variety as well as the aggressive—in distorting nations' perceptions of events and in converting impulses toward peace to a source of violence. But it must be noted that there are a number of thinkers who seem to feel that something like collective defense can be made to work. Certainly tendencies toward self-restraint and communal control could be greatly enhanced if some of the measures discussed below were successful.

D. MORE OR LESS BASIC STRUCTURAL CHANGES

The age of nuclear warfare also raises the question of even more basic change than the evolutionary stabilization or legalization of international affairs we have considered. The discussion of structural changes in the international system has suffered because nothing like the full range is ordinarily considered, and because there are so many possibilities it is hard to single out those to be considered seriously. There is also a natural disinclination to take seriously the prospect of big changes in the world system. Predictions of radical change tend to sound either Utopian or Cassandra-like, and social scientists and others are accustomed to discounting the possibility—a priori—of any large change coming about "naturally" or even by reaction to specific developments. In particular, there is good reason to discount the possibility that great changes can be brought about by choice. Historically such plans tend to miscarry and even when changes occur rapidly, the people undergoing the evolution or revolution often have the greatest difficulty even predicting the outcome—or even recognizing explicitly what is happening—let alone controlling the process.

In any event it is hard to be so confident of the permanence of the current system as to refuse to discuss some of the possibilities for radical change. Some of these are:

1. Development of a bloc system covering most or all of the world with restraints and special institutions or rituals to handle interbloc relations
2. Limited condominiums between some of the major powers that enforce rules of behavior with respect to nuclear weapons and related aspects
3. Concert of large powers (e.g., an active or vigorous United Nation Security Council, a North Atlantic Community, a great power security community)
4. Concert of small powers (perhaps using the U.N. Assembly)
5. Other development of the United Nations
6. World federal government
7. World empire or empires
8. Agonistic rules enforced by community sanctions
9. Setback to civilization

Let us consider these briefly.

1. Bloc System

One can imagine the world lastingly divided into a number of blocs. For example, the following major blocs are presently plausible:

1. North American (or United States-North Atlantic or United States-Atlantic-Pacific)[16]
2. European bloc (most likely the six nations of the EEC, probably including others)
3. Latin American bloc
4. Soviet bloc
5. African bloc
6. Arab bloc
7. Indian bloc
8. Chinese bloc
9. Others

The following smaller blocs might also easily exist or be thought desirable:

10. Balkan bloc
11. Southern Tier (Turkey, Afghanistan, Pakistan)
12. Malaysian-Indonesian-Philippines bloc

[16] A United States-North Atlantic bloc might include England, Ireland, some or all of the Scandinavian nations, and possibly some other European powers. A United States-Atlantic-Pacific bloc could add Australia, New Zealand, and perhaps Japan to either the North American or United States-North Atlantic blocs.

One could imagine each bloc choosing a form of government, including a method of succession. If other blocs refrained from interference in revolutions and civil wars, such a system might last for an extended period. In this case the international system might tolerate a rather high level of sovereignty in each bloc. While the system would amount to a translation of the nation-state system to another level, all of the blocs would be of considerable size and might seem virtually (or practically) unconquerable. In one scenario interbloc frontiers might be mutually guaranteed with a high degree of mobilizable power—both in military and other forms—brought to bear against a transgressor. The larger blocs might feel sufficiently strong interest in maintaining the order to establish permanent interbloc institutions for this purpose. One can imagine a kind of world organization, say a "government" with five "parliamentary houses."

1. *Security Council* (composed of reasonable quotas from each of the blocs or perhaps with equal representation from each bloc)
2. *Economic Council* (primarily represent the "wealth" of the world)
3. A *Social and Welfare Council* (primarily representing the "poor" populations of the world)
4. A *Forum* (consisting of appointed or elected representatives of minority groups and others who speak as individuals)
5. An *Academy* (consisting of scholarly and distinguished individuals who were elected; this in effect acts as sort of "Skill Forum" or the twenty-first century equivalent of a "council of elders")

The Security Council would decide certain political and military questions by various kinds of majorities and would probably have to have access to some kinds of force. One could imagine the second house, based on GNP, wealth, or dues, having limited authority to levy taxes. The third house, which is representative or proportional to population, might allocate development resources, or an important part of them, but this house would not determine how much money would be available for development aid. (In other words, the aid would be in effect a voluntary offering by the rich via the second house.) There might be a house of minorities as in the Forum to inform and mobilize world opinion and to watch over the bureaucracy, with individuals appointed to represent various interests and minority groups or specific classes. The main role of this last would be to guarantee protection, resources, and a platform to minorities, and would also play, to some extent, the role of "Ombudsman" or citizens' protection officer, investigating public complaints against official abuses, as is customary in Sweden. Finally, the "objective" studies of the Academy might go far to raise the level of debate.

Such an elaborate and optimistic view of a bloc system is, of course, tantamount to a prediction of world government—a trend that is further discussed below.

2. Condominiums

It has been suggested [17] that the United States and Soviet Union might sign a one-clause treaty to the effect that they would jointly and separately go to war against any nation that used nuclear weapons against any opponent. It is conceivable that something like this might yet occur. The two largest powers, the United States and the Soviet Union, might do even more than attempt to regulate the *use* of nuclear weapons. They might undertake to try to run the world as a dyarchy.[18] The existing nuclear test ban treaty constitutes a bilateral agreement between the United States and the Soviet Union, ratified by other nations, to discourage the diffusion of nuclear weapons to Nth powers. The condominium could also be so ratified. Such a condominium could have difficulties in management, dangers in application, and defects in consequences. It would not easily be accepted by many of the remaining large and intermediate nations. It could inspire political rebellion, create conflicts in imposition, emphasize the value of and accelerate the acquisition of nuclear weapons if its control faltered, increase suspicions, and generally worsen the climate of international relations. This defect might not occur if the condominiums were clearly a step toward world government and if definite and acceptable steps were taken toward that goal in some reasonably short period of time and succeeding measures governed by some timetable.

Still, it might be argued that fear of the arms race would be so widespread, particularly if there had been one or more nuclear crises, that if such condominiums did not seem to change the existing order too much—beyond controlling the spread and use of nuclear weapons—there might be substantial acceptance of them. Such "limited" condominiums, most likely between the United States and the Soviet Union, though other powers need not be excluded, could limit the freedom of all or part of the world to use violence, or even to develop nuclear weapons systems. If there is an eventual general acceptance of such a condominium—and cooperation among the condominial powers would probably not otherwise continue long—then in the long run such acceptance would be likely not only to transform the basic relationships between the members of the condominium but also of all states in ways as yet not understood.

[17] See, for example, Herman Kahn, *On Thermonuclear War* (Princeton, N.J.: Princeton University Press, 1960), p. 242.

[18] A dual form of government such as obtained in the late Roman Empire or in many provinces in India from 1919-39.

One variation of the condominium might be that in which four great regional groupings based on the United States, Europe, the Soviet Union, and China (perhaps with the cooperation of Japan) dominate the world. The diminished ability of the developing nations to force competition among the blocs, as a consequence of informal modes of dispute settlement that have developed, might in this case produce a reduction in the amount of aid going to them and a diminution in the importance of those international institutions, for example, the General Assembly of the United Nations, in which their voting weight is greatest. The regional great powers might take special responsibility for the resolution of conflict within its sphere of influence, for example, the United States in Latin America, Europe in Africa and the Near East, Russia in East Europe and the Middle East, and China and Japan in Southeast Asia. Each sector might develop its own body of regional law along with an underlying body of international law.

3. *Concert of Large Powers*

This could be a relatively informal working arrangement by comparison with the condominium, and would likely include more than two or three powers. Or it could be formally organized as in the original proposal (and intentions) for the United Nations or in the new structure some have proposed for NATO—that what now is a military alliance be made into a political and economic union. Many or all of the large powers could, by some set of voting negotiating rules for procedures, more or less rigidly enforce the policy consensus through formal or informal machinery. The original hope for the United Nations was that it would institutionalize a concert of the great powers with the Security Council their major organ. The purpose of the Assembly was to give the small powers some representation and a forum but not an overwhelming influence. This was widely understood at the San Francisco conference, and the postwar results of this design show one of the weaknesses of the concept: it is easily broken or negated if one or more of the members of the concert decides to oppose or even to abstain from the consensus, or if there is a sufficiently large and determined power outside the concert. To the extent that no single great power has special responsibilities to control aggression, there is likely to be a real division in any concert as to the relative burden each member of the concert should bear when the issue is not merely deterring aggression but actually accepting costs to correct or punish an aggressor.

The attempts to organize a North Atlantic "Political" Community in succession to NATO provide an example of concert of large and small powers (though some of its advocates, such as Union Now, want a formal confederation or federation). The difficulties of NATO indicate another weakness of these systems—the resistance of the smaller or medium powers to the predominance of the larger when interests begin to diverge and the great issue or crisis that produced the concert begins to fade.

The North Atlantic Political Community was the original form of the "Grand Design" for Europe (possibly to be extended to Japan, Australia, New Zealand, and other democratic nations) envisaged by President Kennedy, many other Americans, and some "good Europeans." This North Atlantic "Political" Community, enlarged or not, would bring a large portion of the earth's inhabitants (one-sixth or more) into a "rule of law" area in which internal war and violence or the threat thereof might be abolished. "Civil War" seems most unlikely in this prosperous, bourgeois community, once established. Many, if not all, of the problems and ambiguities of United States guarantees, extended deterrence, and independent nuclear deterrents would largely disappear. There seem no serious practical objections to such a proposal in the fields of technology, transportation, communication, or defense.

The gross national product (almost one and a half trillion dollars) available to this fabulous combination of nations would dwarf all previous experience. Its existence would greatly accelerate the creation of a postindustrial society and thus raise all the exciting and creative possibilities as well as all the problems we have suggested earlier. The fact that there would be little or no fear of war, and the confidence the leaders could have in the political, economic and military unity of a successful community, could mean a toleration or encouragement of diversity in many areas—while the mixing of cultures could encourage creativity. Thus, while the community would be an affluent bourgeois society, it would not necessarily be wholly materialistic. As we have suggested in Chapter IV, when goods are abundantly available, those who wish to abstain can easily do so—competition for status and wealth might well relax.

One would conjecture that the phrase "wholesome degeneracy" might fairly characterize many of the people who would live in this North Atlantic Community. But that would be up to the citizens of the community. They would have the right to choose the way of life they preferred, less impeded by material or national security constraints than any people in history.

Further, to the extent that resources and will could do it, such a community could also abolish poverty in the world in a few decades. (But this would presume what we have already suggested may be incorrect: that only capital and technology are needed to modernize a country.) No more would man need to live by the sweat of his brow. The promise of automation and technology could be fulfilled throughout the world, and all would share in the fruits of modern science—all who chose to could soon live in a postindustrial culture.

The stable existence of this community could discourage dreams of empire anywhere else. Any theories of the Soviets and Chinese about the inevitability of world revolution would be shattered on the success of the community; there would not be an "increasing misery of the masses" or other obvious "contradictions" from which revolution presumably arises.

Obviously "contradictions" of a novel kind might be expected. It is possible that, as if from sheer boredom, the citizens of the community would take up unreasonable causes and ideologies, possibly risking the community and even human society. Easy success and luxury can be corrupting, and this could be a danger to such a community. But these dangers are no bar to initial success.

More immediate is the possibility of adverse international reactions. A tight union of the advanced, developed, and mostly white nations could not help being viewed to some degree with fear, envy, and distrust by the less-developed and nonwhite nations. Particularly because their power to compete may be small, the smaller nations may feel all the more need for countervailing power. Even if this large community aided them, there would still be feelings of dependency and backwardness. And the community might not be so helpful—the third world might indeed need countervailing power either to protect itself or to stimulate the possibly apathetic and indifferent community to take an interest.

Men are not always interested in the welfare of their fellowmen unless there are special situations to draw—or compel—their attention. While United States interests were adversely affected, at least in the short run, United States policy in Latin America was improved by the advent of Fidel Castro, and United States interest in the Third World generally, particularly in Africa, Southeast Asia, and India, has been stimulated by Communist competition. The success of a NATO political community might make available huge resources for external aid, yet remove most of the motivation to expend it.

Even more ominous is the possibility that such a large and powerful grouping might find itself almost forced to attempt to establish some kind of hegemony or control over the world. There are many motivations for this, but the need for an early control of the arms race—the elimination or discouraging of possible future threats that an ever advancing technology might bring—might itself seem a sufficient (and respectable) motivation. This attempt to create hegemony might work, especially if carried out with some regard for other nations' attitudes, cultures, and sensibilities, but none of these criteria is certain, or probably even likely, to be satisfied. In any case, even a combination of the North Atlantic nations, with the later addition of Japan and Australia and New Zealand, and possibly parts of Latin

America, would not achieve worldwide hegemony easily. Countervailing power, even if much weaker, is almost sure to spring up.

In the immediate postwar era, the United States could probably have taken the lead in establishing such a community. The Europeans, with the possible exception of the British, would probably have been willing to follow, turning away from the seemingly discredited nation-state system. But the larger objectives seem not to have been fully grasped by the Truman administration, when the opportunity existed. It is difficult to believe that the opportunity still exists. Its time may have been, and its time might come again, but it does not seem to be here and now.

4. Concert of Small Powers

It is conceivable that the United Nations Assembly could develop into an effective force for regulating world behavior, though this seems unlikely. This would amount to a concert of the small powers. There is theoretical justification for supporting such a development. A collectivity of small powers is the only available "neutral" that the big powers can permit to arbitrate issues. But the collectivity of small powers today contains a number of states new to the international stage and with relatively primitive societies and unstable governments, and the great powers are unlikely to be willing to submit to its judgments. It would be easier for the great states to entrust the task to the advanced small countries—Sweden, Ireland, Norway, Denmark, Finland, and possibly some of the Balkan states. In practice, how stable, or how reasonable, such a method of organizing international relations would be is an open question. But it is hard to be optimistic about major nations really submitting their fate to the judgment of the small—except in relatively small matters. Such a system could alleviate strains; it could not be reliable.

5. Further Development of the United Nations

The notions of concerts of large and small powers suggest further lines of development for the United Nations. The United Nations might continue in its current structure but gradually become stronger and gain new powers, either by unauthorized development (as, for example, the Russians have argued happened in the case of the Uniting for Peace resolution) or by explicit negotiation and agreement. Many believe that such developments and negotiations could be facilitated by gradually increasing the functions of the international agencies associated with the United Nations—the World Health Organization, the World Court, UNESCO, and so on.

It is difficult to visualize the nature of these developments or even the general directions they might take. But one important turning point might be provided if the United Nations fought a war of some length and magnitude, an extended "Korea" with large participation by many nations, so that it had to carry through important functions under emergency conditions. Another possibility might develop from the radical Asian nations organizing their own international body, and the two organizations competing. A third possibility, particularly plausible if nearly all foreign aid were channeled through the United Nations, would be that the United Nations gradually developed some large degree of legal jurisdiction over questions of great interest to the underdeveloped areas but of less interest to developed areas.

Perhaps the single most important source of support for acquisition of strength by the United Nations might well be those functional areas that are not now of such importance that they invoke important national rivalries but that are likely to become important in the future. One obvious example is control of the mineral resources of the seas. No one has to give up any significant present advantage to agree to this, future advantages are problematical both in terms of technological capabilities and in terms of competitive success, a reasonable access is assured by such agreement, and some potentially dangerous rivalries are avoided. Only a sense of urgency is lacking. If such functional assignments were developed by the United Nations, and if it fulfilled them well (a most important caveat), it might become a kind of world government in limited functional and geographical areas.

6. World Federal Government

The end point, of course, of the possible development of the United Nations could be a functioning world government. This would presumably involve a parliament or legislature and an executive and judicial system, most likely with very explicit powers and constraints, and with separation of such powers on the United States, rather than the British, model. Such a structure is likely to be much more complicated than the United States model, particularly because it would undoubtedly evolve slowly and with many compromises. Examining the growth of economic unity in Europe, one notes that a very large number of different institutions were needed to make the development feasible: the European Coal and Steel Community, EURATOM, the European Parliament, the European Executive, the Council of Ministers, the European Court, and so on. Some feel that a world federal government might grow out of something like the North Atlantic Community—that a world government is most likely to be created if it starts with a core of kindred states and grows by accretion rather than by a single act of creation.

However such a world government came about, it seems clear that the following simple voting systems would not be satisfactory:

1. One man, one vote
2. One nation, one vote
3. One dollar, one vote.

But something like the bloc system described above could be a basis for representation. In any case, even though very complex arrangements were made to mitigate many of the difficulties, the crucial issue would still be where basic political power resided. Idealistic people who wish for, or argue for, some kind of world government as a solution to current international problems, often neglect the important political questions of "who gets what, and when" and "who tells whom what to do." Such questions are almost impossible to settle in the absence of intense external dangers that cause the parties to accept compromises. This is one reason for believing that a world government could only be created out of war or crisis—an emergency that provided an appropriate combination of the motivations of fear and opportunity.

7. World Empire or Empires

A superficial study of the history of civilized man discloses that most civilized peoples, most of the time, lived in empires. From the technological point of view the radius of an empire today is limited only by the size of the earth. A world empire could develop from a thermonuclear war, including a third power emerging relatively undamaged and taking power over the participants. The parties to a thermonuclear war might "tie," and decide "never again," or other survivors, united in this conviction, might proceed, forcibly or otherwise, to confiscate or destroy the weapons of any "small" nations that disagreed with them.

World empire might also be an unforeseen, unexpected, or at least unwanted, result of constitutional world government through a seizure of power by the military or other minority groups or even through the dictatorship of a group that represented a majority but did not command an overwhelming consensus. This is, of course, one of the great risks assumed if a world federal government is ever organized.

There could be several empires. Particularly if these were organized along bloc lines, the imperial characteristics would be much mitigated.

8. Community Sanctions

Modern technology raises the possibility of an unofficial system for punishing violations of the international community's established order.

The missile can be a particularly anonymous weapon, and unless there are very elaborate monitoring systems it could be difficult to tell who fired one. Even with monitoring systems, if a firing occurs in outer space or from a mobile platform at sea, it could be difficult to determine the nation responsible. This potential anonymity could cause extreme problems; it might also act as a regulating and stabilizing influence. A nation that jeopardized the international order might in the future expect to be the victim of an anonymous attack. The anonymous attacker might not be directly affected by its victim's behavior; it might assume the right to strike out of a sense of outrage or of responsibility to preserve the system or because it feared it could later become a victim. Such an event could be a step in a developing process. The mere occurrence of such a bizarre crisis could give rise to pressures both to prevent future misbehavior and the possible misuse of this new form of lynch law—or citizen's arrest.

The possibility of such sanctions might be a powerful stabilizing influence in international systems without war. A system of community sanctions in which nations used modern technologies (perhaps anonymous or official missiles launched by private or internationalized Polaris submarines) to punish infractions of the peace or international standards would constitute an international vigilante committee, but it might also be formally organized—perhaps as part of an alliance using national or even multilateral forces. The United Nations might acquire a small strategic military force whose sole purpose was impartial retaliation against any nuclear aggression in tit-for-tat fashion. Presumably the retaliation could be either "automatic," that is, by doctrine, as in a proportionate nuclear reprisal strategy,[19] or it could become part of an evolving world legal or legislative system.[20] Retaliation by international organization might face some of the problems that undermined collective security during the period of the League of Nations. The obligation that belongs to all may motivate none toward the dangerous actions required, except perhaps in that case discussed above, where the criterion is simple, clear, and virtually automatic in application. Action can perhaps be made particularly credible if an international organization is deliberately designed to operate independently of the member governments, not according to preestablished criteria.

9. Setback to Civilization

Weapons of mass destruction might ultimately disappear either because civilization so retrogresses, presumably as a result of war, to the extent that

[19] Herman Kahn, "Nuclear Proliferation and Rules of Retaliation," 76 *Yale Law Journal* 79 (1966), and Herman Kahn and Carl Dibble, "Criteria for Long-Range Nuclear Control Policies," 55 *California Law Review*, 473 (1967).

[20] Herman Kahn, *On Escalation* (New York: Frederick A. Praeger, 1965), pp. 264-269.

it can no longer manufacture or support these weapons, or because of an immense revulsion against these weapons, which again presumably would be caused by experience of war.

E. HOW DO WE GET THERE?

As important as the question of destinations are questions of directions and routes. A destination may seem very desirable, but if there is no "route" from here to there (or if we cannot find the direction that sets us on this route), then the destination is irrelevant. Below are eight possible routes:

1. Natural evolution ⎫
2. Aided evolution ⎬ Peaceful
3. Negotiation ⎭
4. Crises and "Small Wars" ⎫
5. "Controlled" Wars ⎪
6. Uncontrolled but "Successful" Wars ⎬ Violent
7. "Unsuccessful" Wars ⎪
8. "Armageddons" ⎭

All eight routes are possibilities; in any realistic scenarios, more than one may occur. Many Americans like to believe that only the first three need play an important role in reforming the system, but it seems unlikely that major changes will occur on the basis of normal, peacetime motivation. While we have already experienced slow and peaceful international evolution, we have also experienced major shifts in the system through violence. If a desirable and major change in the system is to come about after a war, it may be necessary to agree upon the essentials "before the dead are buried." If not, even the nations that suffer from the war are soon likely to bargain again for unilateral advantage. Probably an agreement must come while the shock of the world tragedy is still fresh in leaders' minds—or while one side or the other has an advantage. Because some form of violence will probably precede change in the system, a good deal of study is needed on violence as a tool or agent of transition.

Few studies of the use of violence in transition situations have been made. Indeed, until recently almost no attention was paid to ways either of stopping a crisis or war or working within it, if it cannot be avoided, for desirable ends. Today a good deal of work has begun in this area.[21] It is the mechanisms of low-level violence—of crises and "small wars"—that are most

[21] See, for example, A. J. Wiener and Herman Kahn, *Crises and Arms Control* (Croton-on-Hudson, N.Y.: Hudson Institute, 1962).

likely to be involved in systemic change. This is not to say that we should "plot" war or crises. War or crises may nonetheless occur and, whether deliberately chosen or not, may bring about very important historical transitions. If we are not prepared to exploit these mechanisms of transition, we may lose important opportunities or fail to avert great disasters.

Many Americans are distressed by discussions such as this. They believe that to "accept" the possibility of war and violence is to make them more probable. While this objection probably has some validity, it is not a good enough reason for ignoring these possibilities. One might be willing to accept a slightly increased probability of low-level violence in order to be able to deal better with high levels of violence, particularly if this improvement created a decreased possibility of the highest levels of violence. And in actual practice, of course, it is far from clear that discussions of these problems increase the probability even of low-level violence. The best way to avoid crises and wars is probably to understand them; having understood them, it may be possible to influence their consequences.

CHAPTER X

Policy Research and Social Change

A. INTRODUCTION

We have given much attention to the possibility that current technological, economic, and social forces may have extremely undesirable consequences. Increasing wealth and leisure and improved technology are unlikely to have the exclusively beneficial results that are often naïvely assumed.[1] A principal danger in the situation is that a series of decisions can be taken separately for good reasons and yet produce an ultimate condition which—had it been foreseen—no one would have wanted.

This chapter examines (in Part B) some of the ways in which policy decisions can go wrong and suggests (in Part C) ways in which our ability to avoid unintended—or intended, but eventually unwanted—results may be improved. As long as we are in a state of uncertainty about both ends and means, the most important principle may be to refrain from attempting to legislate for the future in detail. Social policies should be devised that leave large amounts of freedom—of choice, of protest, of countervailing action—and that, so far as possible, avoid foreclosing avenues of future

---

[1] There is an analogy in the popular assumption that a family with newly acquired wealth is likely to find this wealth destructive to its character—if not to the first generation than to the second or third. While this is a cliché, it seems to have some basis in fact; and many rich American families have gone "from shirt sleeves to shirt sleeves in three generations," or at least have lost their money. Nor is it necessarily simplistic to argue that many similar effects can occur in a society as a whole, or at least in large sectors of it. But many of these effects can be accelerated, ended, or reversed, by appropriate social choices.

revision and new decision. Yet this delegation of decisions to the future may work better in facilitating progress than in preventing disasters, or even in resisting deterioration. For the latter some degree of firmness and rigidity may be required in policy, as well as some willingness to foreclose some futures—particularly when indecisiveness may display insecurity and itself cause an erosion of values or an acceleration of harmful trends. Yet, a firm plan for avoiding some of the trends that concern us would require a higher degree of consensus and confidence than is likely to be achieved.

Practically all the major technological changes since the beginnings of industrialization have proved at best mixed blessings; that is, they have resulted in unforeseen and unwanted consequences that were not taken into account at the beginning of the process. Most obvious has been the "fouling of the nest": the ecological damage done by the accumulation of the waste products—oxides, isotopes, dirt, and junk—of industrial society. Although this is part of the price we would willingly pay for economic progress, too many of the costs of previous pollution and depredation of resources now seem likely to fall on the current and future generations.

To take another example, consider the automobile's consequences in accidental injury and death, its contribution to the decline of central cities and pollution of the atmosphere, and its thoroughly unexpected contribution to the American sexual revolution by helping to facilitate changes in morality and courtship patterns in the United States in this century. All these changes are irreversible, or nearly so.[2]

Another obvious, and dramatic, example is provided by the advances in public health that helped to bring about the population explosion, primarily by dramatically reducing infant mortality in countries with very high birth rates. The ultimate cost of this medical progress in terms of human suffering in much of the underdeveloped world (doomed to agonizingly slow development unless it can reduce population growth) may eventually far exceed the suffering that would have occurred without such progress. Yet people are unwilling to give up medical progress or to refuse it to popula-

---

[2] We say "nearly so" because there is in 1967 a new consciousness of the problems caused by the automobile. While the automobile casualty rate may now begin to decrease, it is unlikely that it will decrease very much, as the use of the automobile continues to increase. Furthermore, while there have been many proposals for barring automobiles from central cities, recreating pedestrian malls, and so forth, little can actually be done, given the current economics of shopping and transportation in central cities. While it seems likely that mass transport systems, at least in a few cities, such as San Francisco and perhaps New York, will be rehabilitated, in other cities, such as Los Angeles, and in innumerable small cities, traffic problems, urban decay, and suburban sprawl are likely to go on getting worse for at least several more decades—at least under current programs.

tions where too many babies are born; indeed most would judge it immoral to do so even if it were possible.[3]

We noted earlier that it is likely that ways will continue to be developed to prolong human life by means of artificial organs and even, perhaps, through computerized substitutes for damaged (e.g., senile) portions of brains. This raises very starkly several ethical issues,[4] including the possibility of dehumanizing people. While each advance in the capacity to prolong lives is welcomed for good reason, ultimately there is a danger of blurring the difference between human and nonhuman entities.[5] If this occurs a dehumanized view of partly human beings (and, by extension, of all human beings) becomes plausible. In the extreme limit, as humanoid equipment is evolved, maintained, and repaired for various special purposes, it may come to seem appropriate and reasonable to "phase out" this equipment as those purposes change. What begins as an expression of the value of the individual human life could easily become a step toward the treatment of men as objects, manipulatable or even disposable as social purposes dictate.

Thus it is simply not true that if society chooses B over C, and A over B, that A would necessarily have been chosen over C had society been given the choice. Rather, it is all too possible for the following sequence of events to occur:

1. A series of relatively small changes are proposed.
2. In each case the changed situation is thought to be preferable (by, say, vote of the *relevant* decision-makers or community) to the old situation.
3. The changes are cumulative.

---

[3] There are many situations in which calculations would disrupt social ties or personal relationships of utility essential for psychological or social reasons. (For example, it would obviously be destructive to carry out a cost-effectiveness analysis of a marriage, a friendship, or a loyalty to a group or an ideal.) One of the problems of the embourgeoisement and rationalization of social relationships included in our description of the multifold trend is that it tends to break down the moral (and psychologically and socially useful) values of commitment to persons and principles. Recall the quotation from Marx and Engels in Chapter VIII; see also a relevant discussion by Morton A. Kaplan, "Some Problems of the Extreme Utilitarian Position," *Ethics* (University of Chicago), 70 (1960): 228-32.

[4] For example, given limited resources, who shall live? See Harold M. Schmeck, Jr., *The Semi-Artificial Man* (New York: Walker and Co., 1965).

[5] Another possibility is that of adding to world population by bringing about a dramatic increase in average life expectancy. While most of the medical techniques envisioned for the next several decades seem more likely to ensure full life span (say three-score and ten) for nearly everyone (or perhaps only those who can pay for it, either by being a member or a citizen of an affluent society, or an elite in a poor nation), rather than a significant postponement of the general aging process, the latter does not seem impossible.

4. Once the series of changes has been made people think of the situation as undesirable or disastrous, or the situation become that we who initiated the process would judge undesirable.

5. Yet it is now impossible to reverse the sequence because of irrevocable changes, too great an investment, or changed values.

"Deterioration" can be accelerated if the changes create pressure groups that create new changes that create new pressure groups, and so on, accelerating undesirable trends. There is little that one can do about this kind of problem except to try to mobilize, ahead of time, the pressure groups that may be expected to object to the final situation. This may require that the issue be projected so plausibly or with such credibility that people will be effectively mobilized; and it requires, as well, that the causes and remedies be understood. But given the inevitable uncertainties, and the rigidity of any contemporary set of values and their likely endurance to future conditions, posterity will often in retrospect judge such a pressure group ill-advised—particularly if it failed. (We, of course, may not agree with this prospective judgment, and may wish to preclude it if possible.)

B. WAYS TO GO WRONG

Let us consider some of the mechanisms responsible for undesirable (by contemporary values) results in social processes. There seem to be at least ten important—though sometimes overlapping—"pitfalls."

1. Criteria too narrow
2. Decisions at inappropriate point in the structure (for the end in view or consequences actually caused)
3. Inadequate thought
4. Bad luck: unknown issues
5. Bad luck: unlikely events
6. Changes in actors
7. Inappropriate models
8. Inappropriate values
9. Over- or underdiscounting of uncertainty or the future
10. The best may be the enemy of the good (and sometimes vice versa)

While the above are almost self-explanatory, some comment may be useful.

1. Criteria too Narrow

Criteria for decisions are often too narrow because the decision-makers are parochial, partisan, or self-interested, or simply not accustomed to considering the new criteria that are becoming relevant. These new criteria are disregarded simply because they are new; they were not considered in the past so it is not reasonable that they should be considered now. If, for example, the Internal Revenue Service decides, in the interest of efficiency, to place very large amounts of personal information into computers, or the government, in the interests of science and efficiency, decides to centralize the records of twenty or more federal agencies in a National Data Bank, there is no existing pressure group (with the possible exception of Congress or the courts) organized to sound effective warnings of the dangers. If later, in the interests of law enforcement, this information is made widely available to other agencies, or even later, in the interest of commercial efficiency, the information is made available under "suitable" guard to credit groups, the final consequence may be an enormous invasion of privacy.[6] Yet the people who value privacy would not have had an effective chance to "vote" except in a perfunctory hearing or two, or perhaps by means of an *amicus curiae* brief filed by the ACLU if any test cases are fought. Presumably the democratic process provides many opportunities to affect such developments. Yet often enough the appropriate pressure group does not exist in an organized form effectively able to resist the groups that support the innovation. Even the constitutionality of an innovation may be difficult to test; the injured parties may not have "standing" insofar as they do not know or cannot prove how personal harm was done to them, or indeed injured parties may exist only *in potentia.*

Because of new technologies, new wealth, new conditions of domestic life and of international relations, unprecedented criteria and issues are coming up for national decision. But in the usual bureaucratic situation an executive is expected to be concerned with his own immediate responsibilities and not to worry unduly about others except for purposes of "political" bargaining or compromise. The only man who has nominal responsibility for the "overall" problem is the President (or other chief executive), who has little time to spend on anything except already "felt" pressures; and his competence obviously is limited. Furthermore, executives often do not make the crucial design decisions or even have much effective influence on them; they tend to make choices among already designed systems. As a result the principles of contingency design are often neglected, or the choices and compromises that are formulated may be far from optimal.

[6] Carl Kaysen, chairman of the task force which in 1966 recommended to the Bureau of the Budget that such a center be created, discounts this possibility in "Data Banks and Dossiers," *The Public Interest,* No. 7, Spring 1967. While we agree with Kaysen that the advantages of centralizing data are sufficient to make the step worth taking, there are reasons to be concerned that mere general awareness of the possibility of abuse may not be sufficient to prevent the danger from materializing, especially after some years have gone by and people have become complacent about the system.

Thus the national executive viewpoint may be narrow simply because there is no group whose professional and continuous job it is to worry about the appropriate issue. We have seen more than one instance in which a new issue is identified, all the officials to whom it is pointed out agree that it is significant, and it remains neglected simply because no one in the bureaucratic structure has a "mission" that would permit him to take cognizance of the new problem. Similarly it often happens that although there are offices in many parts of the government that are responsible for various parts of a problem, there is no one who has responsibility for the problem as a whole, for fitting the traditionally recognized part into a newly glimpsed total system—except of course the Chief Executive, for whom the problem may be at too high or low a level of abstraction or too low in priority in comparison to more pressing (and possibly less important) demands on his attention. It is one of the most important objectives of a policy-oriented research organization to function as a "lobby for the future": that is, to make a deliberate attempt to take a broad and long-range view of problems, and to try to create intellectual pressures on behalf of considerations outside the institutionalized criteria, particularly those considerations relevant to the long-run future or to the larger community, as in the case of issues such as international security. Policy studies should seek to discover important issues that are not currently recognized and should try to see that they are not unduly neglected in favor of more obvious, more pressing, or better-institutionalized considerations.

2. Decisions at Inappropriate Point in Structure

The above discussion inevitably raises the question of who determines the "good of society." This question is further obscured by the ways in which preferences are modified and decisions changed by the decision-making process. In its simplest form this is evident in the so-called Committee Paradox, in which the result of group voting—depending on the agenda— can be different from the result any member of the group would have preferred.[7]

A closely related common error is to mistake a prescription for macrobehavior as one that will affect microbehavior, or vice versa. For example, a park and a police force are, most people will agree, good things. This

---

[7] Because many readers will be familiar with this basic difficulty in determining social utilities, we will simply make reference to the followng discussions: (1) Kenneth Arrow, *Social Choice and Individual Values* (New York: Wiley, 1951); (2) Leonard James Savage, *The Foundations of Statistics* (New York: Wiley, 1954), p. 207 ff.; (3) Herman Kahn, *On Thermonuclear War* (Princeton, N.J.: Princeton University Press, 1960), pp. 119-26. Daniel Bell has also called attention to the impossibility of a perfect social calculus in his "Notes on the Post-Industrial Society (II)," *The Public Interest*, No. 7, Spring 1967.

does not mean that people will contribute toward them, unless they are public-spirited, for each individual is better off, on a strictly individual utilitarian calculus, if other people will contribute and he does not have to. Since decisions of all individuals are presumably independent, no individual has reason to expect that his behavior will affect that of any significant number of other people, if the community is large. (This is one reason why such goals are best implemented by collective rather than individual action.) The converse of this may also occur. If the price of wheat is dropping, a farmer may want to maintain his income by increasing his production. But the same factors that impelled him to this decision will impel others to the same decision, reducing the price of wheat still further. If it drops only a little they may still gain from their added effort, but if it drops below the marginal planting costs, they will have lost as a result of their extra efforts.

There are many other instances in which decisions that are rational for members of a group lead to results that are undesirable from the point of view of the whole group. If there is tension between two nations, they would both—considered *together*—usually be better off to avoid an arms race or a war; but in view of the uncertainties one nation might rationally decide that its best course is to enter the arms race, or even to fight pre-emptively; the other might then find it better to respond in kind than not.

From the individual point of view, voting may be judged to be not worth the effort, as there is no reason to believe that a tie vote will occur. During the water shortage in New York City, it was not "cost-effective" from the point of an individual for him to conserve water, as the amount he saved spread over nine million people would have been infinitesimal. In this case not only would his use of water not influence any one else, but the more people behaved as he did, the more pressure would be placed psychologically (if not rationally) upon others to save water. Yet if each followed the utilitarian rule for the individual, catastrophe might result. Thus naïve utilitarianism can do considerable social damage; and moral rules are required under a variety of circumstances.

A mistake related to those in the paragraphs above is to mistake agreement on goals with agreement on means of achieving them, or to mistake agreement on a specific set of means with agreement on goals. Thus the fact (if it is a fact) that two states favor disarmament does not mean that they can agree on the rates and categories of disarmament. Many kinds of instabilities and hidden advantages or disadvantages can inhere in any specific means of implementation; no means may be substantially neutral with respect to the interests of the parties in the interim. If these asymmetries are great enough, they may foreclose agreement even though the destination is mutually agreed. Conversely, as was true during World War II, nations may be able to agree on means, for example, the defeat of Nazi

Germany, while disagreeing about their destination, that is, the regime for Europe and the world in the postwar period. Sometimes these disagreements on destinations are obscured in a way that is functional for agreement on present means, say, the war effort, but dysfunctional for the future goals, because of the excessive fear of "rocking the boat" or lack of attention to "less important issues."

3. *Inadequate Thought*

Failures of perspective in decision-making can be due to aspects of the social utility paradox, but more often result from simple mistakes caused by inadequate thought. It is, for example, common enough that unnecessarily poor analyses are made. Obviously some analyses are done badly because they cannot be done well. But often sufficient information simply is not gathered, or there is a culpable failure in understanding theory. Both errors are avoidable if sufficient thought and time are devoted to the problem. Or there may be insufficient attention paid to hedging against complexities and contingencies. It is usually possible to make a plan that will work well if things go according to specially selected assumptions but that fails disastrously if certain not-unlikely variations from the assumptions take place. It is the purpose of such techniques as systems analysis to make designs that are relatively insensitive to changes in assumptions. For a remarkable number of cases this can be done, given sufficient intelligence, care, and interest.[8] While of course there are problems for which no reasonable "contingency design" is possible, there are still a great many plans that simply have not been thought through because custom, doctrine, or disastrous experience have not created any pressure to do so.

Most administrators dislike debating or thinking about fundamentals, even when vague, implicit, and half-formulated views obviously are governing choices, and when some searching debate is clearly desirable. Administrators resist even more "unnecessary" discussions that may become unpleasant or divisive. They tend to resist still more the very basic or very speculative thinking that may be essential to raising issues about the future, in part because of a well-grounded feeling that such thinking and discussing are usually unproductive and expose those who make the attempt to criticism, bureaucratic animosity, or ridicule. Yet it is often necessary to be courageous—or seemingly irresponsible—in suggesting and defending far-fetched issues in argument, if unprecedented but crucial considerations are to be discovered and appreciated. It is necessary to spend some time and energy in a process that frequently leads nowhere for the sake of the instances in which something new is learned.

[8] See Herman Kahn and Irwin Mann, *Techniques of Systems Analysis* (Santa Monica, Calif.: RAND Corporation, 1957), RM-1829-1.

And even when something new is learned, it is difficult to get "responsible" people to take the results seriously or to face up to thinking the issues through and then to providing relatively clear guidance or to making decisions. Again part of the reason is a lack of confidence based on experience of failure with similar issues. The result is a tendency to make important decisions almost arbitrarily, as if there were no way to judge whether any one decision was better than any other. A surprising number of government committees will make important decisions on fundamental matters with less attention than each individual would give to buying a suit.

4. *Bad Luck: Unknown Issues*

Sometimes, of course, certain information is simply not available. Then, in a sense, no mistake is made: the decision-maker did not understand the problem even though he thought he did and perhaps had every right to think he did; it is simply bad luck that there were aspects of the problem that could not be assessed. There are undoubtedly situations in which the theory or empirical data are insufficient not only to supply the information needed, but even to alert the planner to the fact that important information is missing. The recognition of this possibility is one of the reasons one must be both humble and skeptical about relying too heavily on either new "logical" analyses or old intuitions in unprecedented situations. It is one reason why decision-makers lack confidence in their ability to raise and settle basic issues; it is also a main justification for contingency design and for trying to defer irrevocable or firm choices by preserving flexibility as long as possible. Flexibility is not always good; firm and irrevocable policies may be better if the policies are correct, and sometimes almost any policy pursued firmly is better than no policy. More often wrong policies pursued firmly undercut good results that more flexibility would have saved. Unfortunately no single rule of thumb is sufficiently good, and judgment will have to be exercised on each case of assumed importance.

5. *Bad Luck: Unlikely Events*

Sometimes the best-laid plans gang agley for "statistical" reasons. That is, a proper judgment may be made on the basis of the probabilities as they are known, but the improbable occurs; either conditions are met that are *far* worse than anyone could have anticipated, or some bizarre combination of accidents—each one of which was unlikely in itself but could have been handled—takes place, and "swamps" the system. The most dramatic possibility for bad luck today would be an accidental or inadvertent nuclear war caused by some extremely unlikely, but not absolutely impossible, combination of technological and human errors or failures. Good planning is designed to decrease not only the likelihood of bad luck but also the consequences if it occurs, since the "extremely improbable" is not the same as the impossible.

6. *Changes in Actors*

Miscarriages of policy decisions can result from a lack of continuity in the effective actors or pressure groups. In a typical situation one group initiates, another formulates, a third sets up the program, while a fourth actually carries it through. It is this fourth group (or possibly still another group) that furnishes the continuous pressure and determines what the program actually accomplishes. In many cases this turns out to be quite different from what all the previous groups wanted and intended.

7. *Inappropriate Models*

One kind of inappropriate model is simply technically wrong; someone has made a mistake. For example, many people feel that the unrest in under-developed societies results primarily from their poverty. They conclude that foreign aid can decrease the amount of unrest in these countries. Yet one thing that seems very clear by now is that the process of development is disrupting and usually increases violence and unrest. Social change is disruptive and partly destructive, causing many breakdowns and strains in existing systems and creating new systems that clash with the old.

Another kind—the inappropriate analogy—appears, for example, in international relations. Many Americans feel that every step toward integration or union among nation-states is a good thing and amounts to a step toward democratic world government or world community. Many naïve enthusiasms for NATO, North Atlantic unity, and European integration stem from an American model of the constitutional convention as the appropriate solution for fundamental problems among states. This model makes it possible to ignore many issues, among them the simple reality that increasing the integration of a bloc such as NATO is not necessarily a step toward integration of the world community and may, in fact, tend to create cleavage in the world community—and be valuable, if it is valuable, for quite different reasons. This inappropriate model is closely related to the mistake discussed in number two above: what is a decision for integration at one point in the structure may, on occasion, result in unintended (or intended on the part of some of the participants) disintegration at another level.

Another common error in models is to mirror-image. One knows one's self and motives, and one imputes these motives to others. Mistaken mirror images play important roles in foreign policy, in ethnic issues, and in confrontations between classes. Most important of all mistakes arise out of attempts to treat complex and intractable issues by overly abstract or simple models. This is often done in foreign affairs as well as in middle-class judgments on the poor. No matter how much energy or effort one puts into an analysis or the execution of a policy, if the efforts are guided by a badly formulated model they can be ineffective and even counterproductive.

8. Inappropriate Values

Some of our misgivings about the future may simply be due to the fact that our values are inappropriate to the future. Within broad limits the future's values should belong to the future. It is quite possible that our apprehensions about alienations and affluence in Chapter IV, admittedly based upon certain current middle-class and democratic American values, may seem entirely misplaced by the year 2000. We, of course, do not think so; but this may be our limitation.

Almost any decision-maker will find many aspects of subsequent events undesirable. The medieval church doubtless would have more strongly resisted the Renaissance if it had understood that the Renaissance would lead to the secularization of European society. Kings would have fought the rise of the bourgeoisie sooner and more strongly if they had understood that eventually the bourgeoisie would not only support them against the nobles but would eventually take over their role.

Our values may be inappropriate in still another, less easily recognized, way. We may think that we prize a certain aspect of the current system and regard it as an end in itself when in fact it would be better understood as a means to an end. It is common—and very often of great importance—for people to treat means as values, as ends in themselves, since to consider means as merely instrumental is to subject them to questioning. Yet when conditions change, the failure to reconsider the relation of old means to continuing ends can result not only in misdirected efforts but in behavior that becomes destructive to other, more important goals.

9. Over- or Underdiscounting of Uncertainty or the Future

Probably the most important reason apparently reasonable decisions lead in the long run to undesirable results is that, by and large, it is so difficult to discount uncertain and/or distant difficulties appropriately—neither too much nor too little. For example, it is difficult to imagine a Virginia planter's wanting to stop the slave trade in 1620—or in 1800—because in 1861 there might be civil war. Of course, this might have been reasonable and realistic of him; the future is a region of great uncertainty; and it is the present in which we live and have the power to act. Yet *two* kinds of mistakes can be made: those who focus pragmatically on case-by-case decisions may take the long run too little into account, while those who are most concerned with adherence to principles, now and forever (and these principles may be radical or conservative), may fail to deal adequately with problems as they arise in the present.

Of course, the planter in our example might have wanted to stop the slave trade on moral rather than prudential grounds; and events would have shown him right in consequential as well as in absolute terms. One problem of the secular humanist's relativistic "ethic of consequences"—in which the consequences, including both means and ends of each decision, taken together, are weighed against the total consequences of the alternatives—is that it depends so much on fallible assessments of consequences. It could be argued that human judgment on such matters is so typically bad that an absolute morality, which prohibits certain means no matter how comparatively attractive the "total consequences" of means and ends may appear, actually leads to better results, even in consequential terms. On many kinds of issues we find this argument persuasive; [9] and we would find the argument persuasive on many additional issues, if social conditions were not changing so rapidly as to require continual reexamination of means as ends change, lest the means become too much ends in themselves. Under twentieth-century conditions of flux, however, there seems to be more to lose by routinely deciding major policy questions on the basis of received doctrine or principle than by making such decisions on the basis of fallible assessments of the likely results of one choice compared to another.

10. *The Best May Be the Enemy of the Good (and Sometimes Vice Versa)*

Desirability and feasibility may be separable for analytic purposes, but when it comes to making choices they are intimately related. By trying for a great deal one ordinarily increases the risk of failure; by attempting too little one may ensure that at best one does not get very much. On the one hand, if a goal is very desirable it may be possible to arouse a great deal of enthusiasm for it, and its feasibility may be greater than one would have thought; on the other hand a goal that seems within reach looks more attractive than one that is hard to get.

Obviously there can be no general rule for making such choices; they often turn on subtle, difficult-to-evaluate factors. On the whole, our own judgment is indicated in the title above: limited objectives usually do not preclude further incremental progress, but excessive or utopian objectives

[9] As Max Weber pointed out in "Politics as a Vocation" (1918), the (consequential) "ethic of responsibility," which is much more appropriate to political action than the (absolute) "ethic of ultimate ends," nevertheless must sometimes take a stand on principle—provided the stand is "mature" and "responsible," that is, fundamentally consequential, rather than absolute or ideological. See H. H. Gerth and C. Wright Mills, eds., *From Max Weber: Essays in Sociology* (New York: Oxford University Press, 1946), p. 127.

often prevent even limited gains from being obtained. If there is any general idea in this field that we would generally reject, it is the radical or "dialectical" notion that to make things better one should first make them worse, since only then will people understand that something must be done. On this dubious basis Communists resisted meliorating the lot of workers during the depression, since to do so would postpone the revolution; similarly there are those who oppose intellectuals giving constructive advice to the military, political, or economic "establishment," since to cause improvements in policies is merely to cloak the "power structure" in a "veneer" of rationality. While this principle that it is desirable to refuse to improve matters, or to make them worse, no doubt works sometimes, more often it simply makes or leaves things worse than they need be.

C. THE OBJECTIVES OF FUTURE-ORIENTED POLICY RESEARCH

What can policy research do to help avoid undesired results of decisions? Obviously a good deal less can be done than an engineer or doctor is often able to do about problems within his technical expertise. But research can be helpful if carried out with a proper sense of limitations. One can attempt to accomplish one or more of the following objectives:

1. To stimulate and stretch the imagination and improve the perspective
2. To clarify, define, name, expound, and argue major issues
3. To design and study alternative policy "packages" and contexts
4. To create propaedeutic and heuristic expositions, methodologies, paradigms, and frameworks [10]
5. To improve intellectual communication and cooperation, particularly by the use of historical analogies, scenarios, metaphors, analytic models, precise concepts, and suitable language
6. To increase the ability to identify new patterns and crises and to understand their character and significance

[10] We use these rather pedantic words reluctantly, but they seem to be the best available to describe our objectives. By propaedeutic we mean pertaining to introductory instruction, although there is no suggestion of the oversimplified. Because creative integration of ideas must ultimately take place in a single mind, even a very sophisticated and knowledgeable policy-maker, analyst, long-range planner (or member of an interdisciplinary study group) must absorb many ideas from unfamiliar fields. Hence, propaedeutic techniques are indispensable. By "heuristic" we refer to that which serves to discover, or to stimulate investigation, or to methods of demonstration that lead an investigator to probe further. While heuristic techniques are not necessarily scholarly or rigorous, their value need not be belabored. Paradigm, a structured set of propositions, is discussed more fully below.

7. To furnish specific knowledge and to generate and document conclusions, recommendations, and suggestions
8. To clarify currently realistic policy choices, with emphasis on those that retain efficiency and flexibility over a broad range of contigencies
9. To improve the "administrative" ability of decision-makers and their staffs to react appropriately to the new and unfamiliar

A good deal of thought has gone into framing and describing this list of objectives. We believe it is useful and productive for the researcher to go through a conscious process of focusing specifically upon what he is trying to achieve. Doing this may simultaneously open up new opportunities and areas for analysis and limit ambitions in others. We also believe that trying to be explicit and thoughtfully aware of the possible objectives can be an equally healthy exercise for the reader and can help him to achieve desirable objectives.

1. *Stimulate and Stretch the Imagination and Improve the Perspective*

The very process of systematically arranging all the factors that have or conceivably might have a bearing on the issues being studied makes demands on the imagination. Making up such lists forces one at least briefly to make distinctions and to examine nuances that are ordinarily overlooked or disregarded and to give attention and thought to potentially important situations and influences that would normally be outside the range of consideration, possibly because they are nonobvious or improbable or, more likely, because of emotional, professional, or doctrinaire biases. The effort of imagination and intellect required to bring a range of potentially relevant factors into focus is not likely to be wasted. Even if most of them should never acquire significance for action in the real world, some very likely will. Almost invariably some small but important number of the distinctions and nuances that are missed the first time will ultimately become important. In particular, possibilities that do not seem live options today may become worthy of serious consideration overnight as a result of new developments. Surprising developments happen often enough to make worthwhile the spending of valuable time and resources in preparing for them—at least intellectually—despite intellectual, social, bureaucratic, and other difficulties.

It is often the borderline or extreme cases that open up new vistas or new fields. Also, alternatives that no one would choose, either today or tomorrow, may still illustrate important principles in a simpler and more persuasive fashion than complex examples taken from reality. To be fully aware of the shape of reality it is necessary to glance beyond its boundaries on all sides. Proper perspective requires a view of the setting. Perhaps most important, our intuitions are no longer as reliable a guide as they used to be. Many currently useful ideas seemed bizarre or ridiculous when they were first considered. The seemingly improbable or hypothetical may, on analysis, be judged to have been unfashionable, novel, or unpleasant rather than unlikely or unrealistic. Thus research that opens the mind to new concepts and possibilities, fine distinctions, and subtle nuances is essential training and education for the analyst. For this reason alone such research should not shy away from examining extreme, implausible, or unfamiliar situations.

The reader of this volume of speculations on the relatively distant future may believe there is a danger of bringing too much imagination to these problems and a risk of losing ourselves in a maze of bizarre improbabilities. Yet if we review past performance in this field, we find comparatively little evidence of harm through excessive concern with the unfashionably hypothetical, even when short-run policies are at issue. Although there has been the occasional fashionable chimera that diverted attention and resources from projects that later turned out to have been more needful, a brief consideration of unfashionable improbabilities is not open to the same objection. In any case, it has usually been lack of imagination, rather than excess of it, that caused unfortunate decisions and missed opportunities. It is just because the fashionably hypothetical may dominate current planning and discussion that it is important to emphasize the relevance of the unfashionably hypothetical. It is hoped that reality will not introduce some of its acid, but potentially very painful, operational tests.

It may also be important to have some perspective on the role and relative importance of any particular issue or problem. There are important differences here between the roles of the researcher, the policy-adviser, and the policy-maker. In many areas good work can result only from systematic, sustained perseverance, often in the face of intellectual, social, bureaucratic, or other difficulties. Often sufficient motivation for such an effort can result only from an exaggerated estimate of the importance or of the likelihood of success that leads to a dedicated or even fanatic intensity of effort. However, when it becomes time to integrate this work into the total body of policy, the subject must be restored to its proper perspective. While it is the viewpoint of this report that a competent discussion of issues that may arise during the next thirty-three years may be of greater importance than is believed by those who are preoccupied by the present, there is a danger that the importance of "long-range prediction" will tend to be overestimated by those who engage more or less full-time in the activity. Tolerance and forbearance on the part of the generalists toward the more specialized professionals, and vice versa, are more likely to lead to useful communications and eventual balance than an invidious underlining, or even magnification, of the biases observed.

2. Clarify, Define, Name, Expound, and Argue Major Issues

It is occasionally assumed that there is widespread and explicit agreement about (a) what issues are important, (b) what stands on them are possible or reasonable, and (c) what are the major arguments for each of these stands.

In point of fact, no such second-order agreement [11] exists, except possibly within a few close-knit circles or on a few limited issues that have been in the spotlight of attention in recent years. Many other equally or more important issues remain unrecognized, undefined, and undiscussed. Such recognition and definition is of the utmost importance.

Clarification and definition of the issues also involve naming, for a choice of categories is in effect a choice of subject matter. This can lead to difficulties, for any system of categories comprehends some real distinctions and likenesses while ignoring or deemphasizing others. In the long run, problems shift and the nomenclature that is left over from an earlier focus or context makes discussion of later issues more difficult. Thus, for instance, to differentiate international systems according to the degree of nuclear diffusion may enhance clarification of the issues in the 1960's and may confuse them in the 1980's, when some other set of categories may prove more important. Appropriate words are often "used up" by acquiring a special technical meaning. Moreover the technical terminology employed may make it difficult either to see or to discuss these new issues usefully. However, we believe in the convenience of having simple labels for relevant packages of complex issues, even though the future will likely make even the best classification and naming system more or less obsolete. This is why one important aspect of technical competence consists of the ability to learn current classificatory systems with skill and discretion and to modify or replace such systems as their relevance diminishes or vanishes.

We employ the term naming, however, in a more specialized sense here. It functions as a metaphor in calling to mind analogous categories. Thus to label a concession as a "Munich" is to categorize it usefully even though the risk is run that the term will be applied to an appeasement that successfully appeased a world-be aggressor or to a concession that in fact satisfies the dictates of current standards of international justice. Although such names can, and likely will be, misused, we would argue that they carry too much useful information to be dispensed with. Again, one aspect of technical competence will involve using such names in ways that enhance their information-bearing rather than their information-degrading consequences. Their ambiguity also serves a desirable function, for they often initiate de-

[11] By first-order agreement we mean agreement on substance—that is, on assumptions, values, or the policy to be pursued; by second-order agreement we mean agreement on what the agreement or disagreement is about.

bate in a way that clarifies issues further. Thus, just as the clarification and definition of issues involve naming in a more general sense, so this more specialized kind of naming can be used to enhance discussion of the stands that are possible and the arguments that support them.

The main object, of course, is to determine what stands on each issue are reasonable and which are the major arguments for each stand. What is important here is to take each issue seriously enough and to carry the argument deeply enough so that a further superficial examination will not uncover crucial new arguments and factors. The position taken by the participants should be informed enough to stand up under the usual analysis.

It is startling how often in meetings it occurs that the raising of a single not-too-complicated point shifts many positions. Conversely many (unshiftable) positions are revealed as simple and unconsidered, even if strong, reactions to narrow aspects of the problem. In other words, the customary arguments used are often parochial, specialized, mostly unexamined, and sometimes self-serving. This not only leads to unnecessary biases, it may even be counterproductive to the holder's interests. For example, from the viewpoint of efficient political manipulation, it is of some importance to be empathetic with the audience to be manipulated. It is a fair characterization of most reports prepared in various subdivisions of the United States government that they tend to be prepared for audiences of "friends and relatives." They have almost no chance of carrying conviction with or persuading a skeptical, not to say a hostile, audience. Yet to be useful, the exposition and argumentation must be comprehensive enough, as discussed in point four below, to appeal to the relevant "majority." Such an attempt, even if motivated by the most parochial considerations, will still result in better recommendations. From this point of view, in the past even relatively simple concepts were not fully understood until several different analysts in many different studies contributed to their clarification and definition.

3. Formulate and Study Alternative Policy "Packages" and Contexts

One important aspect of exposition and arguing policy issues is the use of proper contexts. Few measures can be evaluated in isolation. They must be evaluated in a context of other measures that are being pursued and also in terms of the criteria and contexts set by the values and assumptions held by the policy-maker (or policy-makers). In order to facilitate such systematic comparisons it is important to assemble a relatively large number of packages of specific measures, so that one relatively complete policy can be compared with another relatively complete policy. The number of packages will, of course, be very small as compared to the total that is possible. However, in a relatively well-understood area, such a small number may still provide a large enough set of examples so that almost all of the relevant people can recognize their views in one package or the other. If it is necessary to make finer distinctions, subpackages within each package can be defined or designed.

It should be clear that people with different attitudes and views may be put in the same package, since these packages are likely to be fairly general and highly aggregated. But to the extent that these issues can be discussed without going into the greater detail that would separate the adherents of the same packages, it is often worthwhile to do so. One can then at least get much of the general discussion carried through in a systematic way. Of course, eventually one must go into details that may be crucial and that will more or less eliminate this superstructure of "packages," but it seems that about 90 per cent of the debates, particularly those conducted in government offices, committees, interdepartmental conferences, briefings, and so on, can be discussed at a relatively general and aggregated level. This discussion can be greatly facilitated by the previous preparation and discussion of specific packages and the creation of shared understandings or even of second-order agreement about most of the major issues raised by the comparison of such packages. A similar set of observations applies to the contexts in which these packages are evaluated and reevaluated. In practice more of the real controversy involves assumptions about overall contexts than about specific details.

In general, the systematic and careful study of the factors affecting the main issues, and the constructing of a number of policy packages in relation to varying contexts, will reveal a great number of interactions among variables, including various incongruities, inconsistencies, incompatibilities, and dissonances as well as mutual reinforcements. A realistic attempt to reconcile and balance the costs and benefits of including, modifying, or excluding important variables and ingredients should lead to an improved synthesis and balance. In particular, the formulation and study of alternatives yields insights into the objectives and assumptions that are behind each choice.

4. *Create Propaedeutic and Heuristic Methodologies and Paradigms*

This was one of the major objectives of this volume; indeed we would have liked to have written a paradigm for speculation about the future, rather than a mere "framework," which was the best we could do in the time available for this phase of the project. By paradigm we mean something a bit more structured than a framework, and a bit more elaborate than a metaphor made explicit, though we mean something much less formal than an analytical model, in the sense of applied mathematics. We mean a relatively structured set of explicit assumptions, definitions, typologies, conjectures, analyses, and questions. Robert K. Merton has argued (and, with examples, has demonstrated) the great value of such paradigms for sociological analyses; [12] his points are equally valid for analyses of problems in public policy. Paradigms, he points out, have five closely related functions:

First, paradigms have a notational function. They provide a compact parsimonious arrangement of the central concepts and their interrelations as these are utilized for description and analysis. Having one's concepts set out in sufficiently brief compass to permit their *simultaneous* inspection is an important aid to self-correction of one's successive interpretations, a result difficult to achieve when one's concepts are scattered and hidden in page after page of discursive exposition . . .

Second, the explicit statement of analytical paradigms lessens the likelihood of inadvertently importing hidden assumptions and concepts, since each new assumption and each new concept must either be logically *derivable* from the previous terms of the paradigm or explicitly *incorporated* in it. The paradigm thus supplies a pragmatic and logical guide for the avoidance of *ad hoc* (i.e., logically irresponsible) hypotheses.

Third, paradigms advance the cumulation of theoretical interpretation. In this connection, we can regard the paradigm as the foundation upon which the house of interpretations is built. If a new story cannot be built directly upon the paradigmatic foundations, if it cannot be derived from the foundations, than it must be considered a new wing of the total structure, and the foundations (of concepts and assumptions) must be extended to support the new wing. Moreover, each new story which *can* be built upon the original foundations strengthens our confidence in their substantial quality just as every new extension, precisely because it requires additional foundations, leads us to suspect the soundness of the original substructure. . . .

Fourth, paradigms, by their very arrangement, suggest the *systematic* cross-tabulation of presumably significant concepts and may thus sensitize the analyst to types of empirical and theoretic problems which might otherwise be overlooked. They promote *analysis* rather than concrete description. . . .

Fifth, and in this accounting, finally, paradigms make for the codification of methods of *qualitative* analysis in a manner approximating the logical, if not the empirical, rigor of *quantitative* analysis . . . (Quantitative) procedures are expressly codified as a matter of course: they are open to inspection by all, and the assumptions and procedures can be critically scrutinized by all who care to read. In frequent contrast to this public character of codified quantitative analysis, the . . . analysis of qualitative data is assumed to reside in a private world inhabited exclusively by penetrating but unfathomable insights and by ineffable understandings. Indeed, discursive expositions not based upon an explicit paradigm often involve perceptive interpretations; as the cant phrase has it, they are rich in "illuminating insights." But it is not always clear just

[12] Merton, *Social Theory and Social Structure,* 1956 rev. ed. (Glencoe, Ill.: Free Press, 1949), see especially pp. 12-16.

which operations with analytic concepts were involved in these insights. There consequently results an aggregate of discrete insights rather than a codified body of knowledge, subject to reproducible research. . . .

Since all virtues can readily become vices merely by being carried to excess, the . . . paradigm can be abused almost as easily as it can be used. It is a temptation to mental indolence. Equipped with his paradigm, the (analyst) may shut his eyes to strategic data not expressly called for in the paradigm. He may turn the paradigm from a . . . field-glass into a . . . blinder. Misuse results from absolutizing the paradigm rather than using it tentatively, as a point of departure.

The paradigms in this book are, without exception, provisional, undoubtedly destined to be modified in the immediate future as they have been in the recent past. But for the time being, these explicit. paradigms seem preferable to tacit assumptions.

Merton's warnings about the dangers and limitations in his book apply with much greater force to ours. Our paradigms must be far more "provisional" and subject to revision than Merton's, since we are not building a cumulative science of society as Merton is, but are only attempting to improve the quality of discussion and analysis of the continually shifting issues of public policy. However, our requirements for explicitness and clarity of notations and assumptions, and for systematic explication and codification of ideas, are equally strong.

As in any field of inquiry in which concerted efforts and possibly even cumulative improvements are sought, propaedeutic and heuristic devices [13] are urgently needed. One of the difficulties with getting enlightened and informed decision-making today is that so many people have to know so much about each other's fields. About half the time of any particular, specialized decision-maker is spent becoming familiar with allied information from complementary and supplementary specializations. It is of extreme importance, under these circumstances, to have in effect a simple "college outline" type of literature that is directly pointed to the needs of these people. Such a literature, of course, can only be produced to order; it is not produced accidentally. By "literature" we include, of course, methodologies for analysis and design.

The kind of work that has to be done on issues such as national security, international order, and the "quality of life" requires the integration, at least at a superficial level, of a large number of different disciplines. Almost anything that would help in doing this should be encouraged. We must maintain standards of depth and thoroughness, but these should not be self-defeating standards that prevent an important job from being begun. Almost necessarily, interdisciplinary workers must rely on "secondary sources," or on the advice of experts whom they have difficulty evaluating, though this

[13] Defined on page 398.

problem can be much alleviated by a suitable playing of experts against each other.[14] "Teams" of experts have important limitations; at some point a plan or solution must be achieved, and this can take place only "within a single skull" (in Clyde Kluckhohn's phrase). Thus one or more specialists must step outside their fields, or one or more nonspecialists must perform the final integration of specialties. However disagreeable such a task may prove, it is necessary and will be done better if better shared concepts and common vocabulary as well as special propaedeutic devices are developed.

5. Improve Intellectual Communication and Cooperation (Particularly by the Use of Historical Examples, Scenarios, Metaphors, Analytic Models, Precise Concepts, and Suitable Language)

One difficulty in devising pragmatic rules and heuristic hypotheses to deal with such novel situations as the proper conduct of international relations in a thermonuclear world is that we do not have a great fund even of intellectual experience to draw upon. Thus the meaningful concepts and metaphors, all of which are useful if not essential for the proper analysis and discussion of any complicated aspect of social relations, are lacking to us. Small groups that work together on these problems tend, in the absence of community experience, to develop special connotations for words and elements of precision in their terms that outsiders do not share, even though it may seem to the outsiders that the debate contains nothing that they fail to follow. The wider the relevant public and decision-making circles, the more this lack of shared experience hampers the communication process that is necessary for adequate decisions. Thus, although it is true that all truly professional groups develop a professional jargon of which outsiders are not fully cognizant, this problem is exacerbated in dealing with public issues. Moreover the jargon is not fully understood and communication is faulty even among many who consider themselves professional, except for some tightly knit small groups. One helpful device for overcoming this problem to some extent would be to create and to use artificial "case histories" and "historical examples" to supplement the paucity of real examples; but we note that there seems to be an insufficient exploitation of the examples that are already available.

6. Increase the Ability to Identify New Patterns and Crises and Understand Their Character and Significance

The major reason why one needs such artificial devices as a specially created "college outline" type of literature and paradigms for policy plan-

[14] Described in Herman Kahn and Irwin Mann, *Ten Common Pitfalls* (Santa Monica, Calif.: RAND Corporation, 1957), pp. 49-52.

ning is the rapidity with which changes occur. If the changes were slower, the various specialists would gradually learn what is needed for them to perform their functions effectively, and the normal methods of providing textbooks, literature, and expert professionals would suffice. So the essence of our problem is that we must cope with new problems and concepts.

By devoting attention to possibilities in a number of future settings it is possible to identify and study patterns and thus to become expert in the recognition of the patterns that are actually developing in the real world. Thus a series of studies like the present one can be of service in facilitating reaction to such patterns. As a result, there may be fewer wrong decisions, fewer unpleasant surprises, and fewer missed opportunities. Understanding developing patterns may not make the future our servant, but it certainly helps us to take advantage of some of its opportunities. Often recognition of a problem in time to cope with it is more of a limitation on adequate governmental action than are expenditures or levels of effort. Therefore, the early recognition of developing patterns has become of the utmost importance.

If subsequent efforts to investigate the distant future achieve some success, many of the new and unusual problems of policy planning will seem much less bizarre and will appear instead as a routine responsibility of the proper staffs. It will be less likely that we fail to guard against or fail to prepare to exploit possible developments because of overconcentration on the current pattern. To the extent the present is emphasized, it will be deliberate, and not by default.

Nonetheless, the pragmatic approach typical of Americans and their government is not going to be—nor would we agree that it should be—replaced by merely technical procedures. Indeed one way to view the whole program sketched out above is as a basis for a kind of planned muddling through. It prevents the foreclosure of options that would make muddling through impossible, and enhances the consensus on basic directions and destinations that makes muddling through successful.[15]

7. Furnish Specific Knowledge and Generate and Document Conclusions, Recommendations, and Suggestions

This volume, unlike the typical policy study, contains few specific conclusions, recommendations, or suggestions. It is intended, as the subtitle suggests, as a framework for speculation and discussion. If we have succeeded in doing useful groundwork for the future debate, the report should result in further studies by ourselves and others that will be more productive in recommendations and suggestions.

Even so, such studies can rarely be definitive. They must necessarily limit themselves to particular aspects of a wide field and cannot be expected

[15] See Wiener and Kahn, "Summary of Recommendations from *Crises and Arms Control*," Hudson Institute-288-RR, September 9, 1963, pp. 5-19, 64-66.

to be conclusive outside rather narrow limits. Furthermore, while they can make the consideration of imponderables more explicit, they can scarcely enable the decision-maker to evade his prerogatives and responsibilities by supplying him with specific solutions for various trades, compromises, and dilemmas.

It is true that on rare occasions a study will be able to make its final recommendations with great force and authority: but such recommendations will almost always be limited to a very narrow area that has been thoroughly covered by the study and in which the basic context and assumptions—at least as to objectives—are not controversial. Broader recommendations and suggestions with respect to more controversial assumptions or values cannot be expected to have as great force.

This is by no means to say that the decision-maker should disregard "narrow" studies. On the contrary, it will nearly always be of advantage to take the results of such studies into account in the process of reaching a decision. There is a great difference between an informed choice and a decision from ignorance or by default.

8. *Clarify Current Choices—Hedging, Contingency Planning, and Compromising*

Current choices are presumably based on the realities, objectives, and assumptions of today. Because all of these can change rapidly, it is important to understand explicitly the relationship of the choice to such realities, objectives, and assumptions, so that the choices can change when the basis on which they were made changes. It is surprisingly hard to do this, because most people—even most professional analysts—tend to forget the original reasons for their choices, and are then not willing to change their positions. It often helps to reconstruct the histories of how individuals arrived at their positions; then they know explicitly what they would be giving up if they changed their minds. But it is not enough to know and remember the reasons for one's choice. No choice is fully meaningful unless its alternatives are also understood and appreciated. It is especially important to understand the negative side of one's choice: the drawbacks and the costs associated with it. A thorough-going satisfaction with all aspects of one's position is often no more than an inability to see its problematic sides. Clarifying a choice involves some awareness of the fact that there was a choice and that something had to be sacrificed or compromised in committing oneself to it.

This underlies the concept of hedging and contingency design. By hedging we mean a modification of the preferred "system" that enables one to cope with "off-design" situations. Inside their own range of past experience, decision-makers usually understand the need for hedging against failure, that is, for acquiring emergency capabilities for dealing with relatively less favorable—including improbable—contingencies than those expected when the choice was made. It is less frequently remembered, but often equally important, that one should be able to take advantage of unexpected but more favorable situations if they arise. That is, one should also hedge to be in a position to exploit opportunities.

Equally important as hedging and analytically very similar to it is the process of attaining necessary accommodation with other people's values and assumptions. This is the process of putting together the relevant majority; and it has many similarities with other political processes. Forming policy is part of political give-and-take, but one of the special problems is that the give and take involves so much time that when the policy is finally set valuable opportunities may have been lost, or points of no return passed. Thus it is important to take into account other points of view in advance. Moreover proposals that do not sufficiently take into account other points of view may be rejected before they receive a "fair" hearing.

9. Broaden and Improve the Basis for Both Political Decision-Making and Administrative Actions in Dealing with New Trends and Crises

Any improvement in the technical or political debates, any improvement in communication and shared understandings, in making basic issues clearer, is likely to result in greater understanding at the upper levels of government, within intellectual elites, and among people generally. But such understanding can be more than intellectual. It can also result in participants becoming morally sensitive, morally informed, and intellectually more serious. Stimulating the study of crucial problems and drawing attention to potentially necessary decisions and acts are minimal requirements for coping successfully with the problems of the future. How much more can be done is problematical. It may be that all we can do is improve our capability to muddle through. But this in itself will be an achievement. It may also be possible to lay down broad guidelines for policies in at least some areas of public and social concern.

D. CONCLUSION: MAN'S INCREASING FAUSTIAN POWER OVER NATURE (INCLUDING MAN)

As we suggested in Chapter I, the Faust legend is a metaphor for a central predicament of modern man. We are interested in it primarily as it gives rise to insights concerning the consequences of the multifold trend characteristic of our culture. For the moment let us set aside the differences in treatments of this legend by several authors, or the same author at different times, as well as divergent critical interpretations. The two most popular literary treatments—those by Marlowe and Goethe—do provide at least poetic insight into the problems we have been raising. Marlowe's version is more faithful to the early folktale, but Goethe's version possesses that poetic ambiguity and complexity that raises the legend to the level of archetype or myth. In both versions, Faust sells his soul to the devil in order to acquire knowledge, power, riches, and women—typical sensate goals.

The object of pragmatic, empirical (sensate) knowledge is to control rather than to comprehend nature—to understand it instrumentally and manipulatively, rather than empathetically, normatively, or mythically. Such knowledge is a tool not for the philosopher but for *homo faber,* man the maker or doer, who gambles with fate (Fortuna or chance is a woman) to seize those rare opportunities that might never recur. Faustian man, or *homo faber,* is secular, profane, and sensate, rather than theological, philosophical, or theoretical.

The medieval play emphasizes the distinction between the sacred and the secular, between the body and the soul. During performances of the play, or puppet show, Faust would often be prompted from the stage (or even from the audience), "Repent, repent, it is not yet too late." Although he replies to the audience, "I have made a bargain and I will stick with it," he nonetheless vainly attempts to repent in the death scene. The lesson is clear: one may pay too high a price for worldly power, and repentance after the penalty is apparent is too late. The myths of Prometheus and Icarus—and even the apple of the tree of knowledge—expressed similar misgiving about the potential consequence of striving for prowess with which to transcend human limitations and to subjugate the forces of nature.

But Goethe's Faust suggests something more complex. Here is the bargain he strikes with the devil:

MEPHISTO:
> So minded, dare it cheerfully.
> Commit yourself and you shall see
> My arts with joy. I'll give you more
> Than any man has seen before.

FAUST:
> What would you, wretched Devil, offer?
> Was ever a man's spirit in its noble striving
> Grasped by your like, devilish scoffer?
> But have you food that is not satisfying,
> Red gold that rolls off without rest,
> Quicksilver-like, over your skin—
> A game in which no man can win—
> A girl who, lying at my breast,
> Ogles already to entice my neighbor,

And honor—that perhaps seems best—
Though like a comet it will turn to vapor?
Show me fruit that, before we pluck them, rot,
And trees whose foliage every day makes new!

MEPHISTO:
Such a commission scares me not,
With such things I can wait on you.
But, worthy friend, the time comes when we
    would
Recline in peace and feast on something good.

FAUST:
If ever I recline, calmed, on a bed of sloth,
You may destroy me then and there.
If ever flattering you should wile me
That in myself I find delight,
If with enjoyment you beguile me,
Then break on me, eternal night!
This bet I offer.

MEPHISTO:
                    I accept it.

FAUST:
                Right.
If to the moment I should say:
Abide, you are so fair—
Put me in fetters on that day,
I *wish* to perish then, I swear.
Then let the death bell ever toll,
Your service done, you shall be free,
The clock may stop, the hand may fall,
As time comes to an end for me.[16]

Thus when Faust builds a new area in which people can find a new life, in which swamps are drained and dikes built to hold back the sea, he rejoices that dikes can never be perfect, since "Freedom and life are earned by those alone who conquer them each day anew." [17]

Faust is less immoral than amoral. He is indifferent to the fate of those who stand in his way rather than brutal; the brutal actions in the play are performed by Faust's agents without Faust's knowledge. However, lest the reader think that Faust would have countermanded this brutality, there is

[16] Goethe's *Faust,* newly translated with an introduction by Walter Kaufmann (Garden City, N.Y.: Doubleday & Co., 1961), p. 183.
[17] *Ibid.,* p. 469.

one episode in which an old couple is ruthlessly evicted from their property by Faust himself even though their property is not essential to his scheme. They are in his way and, like a force of nature, he brushes them aside.

We are far from suggesting that the processes once presented by the basic multifold trend can be overcome. Janus, looking both backward and forward, must be the most disillusioned of all. Few of us are likely to return to the naïve optimism of the Enlightenment, to the rationalistic confidence in historical progress that is still dying slowly in both East and West, slowest of all in the United States, while it continues to gain new adherents in the developing nations and in new nationalistic Communist groups. Some of the more alarming possibilities and some of the nightmares contained in this book are designed to explore possibilities inherent in some of the tendencies present in contemporary society. Some of the technological innovations and the levels of economic development that make these nightmares possible are almost surely not reversible by any means short of holocaust.

Yet, if the cycle cannot be stopped, if the warring elements cannot be eliminated (as indeed they could not without the elimination of man), we can perhaps hope that they can be moderated. Just as the economist hopes to avoid not all the phenomena of business cycles, but only their extreme troughs and depressions, so perhaps we can hope with adequate knowledge and intelligence to control the extreme dips and rises of the cultural cycles. If man may never be completely in control of his fate, perhaps at least he may rise to partial control.

Man is developing enormous power to change his own environment—not only the outside world, but also his own physiological and intrapsychic situation. The prevailing secular humanist view is that this is "progress"— and we would agree that it would be no more desirable than feasible to attempt to halt the process permanently, or to reverse it. Yet this very power over nature threatens to become a force of nature that is itself out of control, as the social framework of action obscures and thwarts not only the human objectives of all the striving for "achievement" and "advancement," but also the various inarticulate or ideological reactions against the process. In the final decades of this century, we shall have the technological and economic power to change the world radically, but probably not get very much ability to restrain our strivings, let alone understand or control the results of the changes we will be making. But if we cannot learn not only to take full advantage of our increasing technological success, but also to cope with its dangerous responsibilities, we may only have thrown off one set of chains— nature-imposed—for another, ostensibly man-made, but in a deeper sense, as Faust learned, also imposed by nature.

If there is any single lesson that emerges from the above, it seems to be this: while it would certainly be desirable and might even be helpful to have a better grasp of how social action may lead to unanticipated or unwanted results, it is not likely to be sufficient. Given man's vastly increased power over his internal and external environment, and, in particular, given the unprecedented opportunities for centralization of social control that follow from the economic and technological changes that have occurred and that are likely to occur with ever increasing impact, the effects of social policies —planned or haphazard—are likely to increase drastically, and the consequences of mistakes are likely to grow correspondingly disastrous. While all decisions are in a sense irrevocable, this existential fact must be appreciated increasingly as it becomes an ever more dominant aspect of all policy decisions.

Of course, it will be worthwhile to try to improve our understanding of future possibilities and the long-term consequences of alternative polices. But the problem is ultimately too difficult, and these efforts can never be entirely successful; almost the only safeguard that then remains is to try in general to moderate Faustian impulses to overpower the environment, and to try to decrease both the centralization and the willingness to use accumulating political, economic, and technological power, or to arrange matters— somehow—so that the centralization of this power is placed in the hands of people who will respect its disastrous potential and will not centralize it further. What is necessary is an unflagging respect for the world as we find it and for dissent and diversity, even for ornery individual stubborness, in spite of the mounting impressiveness of the technical-rational structure bourgeois, sensate society is building. Above all, there must be a concern for perpetuating those institutions that protect freedom of human choice— not only for today's individuals and the pluralistic social groups that would want their views represented, but more important, for those who will follow us—those who in the future may experience their problems differently and would not want to find that we have already—unnecessarily and unwisely— foreclosed their choices and altered their natural and social world irretrievably.

Name Index

Abelson, Philip, 112
Adams, John, 213
Arendt, Hannah, 269
Armbruster, Frank E., xx, 308, 319, 356
Arrow, Kenneth, 391
Ayres, Robert U., 34, 37

Barbarossa, Frederick, 275
Bell, Daniel, xx, 24, 37, 186, 391
Bellamy, Edward, 27
Berdyaev, Nicholas, 41, 343
Berry, Paul, 114
Bertalanffy, Ludwig von, 362
Bishop, J., 106
Bloembergen, Nicholaas, 100
Bogue, Donald J., 151
Bohn, Lewis, 347, 370
Bohr, Niels, 16
Bonner, James, 113
Bose, Subandra, 274
Boulding, Kenneth E., 57, 370
Brezhnev, Leonid, 319
Bruton, Henry J., 135
Burckhardt, Jacob, 27
Burns, Arthur L., 361

Calder, Nigel, 66
Castro, Fidel, 379
Cesaire, Aime, 203
Chamberlain, Neville, 319
Chiang Kai-Shek, 232
Churchill, Sir Winston, 369
Clausewitz, Karl von, 326
Cohn, Norman, 275
Conniff, James C. G., 108
Cromwell, Oliver, 42

Daladier, Edouard, 319
Danilevsky, N. I., 343
Darwin, Charles, 14, 15
Davis, D. M., 106

Deak, Istvan, 269
De Broglie, Louis Victor, 16
De Gaulle, Charles, 324
De Grazia, Sebastian, 125
De Janosi, Nancy Engel, xx
De Riencourt, Amaury, 222
Deutsch, Karl, 372
Dibble, Carl, 247, 383
Dobzhansky, Theodosius, 112
Dollard, John, 198
Dove, John F., 100
Drucker, Peter, 57

Easterlin, Richard A., 136
Eibl-Eibesfeldt, I., 371
Einstein, Albert, 16
Engels, Friedrich, 48, 326, 342, 388
Ewald, William R., Jr., 140

Feuer, Lewis, 200
Feuerbach, Ludwig, 200
Finer, Herman, 268, 269
Franco, General Francisco, 340
Frederick William I, 235
Freud, Sigmund, 16, 41, 199, 200
Friedman, Milton, 21
Friedrich, Carl, 360

Gallois, Pierre, 85, 247, 369
Gandhi, Mahatma, 274
Gastil, Raymond D., xx, 114, 293, 356
Gell-Mann, Murray, 113
Gerth, H. H., 397
Gibbon, Edward, 27
Glass, H. Bentley, 112
Glazer, Nathan, 206
Goethe, Johann Wolfgang von, 31, 410, 411
Goldwater, Barry, 349
Graubard, Stephen R., 271

Subject Index

Achievement-oriented, values and reaction against, 25, 186, 342. *See also* Standard World (Alienation, Bourgeois values, and Humanism)

Advanced Research Projects Agency (ARPA), 88

Affluence, *see* Basic, Long-Term Multifold Trend, Item 6. *See also* Standard World (Alienation and Leisure-Oriented Society)

Africa, messianic movements, 276–277. *See also* Surprise-Free Projections (Worlds and Continents and Dichotomized Standard World) and South Africa

Afro-Asian bloc, rise of, 21. *See also* Canonical Variations (Status Quo-Oriented) and Standard World

Aggressive instincts, and war, 362–363

Agricultural Revolution, 150

Agriculture, *see* Labor force

Air Research and Development Command (ARDC), 76

Albania, 141, 236

Alienation, factor in totalitarianism, 19, 270–271. *See also* Standard World (Alienation)

Alliances, Roman and U.S., 223

Alternative futures, 6

Annamites, 17–18

Anomie, 208, 269. *See also* Standard World (Alienation)

Argentina, 141; and U.S. GNP per capita, 149. *See also* Canonical Variations (Status Quo-Oriented) and Surprise-Free Projections (Nineteen Contender Countries)

Arms control, *see* Weapons systems

Arms race, *see* Weapons systems and Standard World

Aristotle, 31–32

ARPA, *see* Advanced Research Projects Agency

Asia, chiliasm and eschatological factors, 275–277; two epochal events, 16–17. *See also* Surprise-Free Projections (World and Continents and Dichotomized Standard World)

Australia, and U.S. GNP per capita, 149; mass consumption in, 21. *See also* Canonical Variations (Status Quo-Oriented) and Surprise-Free Projections (Nineteen Contender Countries)

Automation, *see* Technology (Selected Areas)

Bacteriological, biological, and chemical warfare, 80, 85

Balance of terror, 225, 327

Ballistic missile defense (BMD), *see* Defenses (ballistic missile)

Ballistic Missile Early Warning System (BMEWs), 78

Baruch Plan, 71

Basic, Long-Term Multifold Trend, 6–7, 23–24, 27, 29, 38–39, 409; postindustrial United States, 185; Roman Empire and Hellenistic Greece, 193

1. Increasingly Sensate Cultures, 7, 25, 65, 186. *See also* Standard World (Alienation)
2. Bourgeois, Bureaucratic, "Meritocratic," Democratic (and Nationalistic?) Elites, 7, 65. *See also* Standard World (Bourgeois values)
3. Accumulation of Scientific and Technical Knowledge, 7, 64, 66
4. Institutionalization of Change, Especially Research, Development,